M

BURNING INHERITANCE

BURNING INHERITANCE

BY
ANNE MATHER

MILLS & BOON LIMITED
Eton House, 18-24 Paradise Road
Richmond, Surrey TW9 1SR

First published in Great Britain in 1987
by Mills & Boon Limited

© Anne Mather 1987

Australian copyright 1987
Philippine copyright 1987
Reprinted 1987
This edition 1992

ISBN 0 263 77941 6

Set in Monotype Times 10.5 on 10.5 pt.
19-9208-55026

Made and printed in Great Britain

CHAPTER ONE

'THE OLD girl must have been senile!' declared Robert Seton angrily.

'But she wasn't,' countered his nephew, from the depths of an Italian leather armchair. 'Vinnie made quite sure you couldn't level that charge at her. She was perfectly sane when she made her will. And there are three medical affidavits to prove it.'

'I don't need reminding of that fact,' retorted Robert Seton irritably. 'I was merely voicing my opinion, that's all. An opinion which will be shared by a majority of the shareholders. For God's sake, Alex, leaving her interest in the company to Isabel Ashley! Is that really the behaviour of a rational human being?'

'Vinnie evidently thought so,' remarked Alex, pushing his hands into the pockets of his trousers and stretching his long legs out in front of him. 'She always did have a soft spot for Isabel. I suppose she saw this as a way of redressing the balance.'

'What balance?' His uncle was impatient. 'Isabel left this family with no more and no less than she came into-it.'

Alex shrugged. 'Perhaps Vinnie didn't consider that was a particularly fair arrangement.'

'What are you trying to say, Alex?' Robert Seton gazed incredulously at the younger man. 'Do you agree with her philanthropy? I wouldn't have thought——'

'Someone has to play devil's advocate,' Alex over-rode him smoothly. But then, as if a little of his uncle's agitation was rubbing off on him, he rose abruptly to his feet. 'After all, if you are going to oppose Isabel's admission to the board——'

'Which I am!'

'—you should consider all the alternatives.'

His uncle snorted. 'There are times, Alex, when that legalistic logic of yours infuriates me. The girl's an opportunist, for heaven's sake! Anyone can see that.' He pressed the balled fist of one hand into the opened palm of the other. 'I should have forbidden Vinnie to see her. I'll never forgive myself for allowing this to happen.'

Alex raised one dark eyebrow, as if doubting his uncle's ability to have forbidden Vinnie to do anything, before leaving him and strolling lazily over to the long windows. With his back to the room, he allowed the tranquillity of the scene beyond the leaded panes to soothe him. His grandmother was dead, after all. And he refused to let his uncle's ugly mood destroy the grief that still lingered.

Outside, the shadows were lengthening across gardens burgeoning with the growth of early summer. The lavish flower beds which Deacon, his uncle's gardener, tended so lovingly, provided a natural frame for lawns as green and well-kept as a bowling green, and the shrubs that marked their borders were as luxuriant as the rest. Deacon had green fingers. It was a well-known fact. And Alex could remember, when he was about six years old, being puzzled because the gardener's hands didn't look any different from anyone else's.

Beyond the perimeter fence, the tree-strewn parkland of the Denby estate stretched towards Peale Bay, and the estuary of the River Naze, which marked the eastern boundary of Denby land. *Seton* land, Alex supposed it was now, with sudden irony. His grandmother's death had marked the passing of the last surviving member of his mother's family. Virginia Denby had outlived both her daughters by some twenty years, but at the age of seventy-seven, she had finally lost the battle. He would miss her. Much more than he had perhaps realised. She had been such a dauntless old lady, and he had loved her very much. For twenty years, she had tried to fill the gap left by his parents' death, and throughout his teens and early manhood, she had been the recipient of all his confidences.

A fold in the downs hid all but a triangle of the sea from view, but the rolling fields and pasture land more than made up for this omission. This was the place where he had been born, where he and his cousin Christopher had played as children, and even though he now had a place of his own in London, he still regarded Nazeby as his home.

'You'll have to go and see her,' announced his uncle from behind him, and Alex turned disbelievingly to face his irate relative.

'*Me!*' he exclaimed ungrammatically. 'Oh, no. You have to be joking! If you want to get in touch with Isabel Ashley, do it yourself.'

'No, I can't.' Robert Seton made a sound of annoyance. And then, changing his tone, he added wheedlingly, 'You know she always blamed me for breaking up the marriage. If I were to go and see her, she'd probably laugh in my face. You know what kind of woman she is. If she thought that by holding on to those shares, she'd be dealing a blow to Denby Industries—*at me!*—she'd never agree to sell!'

Alex had to acknowledge that there was some truth in what his uncle was saying. Not to put too fine a point upon it, Isabel had disliked Robert Seton intensely, and she had accused him of turning Chris against her. Nevertheless, Alex had no intention of getting involved in any vendetta against the woman.

He had his own reasons for despising Isabel Ashley, and nothing his uncle could say would persuade him to act as his emissary. Let the company lawyers do it. There were enough of them, heaven knew.

'Why don't you send Chris to see her?' he enquired now, his lean, intelligent face taking on a distinctly sardonic expression, and his uncle swore.

'Are you mad?' The older man clenched his fists. 'Don't you know your cousin still harbours some kind of feeling for her? Haven't I been the unwilling recipient of his maudlin self-recriminations, when he's been in his cups? For pity's sake, Alex, the last thing I need is for that woman to get her claws into him again. He got out of a difficult situation once, but I wouldn't trust him to be so lucky a second time.'

Alex felt a growing tension in his neck, and tilted his head to relieve it. 'You can't expect me to do your dirty work, Uncle,' he declared flatly. 'If you want to deal with this matter impersonally, get John Frazer or Malcolm Stansfield to handle it. That's what they're paid for. I'm not.'

'You could be.' Robert Seton jumped at the possibility. 'Alex, you know it was your grandmother's dearest wish that you should be a part of the company. Do you think she'd have left those shares to Isabel if she'd thought she could have persuaded you to take a less than half-hearted interest in Denby Industries? Look, I'll make a deal with you. You persuade Isabel to sell, and you can have the shares. Nothing would give me greater pleasure than for you to take Vinnie's seat on the board.'

'No.'

Alex's refusal was polite but firm, and his uncle gazed at him frustratedly. For five years now, ever since Alex left bar school and latterly set up his own tax consultancy agency in London, Robert had been trying to persuade him to join Denbys, but all to no avail. So far as Alex was concerned, his cousin Christopher was his uncle's natural successor and, in spite of the close family relationship, Alex preferred to remain independent.

'It doesn't occur to you that it's what your mother would have wanted you to do, does it?' his uncle persisted now. 'I know she was your grandmother's younger daughter, and I know your father wasn't interested in making money, but, dammit, Alex, he was my brother, and when he crashed the car that killed the three of them, my wife included, that changed the situation somewhat, didn't it?'

Alex's jaw hardened. 'I'm not unmindful of the debt I owe to you and Vinnie,' he declared flatly. 'And if it's family loyalty you're calling in——'

'I'm not.' As if realising he might have gone too far, Robert swiftly interrupted him. 'Alex, Alex, you must know that you're the son I always wished I had. No—don't interrupt. It's true. You're like me. We think alike. I sometimes think there's more of me in you than there is in Chris! He's his mother's son. A Denby through and through. That's how the family fell on hard times, for heaven's sake! Because they bred generation after generation of milk-and-water thoroughbreds, without a shred of honest muscle in them!'

'Vinnie was a Denby,' pointed out Alex harshly, but his uncle scarcely paused in his stride.

'Only by marriage, Alex; only by marriage,' he retorted fiercely. 'And we'll never know what my wife and your mother might have made of the company because they're dead! But we're alive, Alex. You and I, we could make Denby's an international concern. We're already involved in the Brazilian mining operation, but I've got my sights set on Canada and the United States. With you behind me, to run the operation here, I'd be free to travel the world in pursuit of

contracts. Denby Textiles is no longer the corner-
stone of our operation. Denby Engineering and Denby
Electronics outstripped it years ago. I want you with
me, Alex, you know that. I dread to think what will
happen to Denby's when Chris takes over. And he
will do one day, Alex, unless you've got the guts to
take it from him!'

Alex's face was grim. 'Chris is your son, Uncle
Robert!' he exclaimed angrily, but the older man was
not dismayed.

'So what?' he inquired indifferently. 'I'm not saying
that I don't love him. I do. He's my only child, and I
care for him deeply. But that doesn't mean I can't see
his faults, and despair of them. Chris isn't cut out to
be the next managing director of Denby's, Alex. You
are. And you know it!'

Alex drove back to London later that night. As the
sleek grey Ferrari covered the miles between Nazeby
and his own house in Eaton Mews, he had plenty of
time to go over what his uncle had said and he
eventually decided, with some irritation, that Robert
Seton would go to any lengths to get his own way.
Not that Alex entirely disagreed with what his uncle
had said. Chris would find it hard to apply himself to
a real job, when the time came. For the past eight
years, he had done little more than spend some of the
vast sums of money his father's companies were
making, and although he played around a bit as
trouble-shooter for the organisation, his main source
of enjoyment came from gambling. Even so, Alex had
never considered his Denby heritage as giving him any
claim on the company. When Robert Seton married
his mother's sister, the textile trade was failing and,
without Robert's business expertise, Nazeby itself
might have had to be put on the market to help pay
the company's debts. It was Robert's skill which had

turned a losing concern into a thriving industry, and it was only fair that his son should inherit its advantages. Besides which, Alex had always wanted to be independent. He had never been content to bask in the glow of his uncle's generosity, and while Chris was getting sent down from Oxford and wasting his time at clubs and race tracks, Alex had gained a first in law. He could have done almost anything. He was offered jobs by friends of his uncle, other members of the business and banking community, but he had chosen to go to bar school. Then, instead of going on and becoming a famous barrister, as everyone had expected, he had entered a firm of tax consultants and spent the next three years learning what there was to know about income tax, and company tax, and all the other vagaries of the British tax system. In consequence, when he was twenty-six, he was able to set up on his own, and now, at twenty-nine, he owned a very successful company, the rewards of which were quite sufficient to satisfy his needs. It was the knowledge of this that made it comparatively easy to reject his uncle's proposition. He had no burning desire to be the newest director of Denby Industries, and if it meant seeing Isabel Ashley again, nothing could persuade him. Or so he thought.

Ten days later, he had reason to revise his opinion. A telex from New York was waiting for him at his office, when he arrived back from a late lunch, the gist of which sent him rapidly to the telephone.

'What's going on?' he demanded of his uncle's secretary, who had accompanied Robert on his trip. 'I have a message here, which reads: *See Ashley immediately, re sale of Denby shares.* My uncle knows I refused to handle this commission days ago. What game is he playing now? Is he there? Let me speak to him.'

'Mr Seton is in a meeting, and can't be disturbed,'

said Joan Ferris at once, and Alex's mouth compressed at the age-old excuse. 'He thought you might ring, and he asked me to tell you, the situation's changed. Apparently, Miss Ashley does want to dispose of her shares, after all. And as your uncle is out of the country at the moment, he's hoping you'll act as family mediator in his absence.'

'What's wrong with the solicitors handling it?' asked Alex flatly, his suspicions aroused. If Robert had thought he might ring, then why hadn't his uncle done the same? Sending a telex was so impersonal, and it gave Alex little room for manoeuvre.

'Mr Seton was sure you would understand that in a matter as delicate as this, a member of the family should be involved——'

'But not Chris,' Alex interrupted her harshly. 'OK, Joan, but I'll have something pretty strong to say to your boss when next I get hold of him. You can tell him from me, I don't appreciate his methods!'

'But you'll do it?'

'Do I have a choice?' Alex took a grudging breath. 'All right, Joan. You can leave it with me. But don't be surprised if I blow it. I'm not exactly in the mood to be tactful.'

It was not until Alex got back to his own house that night that he allowed himself to give any thought to his uncle's request. His profession entailed seeing clients at all hours of the day and night, and his evening had already been planned before he received his uncle's telex. In consequence, he had been able to put any serious consideration of what he had committed himself to to the back of his mind, and it wasn't until he was undressing for bed that its full import struck him.

It was annoying, because he had had quite a pleasant evening, dining with Howard Marsden and his wife. He had even succeeded in foiling Hilary Marsden's not-unsubtle efforts to attract him, and for once her rather obvious contempt for her husband's feelings had failed to arouse his impatience. Instead, he had concentrated his attention on the problem of Howard's particular tax liability, and he had not even been aware he had been avoiding thoughts of Isabel until the realisation came to him.

Unbuttoning his shirt, and pulling it free of his trousers, he regarded his reflection without liking. It was infuriating that the thought of his cousin's ex-wife should still have the power to disturb him, and he felt a renewed sense of resentment towards his uncle for putting him in his present position. If it wasn't for the affection he genuinely had for Robert, he could even now wash his hands of the affair and let someone else do it. But he had given his word, and was loath to break it, particularly if it meant restoring his grandmother's shares to their rightful branch of the family.

Nevertheless, he took a shower before getting into bed, letting the brittle spray pummel his body and run almost cold before turning it off. Then with a towel wrapped carelessly about his waist, he walked back into his bedroom, using a second towel to dry his hair before shedding them both on to the carpet.

He was tying the belt of a cream silk dressing-gown when he heard a knock at his door. At his resigned summons, a middle-aged man with greying hair put his head into the room, smiling somewhat diffidently at Alex's look of enquiry.

'I wondered if you'd be wanting a drink or a sandwich, perhaps,' he remarked ruefully, widening the door to reveal a small, wiry frame, dressed in a dark woollen dressing-gown over blue and white striped winceyette pyjamas. 'Sure, I was getting ready for bed, and I thought to myself, that's Mr Alex home already, if I'm not mistaken, and maybe feeling a bit peckish, if he's had an early dinner.'

'No, thanks, Kerry.' Alex regarded the cheerful Irishman with reluctant humour. For the past six years, ever since he had had his own establishment, Kerry O'Flynn had looked after him, seconded from the staff at Nazeby at Robert Seton's insistence. 'I don't need anything,' he added wryly, aware of the butler's darting gaze. 'And before you ask, I don't intend to leave those towels to dampen the carpet. I'll put them in the basket in the bathroom before I go to bed. I promise.'

'Now, would I be leaving you to clear your towels away?' demanded Kerry indignantly. Advancing into the room, he gathered up the two offending articles and tucked them under his arm. 'I'll be putting these in the wash tub, first thing in the morning. Like as not, before you're awake, unless you've an early call.'

Alex forced a thin smile. 'Thank you.'

'It's no trouble.' Kerry took his duties very seriously. 'Now, you're sure you've everything you need?'

'Everything.'

'Good enough.' Kerry backed out of the door. 'Then, I'll wish you a good night, sir. You take it easy. You're looking a little tired.'

'Am I?'

But Alex saved his comment until the inquisitive Irishman had closed the door behind him. Then, he walked into his dressing-room and examined his face more closely in the mirror above the hand-basin. It was true, he reflected sourly. The number of nights he had spent working recently were beginning to make their mark. And he'd had some trouble sleeping since his grandmother's will was published.

Grimacing, he rubbed his hand along the darkening curve of his jaw-line. He needed a shave, but what the hell! That could wait. It wasn't as if Penny was here to complain about his designer stubble. She wasn't due back from Kuwait until the beginning of next week and by then the upcoming interview with Isabel, which was making him so irritable, would be behind him.

He had his secretary ring her number, as soon as he arrived at his office the following morning. The sooner he dealt with the matter, the better, he had decided grimly, after spending another restless night. He had too much work on at the moment to prolong the aggravation.

He went into his own office while his secretary made the call, refusing to speculate on the reasons why he could recite Isabel Ashley's phone number from memory. Absorbing the reassuringly familiar atmosphere, he spent the next few minutes flicking through the mail on his desk, only pressing the intercom when it seemed the girl was taking an inordinately long time to make the connection.

'I'm sorry, Alex,' Diana Laurence apologised, when she came on the line. 'But there's no reply from Miss Ashley's number. Do you want me to try somewhere else?'

'Oh——' Alex swore somewhat colourfully, and then, quickly recovering himself, he added, 'I'm sorry. And no, I don't have another number for Miss Ashley.' He sighed. 'Leave it for now, will you, Diana? I'll get back to it later.'

'Very well.'

Diana had been with him too long to be offended by his outburst, but after she had rung off, Alex flung himself irritably into the leather diplomat chair at his desk. He could have given her an alternative number. He knew that eighteen months ago Isabel had joined the Ferry agency, and it would have been a simple matter to call Jason Ferry and have him locate Isabel for him. But that would have meant showing his hand to someone else besides Isabel, and he had no desire

to advertise his mission. *Mission Impossible,* he thought
glumly. He just hoped she hadn't gone off on some
overseas assignment.

Diana rang just then to let him know that his first
appointment of the day had arrived, and realising he
could not allow his frustration with Isabel Ashley to
interfere with his work, he had her send the man in.
What else could he do, after all? He would have to
ring Isabel this evening. If, at that time, there was still
no reply, he'd be perfectly at liberty to tell Robert
that he hadn't been able to reach her.

He had lunch with a graduate friend from Oxford,
and he was quite glad that his afternoon was taken
up with visiting a co-operative in East London. It was
a free service he offered, in conjunction with a govern-
ment-backed grant scheme, and the group presently
running the small engineering company were more
than willing to show him over the workshop. They
wanted his advice about tax allowances, and his
opinion concerning how much they could afford to
invest in new machinery.

'I bet that piece of machinery cost more than we'll
make this year,' commented Brenda Jeffries, one of
the technical trainees, who had taken over the paper-
work, admiring Alex's Ferrari from the window of the
first floor office. 'And you know,' she added, turning
so that he could appreciate her profile, 'I bet someone
like you doesn't need a car to pull the birds. I don't
suppose you need an assistant, do you, Mr Seton? I
have had—secretarial experience.'

'I'm sure you have,' Alex responded humorously,
fitting his papers back into his briefcase. 'And if I
discover we have a vacancy, I'll keep you in mind.'

'You will?' Brenda's round blue eyes sparkled. 'I'll
remind you of that next time you come.'

'OK.' Alex walked towards the door. 'Just don't
forget to tell Ted Ripley I'll be in touch, hmm? G'bye.'

''Bye.'

Brenda bestowed another wistful smile, and Alex's lips were twitching as he descended the flight of iron stairs to the yard below.

But driving back to his office, his humour dissipated. 'Try that number again, will you, Diana?' he requested, as he crossed her office to his own, and then gritted his teeth impatiently when she asked, 'Which number?'

'Isabel Ashley's, of course,' he retorted, and then, realising how unreasonable he was being, he sighed. 'I'm sorry. It's been a long day. Did you take a note of the number? It's——'

'I have it here,' said Diana, unperturbed. 'Oh—and I've left some messages on your desk. Your cousin, Chris, has been ringing you on and off all afternoon.'

'Chris?' Alex suppressed a groan. That was all he needed, for Chris to find out he was trying to see Isabel. In spite of his opposition to his uncle's request, he had to agree with Robert that Chris's seeing his ex-wife again was not a desirable proposition. 'What did you tell him?'

'That you were out at Walthamstow, of course,' said Diana, pressing the buttons that made up Isabel's number. She smiled up at him. 'It's ringing now. Do you want to take it?'

Alex hesitated, and then shook his head. 'I'll wait,' he said, suddenly convinced that Isabel would not be there. Nothing short of a personal confrontation was going to resolve this situation; he could feel it in his bones.

But, amazingly, after a few moments, he heard the connection being made, and Diana looked up at him inquiringly. 'In my office,' he said, striding swiftly across the room, and her 'Miss Ashley? Hold on, will you? I have a call for you,' was terminated by the closing of his door.

'Isabel?' He practically snatched up the phone, grimacing at the sudden acceleration of his pulse. He was out of condition, he told himself fiercely, admitting no other reason for his laboured breathing. Sinking down on to the corner of his desk, he drew a steadying gulp of air. 'Isabel, this is Alex—Seton. My uncle asked me to get in touch with you.'

CHAPTER TWO

THE PHONE rang as Isabel was folding clothes into her suitcase. Jason, she thought immediately, unable to think of anyone else who might be ringing her at a quarter to five in the afternoon and, abandoning her packing, she went to answer it. Perhaps he was ringing to say the trip was off, she reflected hopefully, reaching for the receiver. A long weekend in Scotland at this particular point in her life was something she could have done without.

The girl's voice at the other end of the line was unfamiliar however. 'Miss Ashley?' she said. No one Jason employed would address her as 'Miss Ashley'. 'Hold on, will you? I have a call for you.'

Isabel moistened her lips. All of a sudden, she was back in the intimidating splendour of the lawyer's office, hearing the dry tones of Virginia Denby's solicitor telling her that she had inherited the old lady's shares in Denby Industries, and she instinctively knew that this call had something to do with that. Who else but Robert Seton would address her as *Miss* Ashley, losing no opportunity to underline his achievement in severing her connection with the Seton family?

She was tempted to ring off without speaking to the man. His company solicitors had already been in touch with her own, offering to buy back the shares at a substantially increased premium, and she had told them she was not interested. Evidently Robert Seton was not satisfied with her answer. She knew he would do anything in his power to prevent her from seeing Chris again. If he only knew . . .

'Isabel?'

Her hand trembled at the unwillingly familiar tones. She did not need his 'Isabel, this is Alex,' with 'Seton' added, almost as an afterthought, to identify her caller. Now she really wanted to slam down the receiver, and only the knowledge that Vinnie had expected more of her forced her to suffer his introduction.

'Alex,' she acknowledged flatly. And then, with irony, 'What a surprise!'

'Is it?' Unexpectedly, his voice was curt. 'Yes, well—Uncle Robert is out of the country at the moment, so he asked me to—stand in for him, so to speak.'

'Who better?' put in Isabel caustically, and his intake of breath proved her gibe had found its mark.

'Nevertheless,' he persisted, and she could tell it was an effort for him to control his temper, 'I wonder if it would be convenient for you to call in at my office tomorrow morning at—say——' She heard him flicking through the pages of his diary. 'Um—twelve-thirty?'

'I'm afraid not.' The Scottish trip was suddenly very attractive to her. 'I shall be out of town for the next few days. The earliest I could see you would be—oh——next Wednesday.'

His impatience was almost palpable. 'Next Wednesday,' he echoed through his teeth. 'I see.'

'It's the truth.' For some reason it was important that he should believe her. After all, the last thing she wanted was for him to think she was afraid to see him. Sooner or later, she would have to. She had accepted that when she accepted Vinnie's shares. 'I'm leaving for Perth first thing in the morning. I work for Jason Ferry now, and he's leased a castle over-looking Loch Tay for the weekend.' She crossed her fingers. 'It should be quite an exciting trip. I'm looking forward to it.'

'In May?' Alex was sceptical. 'I hope you get to keep your clothes on.'

Isabel's teeth dug into the soft skin of her lower lip. 'I always do,' she countered tautly. 'You should know that.'

'People change,' he retorted carelessly, and she knew an overwhelming desire to slap his lean, sardonic face. 'In any case,' he continued, 'I should have thought your unexpected windfall would have enabled you to give up an occupation you always professed to dislike.'

'Ah, but that was before I knew the Setons, Alex,' she declared maliciously. 'Compared to living with your family, photographic modelling is a breeze! And I wasn't working for Jason when I married Chris.' And let him make what he liked of that!

However, Alex let her remarks go without retaliation, and she wondered uneasily if she wasn't handling this badly. Surely she ought to be able to speak to him without resorting to insults. When she had first learned of Virginia Denby's generosity, she had determined to face her erstwhile in-laws with dignity and discretion. Yet, here she was, on the verge of kicking and clawing, like the ambitious bitch he had always thought her.

'Anyway,' she said now, adopting what she hoped was a conciliatory tone, 'I can't imagine why you should want us to meet. Any company business can surely be dealt with by my solicitors, and as you're not a member of the Denby board——'

'I've just told you,' Alex interrupted her smoothly. 'My uncle has asked me to deal with the situation in his absence, and as you were, nominally at least, a member of the family, a less—shall we say, formal transaction seems appropriate.'

Isabel's tawny brows drew together in some confusion. 'I'm afraid I—what particular transaction are you talking about?'

She heard him sigh. 'What transaction do you think I mean?' he enquired evenly.

'I don't know.' She frowned. 'Are there some papers I should have read and haven't?'

'Papers?' Alex snorted. 'Look, let's stop playing with words, shall we? I mean the shares, of course. Lady Denby's shares. You do remember them, don't you?'

Isabel's hand sought the cushioned back of her rocking-chair. Almost objectively, she admired the peach-coloured lacquer of her nails, that were such a subtle contrast to the dark green velvet of the cushion, but all the while her brain was racing with the turmoil of her thoughts.

'Are you still there?'

Her silence had initiated the question, and shaking her head in an effort to clear her reasoning, she said quietly, 'I thought I had made my position plain. Your grandmother left those shares to me. I—I intend to respect her wishes.'

There was a brief, but charged, pause, and then Alex said harshly, 'So why am I speaking with you now?'

Isabel swallowed. She could have asked him the same question. Indeed, if his uncle had asked him to contact her, it might be difficult for him to find a convincing answer. Or maybe it had been his idea. Just what was he playing at? Surely he didn't imagine he could trick her into handing the shares over. Her face burned at the thought that he might think he could succeed where his uncle had failed.

'Maybe you should ask yourself that,' she retorted now, refusing to be daunted by the prospect of his anger, but she could almost feel his antagonism.

'What is that supposed to mean?' he enquired, with

biting coldness, and throwing caution to the winds, she told him.

'You never could keep away from me, could you, Alex?' she taunted. 'That's what made you so mad. The fact that I had married Chris, when you were still available!'

She put the receiver down then, without waiting for his response. Whatever it was, whatever form his counter-attack might take, she had no wish to hear it, and she hoped that by the time she came back from Scotland, the whole thing would have blown over. It was obviously an attempt to get her to think again about the advisability of retaining the shares, and she wondered if, in spite of his oft-professed determination not to get involved in Denby business, Alex had finally accepted his heritage. After all, his mother had been a Denby, and he was too like his uncle to ignore the family trait.

Shaking her head, dismissing the faint feeling of unease that still lingered, Isabel walked back into the next room to continue her packing. The suitcase she intended to take with her was open on the bed, and she struggled to remember what she had put in and what she hadn't. The phone call had distracted her, and it was difficult to concentrate on a mundane chore like packing when her brain was still troubled by the things Alex had said. Nevertheless, she had to be ruthless and put all thoughts of the Seton family to the back of her mind, even if Alex's call had rekindled all her doubts about the legacy.

The suitcase wasn't full when she had completed her task, but although she and the other models would be away for five days, most of the time would be spent wearing the clothes sent by the agency. All she really needed was a couple of gowns suitable for evening wear, some casual gear and her toothbrush. Even her make-up would be put on by an expert, and her own

selection of creams and eye make-up slotted easily
into the canvas tote bag she carried.

Moving across to the mirrored vanity unit, Isabel
made a half-hearted attempt to sort out the perfumes
she intended to take with her. Her favourite, by Nina
Ricci, she wore all the time, but for evenings she
preferred something a little heavier. However, her
attention was soon diverted by the image of her hands
in the mirror, and resisting the urge to turn away, she
let her gaze drift upward.

How long was it since any of the Setons had seen
her, she wondered, running her fingertips along the
line of her cheekbones. Three years? Four? Or was it
longer? Certainly, it was all of four years since she
had severed her connection with the family. Four
years! It seemed a lifetime. So much had happened,
and there had been so much she wanted to forget.

Smoky grey eyes encountered their reflection in the
mirror, and she glimpsed a fleeting shadow in their
depths. But the shadow was quickly banished, erased
by a determination not to betray any emotion, even
to herself, and instead she acknowledged their dark-
lashed beauty. Her eyes had always been her best
attribute and, together with features of reasonable
attractiveness, had made her living, if not her fortune.
Her nose was long, but at least it was straight, and
high cheekbones could be a bane, particularly if she
allowed herself to get too thin. After the divorce, her
face had looked almost angular, and it had taken
many months before the hollows filled out again. Her
mouth was too wide, the upper lip too narrow, the
lower lip too full. But it parted over teeth that were
square and white and even, and Jason always said it
had a sexy curve.

She grimaced now. Jason would say anything to get
his own way, and lately he had revealed a totally
unexpected possessiveness where she was concerned.

She hoped it wasn't going to become a problem. She liked Jason. She was grateful to him for giving her the chance to re-establish her career after her marriage failed. But she didn't love him. She didn't love anyone. Love was an emotion she couldn't afford. She had tried it once and it was far too destructive.

It was almost six and, deciding she deserved a cup of coffee, she walked back into the living-room and through it to the kitchen. The apartment was not large. In many ways it was small and inconvenient, in that all the rooms led out of one another, a fact which afforded little privacy when she had guests. But she lived alone, the place was hers, and mostly she didn't mind its shortcomings. It was the first real home she had known, and certainly it was the first home she had ever owned.

She had been brought up in a children's home. Her mother had abandoned her when she was only a few days old, and the somewhat ugly little girl she had become had not attracted would-be adoptive parents. She had always been tall for her age, and her long skinny limbs had contrasted unfavourably with those of smaller, chubbier children. In addition to which, red hair did not seem to find approval among the home's visitors, and the tight braids it was always confined in had accentuated her naturally pale skin. She had never looked strong, and the fact that she was as healthy as an ox had not convinced anyone. It wasn't until she was about fourteen, and her body began to fill out, that people's opinion started to change. The carroty hair had mellowed with age into a rich, dark red, the thin features had acquired a narrow-boned beauty, and the long, awkward limbs had become shapely and elegant. The ugly duckling had turned into a swan, and the trustees at the children's home didn't quite know what to do with her.

She supposed it was natural that she should turn to modelling as a career. In that respect she had been lucky, for one of the governors of the home had had connections with one of the larger model agencies in the city, and by the time she was twenty, she was fairly well established in commercial advertising. And then, she had met Chris, they had got married, and in her innocence, she had imagined they would live happily ever after. How wrong she had been . . .

The sound of her doorbell interrupted her thoughts. Strangely enough, it was not the intercom from downstairs, that visitors usually used to gain access to the building. It was the bell attached to her front door. And although she realised her caller could be one of her fellow tenants, she had purposely kept aloof from the occupants of the other apartments. It wasn't that she was unfriendly. But her privacy was important to her. That was why a troubled expression entered her eyes as she heard the bell peal again.

She wasn't prepared for visitors, she fretted, glancing down at the sloppy yellow track suit she had worn home from the gym. Her feet were bare, her face was devoid of any make-up, and the tangled mass of her hair would need a thorough brushing to tame it. She had intended to do her packing, give herself a facial, enjoy a long luxurious soak in the bath, and then eat a snack supper as she watched the late film. Who could possibly expect to thwart her plans? She could only think of Jason, and her lips compressed impatiently as she walked towards the door.

Even so, it paid to be cautious and, attaching the chain, she called, 'Who is it?' before releasing the latch.

There was a moment's silence, during which time she wondered if her caller had given up and gone away. But if it was Jason, she knew better than to believe that this was so, and waiting for his answer, she expelled a heavy sigh.

'Isabel?' said a voice at last, and although it was male, it was definitely not Jason's. He did not have that distinctive timbre to his tones, nor did his voice send a wave of shocked resentment sweeping over her. 'Open the door! We didn't finish our conversation.'

Isabel swallowed, turning to press her shoulders against the panels. Alex! Here! She couldn't believe it.

'Isabel!'

The edge to his voice was unmistakable, and she thought how typical it was of all the Setons, that they should believe she would jump to their tune. Did Alex really believe that by side-stepping the building's security system, he could barge in here, uninvited? He was totally intractable, and too arrogant to be true.

'Isabel! I know you're there. Don't you have the guts to open the door? Or does hanging up on someone constitute the whole gamut of your resolution?'

Isabel's jaw clenched. This was ridiculous. She was standing here, cringing, and letting the man she despised most in the world threaten her from the other side of a door. He was wrong. She did have guts. And if she hadn't rushed to speak to him, it wasn't because she was scared to do so.

Turning, she hurriedly lifted the latch, and knew a sense of irritation when she fumbled with it. She didn't want him to think he had disconcerted her, though she still kept the safety chain in place.

The door opened to the width of the chain, and steeling herself, she faced the man outside for the first time since her divorce from his cousin. 'Well, Alex! How nice,' she greeted him tauntingly. 'I didn't know you stooped to breaking and entering. But then, nothing the Setons did would ever really surprise me.'

Alex propped his shoulder against the door. 'I don't propose to stand here all night, Isabel,' he said, almost pleasantly. 'Either you open the door properly and let me in, or I break it. It's up to you. Make up your mind.'

Isabel's tongue circled her lips. 'You wouldn't dare.'

'Wouldn't I? Try me. And I'd hazard a guess that you'd have more to lose than I would. Your neighbours wouldn't like it. They might even call the police. Think how embarrassing that would be in a conservative building like this.'

'You bastard!'

'That's more like the Isabel I remember.' He straightened up. 'Open the door.'

Isabel slammed it shut, but only to dislodge the chain and secure the catch. 'It's open,' she muttered, backing away into the living-room, and then turned her back on him as he came into the flat.

He hadn't changed, she thought bitterly. She might have gone through a personal trauma, but Alex Setón looked just as enigmatic as ever. She didn't even have to look at him to recall the dark, almost black, eyes, set between thick, stubby lashes, in a face that was too hard to be called handsome. He was the only man whose height had topped hers by some four inches, and whose lean muscular body owed its fitness to a high metabolism, rather than to a grim devotion to athleticism. So far as she remembered, he had always avoided sports, though he used to swim regularly at a health club in London. He was rich and successful, and immensely attractive to women. But he was also ruthless, as Isabel had learned to her cost.

He came into the living-room of the apartment now, his hands pushed carelessly into the pockets of his jacket. His suit was dark blue, and expensive, she surmised and, like all the clothes she had seen him wear, it fitted his lithe frame with loving indulgence. As he moved, the width of his shoulders was clearly outlined beneath the fine fabric, while the narrow cut of the trousers exposed the powerful muscles of his thighs. She didn't want to look at him, but she couldn't avoid it, particularly as any show of reticence was likely to work to his advantage, not hers.

Alex, meanwhile, was looking intently about the room, and she wondered what he thought of her modest domain. Certainly it could be nothing like the apartments he was used to, and compared to the spacious elegance of Nazeby it must appear cluttered and restricted. After all, much of the furniture had come from the saleroom, the actual purchase price of the flat straining her resources to the limit.

'What do you want?' she demanded now, deciding it was safer to take the initiative than wait for him to do so, and he turned his appraising gaze in her direction.

'You don't change, do you, Isabel?' he remarked obliquely, and she knew an angry sense of frustration. 'I don't think you've ever felt anything deeply in your whole life. That's what makes it so unbelievable that Vinnie should have been taken in by you.'

Isabel drew a breath. 'Is that why you've come here? To talk about your grandmother?' She shrugged. 'She was a dear old lady, and I loved her very much. What more is there to say?'

'Loved?' Alex's thin-lipped mouth curled. 'Oh, spare me that, please! You've never loved anyone, but yourself. Not Chris, not my uncle——'

'You're wrong. I did love Vinnie,' broke in Isabel indignantly, and then, realising that once again she was letting him put her on the defensive, she forced a mocking smile. 'What's the matter, Alex?' she countered lazily. 'Are you jealous?'

The faint trace of colour that entered his narrow face at her words was worth the effort. So, she thought ruefully, that was the only way to deal with him. More difficult, perhaps, but oh, so rewarding!

'As I said, you don't change,' he retorted, spearing her with a crippling gaze. 'Beautiful, but immoral. And selfish to the core. Thank God, Chris had the sense to walk away from you. He may not have found anyone else yet, but at least he's happy.'

Isabel stiffened, but she refused to let him see his words could still hurt her. After all, she had heard them before. She ought to be used by now to that particular offensive. But it was some time since she had come under attack, and she hadn't yet marshalled her defences.

'Anyway, I didn't come here to get involved in old hostilities,' Alex went on presently, and Isabel shrugged.

'To create new ones instead?' she suggested provokingly, and had the temporary satisfaction of another minor victory.

'To talk about your change of heart,' he corrected her grimly. 'Although, as you don't appear to have a heart, perhaps that was an unfortunate choice of phrase. Your change of—mind, shall we say? The reasons behind your communicating with my uncle, which seem at variance with your present attitude.'

Isabel blinked. 'I beg your pardon?'

Alex gave her a weary look. 'Let's cut the chaff, shall we? Just tell me what you want, and I'll try to accommodate you. Uncle Robert will pay whatever it takes to get those shares back. Name your own price. You have the advantage.'

Isabel stared at him. 'Would you believe me if I told you I didn't know what the hell you were talking about?'

'No.' Alex rocked back on to his heels and then forward on to the balls of his feet. 'Isabel, there only is one subject on which we can still communicate. Don't play me for a fool. You know what I'm talking about.'

Isabel shook her head. 'All right. I accept that you've come here to try and persuade me to sell the shares, but I don't see where your uncle comes in. Any communication I've had with him has always been through my solicitors.'

'Has it?' Alex absorbed this in silence for a moment. And then he pulled one hand out of his pocket and pushed long brown fingers into the thick dark hair at his nape. 'So, Uncle Robert didn't tell me that, but no matter. Evidently, your solicitors intimated your desire to discuss it further. As I say, tell me what you want. I'll speak to my uncle and get back to you tomorrow—or next week, if you are going away for the weekend.'

'*If* I am?' Isabel controlled her resentment with an effort. 'Look, I'm sorry, Alex, but I still don't know anything about this.'

'You're lying.'

'No, I'm not!' She was incensed by his intransigence. 'I think you'd better go back to your uncle and find out exactly what he's playing at. I didn't contact him. My solicitors didn't contact him. And what's more, I don't believe your story any more than you do mine.'

Alex stared at her angrily now. 'You're saying you've never thought about selling the shares?'

Isabel nodded. 'Yes.'

'Then why would my——?'

Alex broke off in the middle of his question, and she saw the flash of illumination that crossed his face. As if a veil had lifted, she glimpsed the sudden comprehension in his expression, but then the mask descended, and she could no longer guess his thoughts.

'I think I'd better go,' he said abruptly, pulling his other hand out of his pocket and fastening a single button on his jacket. 'It seems I was mistaken. I've evidently misunderstood my uncle's message. He must have hoped you'd come to your senses. Vinnie may have left you the shares, but she never expected you to keep them.'

'What you mean is, your uncle hoped you'd have more success than he did,' exclaimed Isabel contemptuously, disgusted by the realisation that Alex would support his uncle, whatever the circumstances. For a moment, just for a moment, she had thought she had seen disillusionment in his face, and she had actually felt sympathy for him. But whatever she had seen, it was firmly controlled now, and it was galling to hear him defend a man who was totally unscrupulous.

'I have no intention of debating my uncle's intentions with you,' Alex stated, walking towards the door and, watching him, Isabel wondered if he was really as indifferent as he seemed. In his place, she would have been as mad as hell, but Alex, as always, revealed none of his feelings.

'You've had a wasted journey then,' she ventured softly, curiously unwilling to let it lie. 'Uncle Robert must be laughing up his sleeve at the prospect of you and me being at cross purposes. I mean, he couldn't actually have hoped that you would influence me. Doesn't he know that you hate my guts?'

Alex's expression hardened. 'You put it too strongly, Isabel,' he retorted, pausing in the act of reaching for the Yale lock. 'To hate someone, one must first have feelings towards them. Thankfully, that was not the case so far as I was concerned. I admired you, as one does any unusual object. But I didn't desire you, Isabel. That's where you made your mistake.'

Isabel caught her breath. 'That's not true.'

'I'm afraid it is.' With a jerk, he had the door open, and had stepped outside. 'Keep your shares, Isabel. Take them to bed with you. As you judge everyone in terms of their bank balance, you should find them very reassuring.'

The door slammed on her angry retort, and although

she longed to charge after him and rake her nails
across his smug, complacent face, she didn't. Instead,
she dropped the latch, slid the bolt and put the chain
back into position, as if by shutting out his material
presence she could eliminate him from her thoughts.
But, of course, she couldn't. Apart from anything else,
the faint aroma of some tangy soap or shaving lotion
he used still lingered in the apartment, and even
though she opened the windows she could still smell
it when she went to bed.

CHAPTER THREE

'YOUR cousin is here to see you, Alex . Shall I send him in?'

Diana Laurence's enquiry was voiced from the intercom at his elbow, and Alex gave an impatient sigh. 'Why?'

'Why is he here, or why send him in?' queried Diana drily, and, as her boss revealed his irritation, 'I don't know. Do you want me to ask him?'

Alex hesitated. 'What time is my next appointment?'

'You don't have one.'

'I do now.' Alex's response was clipped. 'Give us—oh, fifteen minutes, and then break it up, hmm?'

'If you say so.' Diana sounded reluctant. 'So—shall I send him in? He can hear this conversation, you know.'

'Only your side of it,' declared Alex curtly. 'OK, Diana. If you must. But don't forget; fifteen minutes only.'

Alex was putting aside the file he had been studying when his cousin, Christopher, entered his office. Sliding the calculator he had been using into a drawer, he rose to meet the man who had once been Isabel Ashley's husband, and he was annoyed by the realisation that he should think of Chris in that way.

'Sit down,' he said, after their initial greeting. 'To what do I owe the pleasure; or is this a social call?'

Christopher Seton laughed and lounged into the chair opposite. Crossing his legs, he rested his hands loosely on his knees. Like his cousin, he was wearing a three-piece suit, but whereas Alex's choice was dark

34

and conservative, Christopher's outfit was much more flamboyant. He was wearing a cream tweed jacket with a matching waistcoat and pants, and instead of a tie, a cream and yellow cravat filled the neck of his shirt. They were clothes more suited to the race-track than the office, and Alex guessed this visit had been an afterthought. He and Chris seldom saw one another these days. It wasn't that he avoided his cousin; if they met at Nazeby, they were always civil to one another. But since they had both become adults, they had found they had nothing in common, and the affair of Isabel had only served to widen the breach.

'How are you, Alex?' Chris asked now, and his cousin knew a sense of irritation out of all proportion to the inconvenience Chris's arrival had created.

However, he hid his feelings admirably, as he responded, 'I'm fine. How about you?'

'Fine, fine.' Chris's lips twitched. 'Losing more than I'm winning, but what's new? It helps to pass the time. You should try it.'

Alex's expression was controlled. 'Not my scene, Chris. You should know that. I prefer a surer way of earning a living.'

'Oh, yes.' Chris's fuller features took on a familiar expression. 'Good old Alex! The example to us all. Well, you ought to lighten up, old man, or Dad will mould you in his image. You know you're his favourite. I never stood a chance.'

Alex sighed. 'That's not true, Chris.'

'Isn't it?' His cousin regarded him shrewdly. 'You wouldn't say that if you could see him. This business over Isabel is tearing him apart.'

'So that's it.' With an exclamation of disgust, Alex pushed back his chair and got abruptly to his feet. 'Your father sent you here, didn't he? To try and justify what he did. You don't really believe I'm your father's favourite. That was just a ruse to try and get my sympathy.'

Chris expelled his breath on a weary sigh. 'Would I do that?'

'If he made it worth your while, yes.' Alex had no illusions about his cousin.

'That's not fair!'

Alex regarded him resignedly for a moment, then he shook his head. 'What did he say?'

'Who? Dad?'

'Who else?'

Chris flicked an imaginary speck of dust from his cuff, and then said carefully, 'He's very upset, Alex. You hurt his feelings. He's not used to anyone treating him like that.'

'Tough.'

'And over Isabel, too!' Chris looked up at him incredulously. 'I mean, if there was any way we could get those shares back again, we should try it. I don't know what Vinnie was thinking of to do such a thing. They were my shares, Alex; mine! How could she leave them to her?'

Alex's lips tightened. 'As a consolation, perhaps?' he remarked sardonically, and Chris was considering his words when he looked up and caught his expression.

'Oh, very funny,' he muttered, realising Alex was being sarcastic. 'Well, anyway, I think you're behaving very badly. Dad was only thinking of the company, you know. And you'll expect a share of that, as well as me.'

'I don't expect anything,' retorted Alex flatly. 'Denby Industries is all yours. Now, if that's all you came to say, I do have work to do——'

'What's she like?'

Chris's unexpected intervention caught Alex unawares, and he felt the warmth invade his neck around his collar. 'I beg your pardon?' he said, though he knew perfectly well what Chris had said, and his cousin moistened full red lips before repeating his enquiry. 'Isabel. Has she changed much?'

Alex considered his answer. 'I—not a lot,' he admitted reluctantly. 'She's older, of course, but aren't we all?'

Chris leant forward. 'Is she—is she still as beautiful?'

'If you like that sort of thing.' Alex took a deep breath. 'Look, what is this, Chris? Why do you care what she looks like?'

'I don't. At least, not really.' Chris lay back in his chair again, and Alex's fingers itched to pull him out of it and eject him from his office. 'But you have to admit, I had good taste. I used to get quite a kick out of taking her places. People used to look at her, you know. Men, especially. They used to envy me.' He shook his head. 'What a pity!'

Alex kept his temper with difficulty. 'Chris,' he said warningly and, with a gesture of compliance, the younger man got to his feet.

'All right, all right, I'm going,' he exclaimed defensively. 'Can't a fellow reminisce from time to time? I wasn't to know she'd turn out to be a super-bitch, was I? Thank heavens you weren't attracted to her. It was bad enough finding out she was cheating on me. Imagine how I'd have felt if you'd been involved.'

Alex's mouth compressed. 'She's not my type.'

Chris snorted. 'Oh, thanks. That's some consolation, I suppose.'

'You know what I mean.'

Chris got to his feet. He wasn't as tall as his cousin, and he looked at him now from beneath lowered lids. 'I suppose I do,' he conceded. Then, 'But what about this business over Dad? Are you going to let that cow ruin your relationship?'

Alex groaned. 'Chris——'

'Well, as you guessed, it's why I came. The old man's like a bear with a sore head these days. What with Isabel's solicitors refusing to discuss any sale, and you treating him like a leper! Can't you see his motives were honourable, even if the way he went about it wasn't? Go see him, Alex. Make your peace.'

Penny Hollister seconded Chris's request later that day. Penny, who was a stewardess with Middle European Airlines, had arrived back from Kuwait the day before, but Alex had had a dinner engagement that night, and they had been unable to get together until this evening. Now, as they shared a bottle of wine at the small Italian restaurant near Alex's house in Knightsbridge, he had been forced to admit they would not be spending the weekend at Nazeby that he had previously suggested. He had glossed over the more personal details of his encounter with his cousin's ex-wife, but he had had to tell Penny why he had gone to see her.

'Well, I think your grandmother must have been a little dotty, whatever her doctors say,' Penny declared now, her disappointment at being denied her trip to Nazeby colouring her tones. 'What was she trying to prove? I mean, they were divorced, weren't they, your cousin and this woman? Why should she make her a beneficiary when she's no longer a member of the family?'

Alex was non-committal. He didn't like to hear his grandmother described as mildly demented, no matter how upset Penny might be feeling, and he was glad when their bolognese was served, and he could concentrate on that.

'What's she like, anyway?' Penny asked, winding a long string of spaghetti round her fork, and Alex watched her for several seconds before saying dismiss-ingly, 'She's a woman.'

'I know that.' Penny grimaced in mock-reproval. 'But what does she look like? Is she good-looking? She must have something to have attracted your cousin.'

Alex didn't really want to discuss it, but he realised any reluctance on his part could be construed as prejudice. And the last thing he wanted Penny to think was that he had any personal reason to deny her request.

'Um—well, she's a bit like you,' he replied at last, and as he did so, he realised how true that was. The two girls were alike, although if he was honest, he would have to admit that Penny was only a pale reflection of her *alter ego*. Isabel's hair was richly coloured; Penny's was amber; Isabel's eyes were a greenish grey; Penny's irises were hazel; Isabel's mouth was wide and provocative; Penny's lips were unre-markable . . .

'Like me?' Penny said, looking at him archly. 'How intriguing! Tell me more.'

'There's nothing more to tell.' Except that Isabel was taller, and slimmer; and he resented the suggestion that he had made any connection.

'You don't like her, do you?' Penny ventured now, sliding her hand across the table and caressing his wrist. She had sensed his irritation, and she was eager to restore his humour. 'If it makes you angry, we won't talk about it any more. But do you think she's worth the sacrifice of being at odds with your uncle?'

Alex's nostrils flared. 'I don't think the two things are mutually compatible. My opinion of Isabel has nothing to do with my argument with my uncle. Let's leave it at that, shall we? I dare say Uncle Robert and I will sort out our differences eventually.'

'But not before this weekend,' bemoaned Penny

ruefully. 'Damn Isabel Ashley! And damn your grandmother, too.'

Alex made no comment. He was grateful for the
opportunity to change the subject, and for a while
their conversation turned to less controversial matters.
But then, after the meal, when they were waiting for
a liqueur to round off the evening. Penny suddenly
said, 'What does she do?' and Alex's feeling of tranquillity fled.

'What does who do?' he asked. But he knew. It was
as if the subject fascinated Penny. Hearing that they
looked alike had evidently aroused her interest, and
although she knew he wouldn't like it, she had to take
the chance.

'Isabel Ashley,' she said at once, giving him a
pleading look. 'Don't be mad. I'm curious, that's all.
Maybe she doesn't work for her living. I just wondered
if she did.'

'She's a photographic model,' said Alex flatly. 'She
does layouts for catalogues and things, and occasionally she appears in TV commercials. Does that satisfy
you?'

Penny's eyes widened. 'Would I know her face if I
saw it?'

'I doubt it.' Alex was impatient. 'She's no Marie
Helvin. There are dozens of girls, just like her. Few of
them ever make it big.'

'I suppose not.' Penny was thoughtful. 'All the
same . . . ' She shrugged. 'She did meet your cousin.'

'Yes, she did that,' agreed Alex sardonically, and
when his brandy came, he swallowed it in two gulps.
'Right. Shall we go? Before I begin to wonder if Chris
is the reason you so desperately wanted to spend the
weekend at Nazeby.'

'As if that was a possibility!' Penny exclaimed later,
hugging his arm as they walked the short distance to
where Alex had left his car. 'I have met him, you

know. He came to your apartment that Sunday, wanting to borrow some cash because all the banks were closed.' She grimaced. 'He's not my type at all. He has such a weak face, don't you think?'

Alex regarded her tolerantly as he unlocked the Ferrari. 'Well, that's my grandmother and my cousin you've insulted. Anyone else?'

Penny coloured. 'I'm sorry. I just didn't want you to even think I was interested in Chris. No, I was just curious about his ex-wife, that's all. I don't believe you ever told me why they split up.'

'Some other time,' said Alex briefly, swinging open his door. 'I've got some work to do after I've taken you home.'

Penny's face dropped. 'You're not coming in?'

'Not tonight,' said Alex, reaching for the ignition. 'I've got to have a report ready for tomorrow morning, and right now, it's only half written.'

Penny gave him a sulky look. 'You should have said. I could have easily got a Chinese take-away, and washed my hair instead.'

Alex glanced her way. 'Who's complaining?'

'I am.' She hunched her shoulders. 'First of all, our weekend's been blown out of the water by this silly disagreement you've had with your uncle, and now you don't have time to go to bed with me because you've got some stupid report to write! What did you expect?'

'All right, all right. We'll go to bed together then,' said Alex expressionlessly. 'But I shall have to leave straight after——'

'No, you won't!'

'The report won't write itself.'

'That's not what I meant.' She sniffed. 'If you think I'd just let you *use* me——'

'I understood we used each other,' Alex overrode her coldly. 'I thought we agreed our work would always come first. I don't object when you fly off to Cairo or Bahrain, or some European capital at a moment's notice. Why should you complain when I tell you I have commitments, too?'

'Because I've just come back from the Middle East,' she exclaimed indignantly. 'We haven't been together for over a week! I need you, Alex.'

'I'm sorry.'

'No, you're not.' She flung herself away from him. 'And I can't help wondering why it isn't the same for you as it is for me. How do I know what you get up to while I'm out of the country? You could have another woman. I'd never get to know.'

Alex expelled a heavy breath. 'This is ridiculous!'

'Is it? Is it?' Penny slumped in the seat. 'I wish I could believe you.'

Alex slowed to accommodate a pedestrian crossing. 'Does it matter?' he queried wearily. 'I don't put any conditions on you.'

'No, you don't, do you?' she countered bitterly. 'So what am I supposed to glean from that? Is there someone else?'

Alex's face was set. 'I don't think that's part of our agreement.'

'So there is,' she cried tearfully.

'I didn't say that.' Alex swung the car into the forecourt of the apartment block where Penny lived, and brought the car to a standstill. 'But would you believe that I was telling you the truth if I denied it?'

Penny gulped. 'If—if we could trust one another——'

'Trust is for kids, Penny. And for those rare beings who find a lasting relationship. It's not for us. We each professed to want our independence.'

Penny's lip quivered. 'And if I've changed my mind?'

'I haven't,' said Alex callously and, getting out of the car, he walked round to open her door for her.

'Good night, Penny. Sleep well.'

He was getting into the car again when she seemed to come to her senses. 'When will I see you again?'

'I'll give you a ring,' he promised glibly, and then, before she could put any further restraints upon him, he set the wheels in motion with a spinning of the tyres.

Kerry was still up when he got back to Eaton Mews and his bushy brows arched enquiringly when his employer walked in.

'Sure, and you're an early bird,' he exclaimed, switching off his television and following Alex into the kitchen. 'Now what can I get you? Some coffee? A cup of tea? Or would you rather have something stronger? There's that bottle of fire-water your uncle brought you back from Brazil.'

'Coke will do,' Alex assured him flatly, extracting a can from the door of the fridge. 'And I don't want anything to eat either. I've just had dinner, and I've got some work to do.'

'Ah.'

Kerry nodded, and Alex drank half the can before wiping his mouth on the back of his hand and regarding the smaller man dourly. 'Ah what?' he demanded.

Kerry shifted a little awkwardly now. 'Ah—that's why you're back so soon,' he volunteered defensively. 'Because you've got some work to do. I assumed you'd be spending——'

'You should never assume anything, Kerry,' said Alex, brushing past him on the way to his study. Shrugging off his jacket with one arm, he drained the can with the other. 'I don't want to be disturbed, understand? I'll see you in the morning.'

'Yes, sir.'

Kerry watched his employer disappear through the door that led into his private sanctum and pulled a wry face. If he was any judge, it wasn't just the weight of work that was bugging the man tonight. Mr Seton had something else on his mind, or he was a leprechaun's uncle!

In all honesty, Alex was admitting much the same thing to himself. Flinging himself into the chair at his desk, he acknowledged that the excuse he had given Penny wouldn't quite hold water. Oh, he had a report to write, but there was no specific urgency for it. He had actually told his client it might take several days to compile, and he had only used that as an excuse to get out of an unwelcome situation. But why? Why hadn't he wanted to go to bed with Penny tonight, when for the past six months they had had a more than satisfactory relationship?

One solution to his dilemma was totally unacceptable to him. The idea that his recent encounter with Isabel Ashley should in some way have influenced his decision tonight was almost laughable, only he wasn't entertained. Apprehensive, perhaps; angry, certainly; but not in any way amused.

Pulling his tie away from his collar, he tore the knot free and tossed it impatiently across his desk. For once, the elegantly appointed room gave him no pleasure, and the lamplight glinting over polished mahogany and Moroccan leather was just a means of illuminating his unease. He didn't feel like working. He didn't feel like doing anything. But he was sensible enough to realise where too much introspection might lead and, gritting his teeth, he reached for the pile of documents arranged neatly in a metal tray. He had always been able to find peace of mind in his work, and when Kerry risked poking his head round the door before going to bed, he found his employer firmly engrossed in a complicated financial analysis.

Robert Seton rang Alex the next morning.

'Do you want to speak to him?' asked Diana, mindful of her employer's mood the previous day after his cousin had departed. 'You have an appointment at eleven.'

Alex hesitated. Then, 'Why not?' he conceded, after a moment. 'OK, Diana. Put him through.'

His uncle was evidently delighted at his success. 'Does this mean you've forgiven me, Alex?' he exclaimed, causing the younger man no small feeling of self-derision. 'Chris told me that he's spoken to you. I don't usually approve of his interference, as you know, but in this instance, I'm inclined to reserve judgement.'

Alex caught his lower lip between his teeth for a moment before replying. He was not unaware that his decision to speak to his uncle was due in no small measure to the restless night he had just spent, rather than to any persuasion his cousin had exerted. But why shouldn't Chris take the credit? he mused wearily. He had no intention of telling Robert that Isabel Ashley had disturbed his sleep.

'What do you want, Uncle?' he inquired now, leaning back in his chair and resting the ankle of one leg across the knee of the other. 'I have an appointment in exactly four minutes. I'm not being rude, but I really don't have a lot of time.'

'I know what a busy man you are.' Robert Seton was conciliatory. 'And what I have to say won't take more than a couple of minutes. I just wanted to tell you that I'm still expecting you at Nazeby this weekend. And your charming friend of course. Chris is looking forward to seeing her again. He tells me she's a lovely girl.'

Alex sighed. 'I'm afraid I won't be able to make it this weekend after all, Uncle. Something has—come up. I'm sorry.'

Robert sighed, too. 'So you haven't forgiven me.'

'My decision has nothing to do with the affair over Isabel,' declared Alex shortly. 'It's simply that——'

'How can I believe you?' His uncle sounded desperate. 'Alex, the last time we met, face to face, you said some pretty scathing things about me, and about my business methods. All right. Maybe I did behave badly. Maybe I did send you to see that woman with some crazy idea that you might succeed where I failed. She always had a soft spot for you, you know that. Was it so unscrupulous to try and exploit the fact?'

'Yes.' Alex was adamant.

'Well—so be it. If you say so. But we're *family*, Alex. We can't allow that woman to be the cause of any more unpleasantness between us. Please, say you'll forget what I did. I really do want to see you.'

'Why?'

Robert gasped. 'Why do you think?'

Alex considered. 'The board meeting next week, perhaps.'

There was a pause, and the silence that ensued was heavy with frustration. A home run, reflected Alex shrewdly. Robert must be more distraught than he thought. He had evidently overlooked the fact that, as financial consultant to the company, his nephew received regular bulletins about all company matters. He already knew there was a meeting on Thursday.

'So,' Robert's voice was flat now, 'I could invite you in your business capacity.'

'In business hours.' Alex conceded the point.

'Oh, come on.' There was an edge to his uncle's voice. 'Not all your dealings are conducted in business hours. Can't you spare me one weekend? I really do need to talk to you.'

Alex paused. 'What about?'

'I thought you said you had a client pending.'

'I do.'

Robert grunted. 'Well, this may take longer than a few minutes. Have dinner with me this evening. We can talk about it then.'

'I'm afraid I have a dinner engagement,' said Alex flatly. 'If you could come here tomorrow——'

'Lunch, then,' said his uncle harshly. 'Or are you booked for lunch, too? What are you trying to do to me, Alex? Don't you think you owe me a few minutes of your time?'

Alex could have said he couldn't make it, but the affection he had always had for his uncle won out. At half-past twelve, he walked through the doors of the select Soho restaurant Robert had suggested, and joined his waiting relative in the adjacent bar.

'Gin and tonic?' enquired the older man, indicating his own glass, but Alex shook his head.

'Perrier water,' he insisted, sliding on to the stool beside him. 'I've got a heavy afternoon ahead of me.'

Robert grimaced, but he gave the bartender the order and then surveyed his nephew with unconcealed relief. 'I can't tell you how pleased I am to see you, Alex. And to know that we've ironed out our differences, too. We have ironed them out, haven't we?' he probed, when the younger man arched a sardonic eyebrow, and after a moment Alex inclined his head.

'I guess so,' he conceded drily, accepting the glass of iced Perrier water from the barman. 'So long as you're not about to ask me to undertake any more of your dirty work.'

Robert's mouth compressed. 'It wasn't like that, Alex. You know why I did it. Isabel—if she was going to listen to anyone, it had to be you.'

'But I had already refused that assignment,' Alex reminded him tersely, still feeling the tug of frustration in his stomach when he remembered how Robert had tricked him. 'Look, as far as Isabel Ashley is concerned, you're just going to have to live with it.'

'I can't.' Robert brought his balled fist down on the bar in silent protest. 'You don't realise what that woman's trying to do to me.'

Alex contained his impatience with an effort, looking away from his uncle to survey the discreetly lit restaurant that was visible beyond the curtained entrance to the bar. He should have known better than to believe Robert was prepared to let the situation ride. It was eating him up. That much was evident from the agitated way he kept toying with his glass, and the air of tension about him was not just a reaction to this meeting. He needed Alex, but mostly he needed someone to confide in.

Bringing his gaze back to his glass, Alex lifted it to swirl the ice around in the faintly sparkling mineral water. 'So,' he said, submitting to an unwilling stir of conscience, 'tell me. What is she doing?'

'Do you really want to know? You're not just humouring me?'

'I'm asking, aren't I?' Alex hid his resignation.

'All right.' Robert drew a steadying breath. 'All right, I'll tell you. She's blocking Denby's bid for Mattley Pharmaceuticals.'

Alex frowned now. 'Blocking your bid?' he echoed. 'How can she do that?'

'Don't you believe me?'

Robert was aggressive and, realising he was being presumptuous, Alex urged his uncle to go on.

'It's quite easy, really. She's voting her shares against mine. I've had prior notification from her solicitors, before the board meeting next week.'

Alex was confused. 'But Vinnie's shares only amounted to—what? Fifteen per cent, wasn't it?'

Robert groaned. 'I let her have your Aunt Ellen's shares when she died,' he admitted painfully. 'Vinnie had lost both her daughters, and I thought that by giving her Ellen's shares, it would help to keep one of them alive. I always assumed that when Vinnie died, they'd come back into the family.' He shook his head. 'And this is how she repays me!'

Alex stared at him. 'So that was why——'

'—why I was so shattered when the will was read?' Robert's lips twisted. 'Yes. It was quite a blow.'

'And you need a seventy-five per cent majority to push through the Mattley deal.'

'You've got it.'

Alex hesitated. 'So how many shares does Isabel —own?'

'Thirty per cent,' said his uncle flatly.

'*Thirty!*' Alex was stunned.

'Yes.' Robert shrugged. 'It's my fault, of course. If I hadn't been so stupidly sentimental, I wouldn't be in this position now. That's why I need your help, Alex. I don't expect you to get actively involved again, but perhaps you can give me some advice.'

CHAPTER FOUR

IT WAS after one o'clock when Isabel hurried into the restaurant. She had spent the morning at the hairdressers, having the ends of her hair trimmed, and a thorough conditioning had done much to tame its unruly wildness into a manageable state. Now, it was caught up on top of her head in a loose knot, with delicious tendrils of dark red silk nudging the collar of her dark blue jacket. Underneath the jacket, a purple suede button-through dress hugged the shapely contours of her thighs, and even without the heels that added inches to her height, she would have attracted attention.

Not that Isabel enjoyed her notoriety. She was indifferent to the fact that her entrance had caused a minor stir. Her years as a model had enabled her to acquire an immunity to inquisitive eyes, and right now her mind was focused on the fact that Jason had been waiting for over half an hour.

'I know,' she murmured unhappily, responding to his censure, as he rose to hold her chair for her. 'I'm late. But it wasn't my fault.'

Jason Ferry resumed his seat and regarded her sombrely. 'So whose fault was it, then?' he enquired coldly. 'Don't tell me you've just left the salon.'

'But I have,' protested Isabel anxiously. 'You know what it's like trying to get a taxi at this time of day. And then, when I did manage to get one, we got stuck in Charing Cross Road.'

'You should have phoned,' said Jason unreasonably, summoning the waiter. 'Two glasses of white wine, Claud. One with ice.'

Isabel sank back in her chair, slipping off her jacket as Jason gave the order. It no longer annoyed her that Jason hadn't asked her what she wanted before ordering. She was used to his high-handedness now, and besides, today she was relieved that he had not caused a scene. He was a strange man, in some ways. Childishly temperamental at times, and at others, infinitely kind and understanding. He was a conscientious worker, tireless in his pursuit of success for his models. Yet, at the same time, he could be sulky and impatient, taking offence at the slightest thing, and venting his spleen on those who were nearest to him.

She supposed he was a handsome man, although she had never been attracted by his fair good looks and stocky frame. Apart from the fact she wasn't interested in men, he reminded her too much of her ex-husband. And that was why she hoped his present proprietorial attitude towards her was not going to create problems.

'Well, at least the appointment was a success,' he remarked now, capturing her hand on the pretext of examining her nails. His thumb rubbed over the mauve lacquer the manicurist had applied before he brought her fingers to his lips. 'I'm sorry if I was rude. But I was getting quite worried about you.'

Isabel offered a smile, but she withdrew her hand from his grasp. 'No problem,' she said, picking up the glass the waiter had just set beside her and, avoiding Jason's possessive gaze, she looked round the room——straight into the eyes of Alex Seton.

To say she was surprised would have been an understatement. She was shocked, stunned, and not a little resentful that he should be there. After all, she had never seen him here before, and the thought immediately occurred to her that his presence was intentional. But why? What did he have to gain? After their recent encounter, it was the last thing she would have expected. But then she saw his companion, and the doubts she had been feeling crystallised.

Unknown to her, a little of the colour left her cheeks at this discovery, and although she quickly looked away, she could not hide her dismay from Jason. The make-up the beautician had employed with such effect earlier in the day only accentuated her sudden pallor, and his brows drew together when he noticed her expression.

'What is it?' he exclaimed, at once concerned on her behalf. 'Is something wrong? Aren't you feeling well? You can tell me.'

'It's nothing.' Isabel had no wish to draw Jason's attention to the Setons. 'I—I just felt a bit faint, that's all. I'm probably hungry. What shall we eat?'

Jason frowned. 'Are you sure you're telling me the truth?'

Isabel gathered her defences and levelled a cool gaze in his direction. 'I'm not in the habit of lying,' she declared, lifting her glass to her lips. But although she performed quite convincingly to Jason's wary eye, she was intensely conscious of another, hostile, scrutiny.

'Very well.' Jason was obliged to believe her. He picked up the menu the waiter had left lying by his plate, and gave it a swift appraisal. 'What would you like to eat?'

'Hello, Isabel.'

The much-hated, yet undeniably attractive, voice relieved her of an immediate decision. Instead, as Jason's features mirrored a taut reflection of his feelings at this interruption, she was obliged to acknowledge the man who had paused beside their table.

'Alex,' she greeted him coldly, leaving him in no

doubt as to her reaction to his presence, and to her irritation, he smiled.

'It's Ferry, isn't it?' he added, turning to her companion. 'Jason Ferry? You probably don't remember, but we met once at a charity gala. You were with Yvonne Hemmingway, and I was with her cousin, Meryl French. I'm Alex Seton. Isabel was married to my cousin.'

Jason was forced to get to his feet then to shake hands with the other man, and Isabel's nerves tightened. It wasn't like Alex to be so civil, and she couldn't help but suspect his motives.

She hardly heard what Jason said in response, but then Alex turned to her again. 'I hope you don't mind me barging in like this,' he said smoothly. 'But my uncle and I were just talking about you. We wondered if you'd—both—like to join us for a drink.'

Isabel stared up into his lean, sardonic face with unconcealed disbelief. 'You can't be serious!'

'Why not?' Alex's eyes were dark and enigmatic. 'Just because you're no longer family doesn't mean we can't be friends. I realise we've had our differences in the past, but that's over now. We—that is, Uncle Robert and I—want to mend bridges. Can't you at least meet us half-way?'

Isabel caught her breath. 'I don't believe this,' she choked. 'The Setons don't mend bridges; they destroy them!'

Alex gave a convincing impression of being taken aback at this, and to her astonishment, Jason came to his aid. 'Isabel,' he said mildly. 'I think the man is only trying to be friendly.' He resumed his seat to take her hand, giving Alex an apologetic smile. 'I'm afraid she's not feeling well right now. A few moments ago, I thought she was going to faint——'

'Will you please stop talking about me as if I wasn't here?' Isabel exclaimed angrily, snatching her hand

from him. Taking a deep breath, she forced herself to
look at Alex again. 'Thank you, but I have no wish
to share anything with either you or your uncle! I'm
not sick—only sickened, if you get my meaning.'

Alex's expression never faltered, but she thought
she saw a fleeting savagery in his eyes. But then, with
a rueful shrug in Jason's direction, he strolled back to
his own table, leaving Isabel with the unpleasant task
of explaining herself to her escort.

'Well,' he said, as soon as Alex was out of earshot.
'That wasn't very sensible, was it? And why didn't
you tell me your ex-husband was one of those Setons?
My God, I assumed he was some little salesman or
something.'

Isabel felt inestimably weary suddenly. 'Does it
matter?' she countered, wishing Jason would just forget
about it. She determinedly picked up the menu. 'We
were about to decide what we were going to have to
eat.'

But Jason wasn't listening to her. 'Denby Textiles,'
he was saying wonderingly. 'They have their own
catalogue, you know. All very exclusive stuff, especially for the American market. That's one contract
the Ferry agency could use.'

'No, Jason.' Isabel was quite definite now, and he
pulled a wry face.

'No?'

'That's what I said.'

'Still painful, hmm?' he probed, his sharp eyes alert,
and Isabel sighed.

'Just—distasteful,' she corrected him tersely. 'Now,
can we talk about something else? The food, for
example?'

It took an immense effort of will, but somehow she
managed to swallow smoked salmon mousse and a
salad. At least, she ate enough to convince Jason that
whatever had disturbed her earlier no longer was a

problem, and by the time they left the restaurant, she was convinced she had handled herself with aplomb.

Alex and Robert Seton had departed much earlier. She had known the minute that inimical gaze was withdrawn, and from then on it had been easier to sustain her self-assurance. She was sure now that Alex's presence in the restaurant had not been coincidental, and she hoped Jason would not object if she refused to eat there any more.

Thankfully, Jason had an afternoon engagement, and she did not have to find excuses to go home. His suggestion that they meet up later for dinner, to discuss a projected trip to Paris, was less easy to avoid, but she had left it until the last minute to demur, and Jason did not have time to try and persuade her.

'Very well. I'll see you in the studio tomorrow morning,' he conceded at last, his fair good looks marred by an angry scowl. 'And don't be late this time. Or I may just decide to terminate your contract.'

The words *'Do it!'* trembled on her lips, but she bit them back. It was no use letting her frustration over Alex Seton and his uncle colour her professional judgement. And that was what she was doing. Oh, Jason could be awkward, and his possessiveness where she was concerned was becoming a nuisance. But she convinced herself that she could handle him, and it would be stupid to sacrifice a well-paid occupation just to prove her independence.

She came out into Oxford Street and summoned a taxi, giving the driver her Dorset Place address before sinking back against the worn leather upholstery. It was such a relief to relax at last, and she couldn't help wondering if it was going to be worth the effort to hang on to Vinnie's shares after all. Because that was why Alex was hounding her. No matter how friendly or polite he had seemed, his real motive was plain to see. They had intimidated her and threatened her; Alex had even come round to the flat in an effort to prise her legacy from her; but none of that had worked. Her solicitors had politely, but firmly, denied any attempt to gain possession of the shares, and now they were trying different tactics, pretending to offer her an olive branch.

She shook her head. Why had Vinnie done it? Why had she pushed her gently, but firmly, back into the middle of the ring? It wasn't as if she hadn't known how Isabel felt about her ex-husband and his family. In those dreadful, traumatic days, following the break-up of her marriage, Vinnie had been her only confidante, and the only person she could turn to when she first left Nazeby. She must have known how Isabel would feel, having to deal with Robert Seton again, and if her intention had been to give the girl the means to take her revenge, Isabel wished she had asked her first before putting the onus on her.

Dorset Place ran at right angles to the road that circled Regent's Park. Near the end of the street, the upper windows of the converted Victorian town house, where Isabel's apartment was situated, overlooked the cricket ground, and the open aspect from her living-room was one of the reasons why she had bought it. But as well as that, it was in a reasonably quiet area, and as she sometimes worked at odd times of the night, she was able to sleep undisturbed during the day. Her fellow tenants were professional people for the most part. As Alex had taunted, they were a conservative group, and although she knew them all by sight, she remained an enigma to them.

It was only a little after three when she let herself into the apartment and, kicking off her shoes, she padded into the living-room. Then, shedding her jacket on to the cream linen cushions of the sofa, she trod into her bedroom, to get into something more casual.

The bedroom was the one room in the apartment in which she had allowed her imagination free rein. From the folded Chinese screen behind the bed to the adjoining cubicle with its whirlpool bath, she had spent rather more lavishly than she had intended, but the resulting blend of ancient and modern was a more than pleasing compensation. The walls were pale amber, the radiator was concealed behind a lattice-work screen, and the warm, stencilled fabric of the bed quilt was echoed in the long, draped curtains at the windows.

But today, even the beauty of her bedroom failed to lift her spirits. She was still torn by doubts about what she was doing, and troubled by the uncertain wisdom of pursuing revenge. She was not naturally a vindictive person. Until Virginia Denby had put the means into her hands, she had never thought of making Robert Seton pay for the pain and humiliation he had wreaked upon her. She didn't want to think about Chris, or Alex—and as time went by, she had begun to believe that period in her life was behind her. She had even convinced herself that she wasn't the marrying kind, and her relationship with Jason had reinforced that opinion.

Now, pulling her track suit out of the wardrobe, she stepped into the baggy yellow trousers. Then, tugging the top over her head, she rummaged for her running shoes. Her careless dressing had dislodged her hair from its knot, and she grimaced resignedly. Still, an elastic band soon secured it at her nape and, taking a deep breath, she collected her key and left the apartment.

Although it was May, it was still chilly, and though the tulips were out in the park, there were not many admirers. At this hour of the afternoon, her usual companions were children with their mothers or nannies, people walking their dogs, and a few elderly

gentlemen, out to take the air. And today was no
exception. As Isabel jogged round the lake, she saw
several faces she recognised, and her tense nerves
responded to the comfort of familiar surroundings.
She felt almost content as she trotted back across the
Broad Walk, and not until she saw the gun-metal grey
Ferrari parked outside the house in Dorset Place did
a feeling of apprehension take a hold of her.

Alex! she thought unsteadily, coming to an abrupt
halt. Or Chris? She took a ragged breath. Or maybe
just someone entirely different, she fretted. But who,
in these fairly modest apartments, was likely to own a
Ferrari? Or even know someone who did!

She sighed. Was she being absurdly melodramatic?
A car parked in Dorset Place meant nothing. Good
heavens, it could belong to anyone. Just because Alex
used to drive another expensive car was no reason to
connect the two.

Nevertheless, her pace was considerably slower as
she approached the vehicle, and only when she had
satisfied herself that it was unoccupied did a little of
the tension leave her. All the same, as she mounted
the stairs to her apartment, she couldn't help
wondering if some unwelcome visitor might not be
waiting for her outside her door.

But the landing was deserted, and she chided herself
for her own conceit. She was not that important and,
although she had been a little anxious after the way
she had snubbed Alex in the restaurant, he had more
important things to do than seek an unwilling apology.

After another reassuring look around her, Isabel
took out her key and unlocked the door. Then, letting
herself swiftly into the apartment, she carefully dropped
the latch and slid the bolt and security chain into
place. Fort Knox, she mused, a little ruefully, and
turning away from the door, she walked more confidently into the living-room.

The man standing indolently in the bay of the window, staring out on to the park, turned at the sound of her approach. His shadow was the first inclination Isabel had that she was not alone, but her initial surge of panic quickly gave way to a stinging shock of resentment. 'H—how did you get in here?'

She was clutching her keys to her chest as she spoke, and Alex's lips twitched mockingly. Then, withdrawing one of his hands from the pockets of his pants, he displayed the key dangling from his fingers. 'Snap,' he said, putting it away again. 'You ought to know by now, Isabel, I can get most things I want.'

Isabel squirmed beneath his sardonic appraisal. 'I should have trusted my instincts,' she exclaimed bitterly. 'When I saw the trap downstairs, I should have known the rat would be about somewhere!'

Alex's mouth tightened a little at the deliberate insult, but he didn't respond in kind. Instead, he came round the sofa, and lowered his lean length on to the cushions. 'Thank you, I will sit down,' he declared smoothly, occupying the central position and spreading his arms out along the back on either side. 'And yes, I would like a drink, if you're having one.'

'Get out!'

Isabel could think of nothing else to say, but as she had expected, Alex didn't comply. Instead, he remained where he was, cool and relaxed, watching her frustration with bland, untroubled eyes.

Think! she told herself fiercely, when a sense of impotence threatened to overwhelm her. So long as she remained the aggressor, Alex held all the cards. He was bigger than she was; he was certainly stronger than she was; and in any verbal battle, his vocabulary would always outstrip hers. Her only chance lay in turning his anger against himself, and she wouldn't do that by stamping her feet.

'You look hot,' he said now, and she turned away

from the blatant mockery of his regard. Keep calm, she told herself grimly. Let him think that you're frustrated. And don't be discouraged by his attempts to bait you.

All the same, she couldn't help being aware of him, and not just as her tormentor either. Seated, as he was, with the two sides of his jacket opened over a white silk shirt and striped grey tie, she found her eyes were drawn to the spot where one small pearl button had parted from its fastening. The hint of brown, muscled flesh revealed by that errant stud caused a wave of unwelcome remembrance to sweep over her, and she tore her eyes away before he noticed her confusion.

'Um—is coffee all right?' she asked determinedly, and she had the momentary satisfaction that came from a delayed response.

'Coffee's fine,' he conceded at length, his tone just a little less confident now, and Isabel drew a triumphant breath as she walked into the kitchen.

Her triumph was premature. As she set the kettle to boil, and spooned coffee into the filter, Alex came to the kitchen door, propping his weight against the jamb, and watching her unblinkingly. With one hand in his pocket, and the other toying absently with his tie, he was a disturbing presence, and it took the utmost self-control not to spill grounds all over the marbled working-surface.

'Why did my grandmother leave those shares to you?' he asked unexpectedly, and Isabel felt the hot colour running up underneath her skin. 'She must have known how Uncle Robert would react. She was an intelligent woman. If she wanted to leave you something, why not money?'

Isabel refused to let his words upset her. It was a reasonable question, after all. If she took it at face value, she might yet retain some dignity. Why had

Vinnie left her the shares? She really wished she knew.

'I don't know,' she said now, setting out two earthenware cups and saucers. 'Do you take cream and sugar? I can't remember.'

'Can't you?' Alex straightened. 'Sugar, but no cream,' he advised her distantly. 'And you must know more than you're admitting. Was it your idea to grab a piece of Denby's?'

'My idea?' Isabel's voice rose, but she caught herself just in time. 'Of course it wasn't my idea,' she denied less vehemently, putting the sugar and cream jug on a small silver tray. 'I—would you like a biscuit? I believe there are some in the tin.'

Alex's response was to suck in his breath and turn away and, congratulating herself on her success, Isabel turned to attend to the boiling kettle. Even the fact that her hands were trembling now, and she had to dodge several scalding splashes of water, couldn't prevent her feeling of victory. If only she could keep this up, she need never fear the Setons again.

When she carried the tray into the living-room, Alex had resumed his position on the sofa. It meant that if she sat beside him, she would be uncomfortably close to his lean body, and in consequence she was forced to take the easy chair opposite. It meant that she was obliged to look at him instead of away from him, but there wasn't any alternative.

The glass-topped table between the chairs provided a suitable place to set the tray, and for the first few minutes she could direct her attention to pouring the coffee. But when that was done, and Alex's cup pushed towards him—to avoid unnecessary contact—she couldn't go on evading his gaze.

'You—er—you know Jason?' she remarked, with what she hoped was casual interest, and Alex inclined his head.

'Slightly,' he conceded tersely.

Isabel's tongue touched her upper lip. 'He's a good photographer.'

'I'm sure.'

'I've worked for him for the past eighteen months.'

'Really.'

'Yes.' Isabel relaxed a little. This was going to be easier than she had thought. If she could only sustain this rather one-sided conversation until Alex had drunk his coffee, there would be no further reason for him to stay. 'We did a shoot in Scotland a couple of weeks ago. Oh—but, of course, you know that. It—er—it was fun. The weather wasn't very good, of course, but we spent the weekend in this old castle——'

'Why, Isabel?'

Alex's weary interruption momentarily silenced her, but then, licking her lips, she said innocently, 'Why what?'

'Why this charade?' he demanded, ignoring the coffee. Moving to the edge of the couch, he spread his legs, his hands linked loosely between. 'Who are you trying to hurt? Robert? Chris?' He paused. *'Me?'*

Isabel caught her breath. 'You flatter yourself!'

'Do I?' He regarded her narrowly. 'What is it they say about a woman scorned?'

'A woman scorned?' Isabel knew another surge of fury at his arrogance. The adrenalin was rushing through her blood, and she badly wanted to give in to its insistence and order him out of the apartment. But, somehow, she managed to quell her upheaval, and although she couldn't sit still under such an onslaught, she got to her feet with admirable control. 'A woman scorned,' she said again. 'Oh, Alex! How you deceive yourself!'

Alex rose then, his dark face grim with menace. 'You like playing with fire, don't you, Isabel?' he grated. 'Well, have a care. You may still get burned!'

'I'm shaking in my shoes.' In honesty, she was, but

he would never know it. 'You can't frighten me any more, Alex.'

A spasm of some emotion she couldn't identify crossed his face at her words, and then, sighing deeply, he said, 'I'm not trying to frighten you. I came here this afternoon—as I came to your table at lunchtime—to try and salvage something from the mess Vinnie has left.'

'Really?' Isabel couldn't prevent a thread of bitterness from entering her voice at his facile explanation. 'And I suppose breaking into my apartment was all part and parcel of making up!'

'I didn't break in,' said Alex between his teeth.

'I didn't give you a key.'

'No, and I knew you wouldn't have let me in if I'd come to your door uninvited.'

'Which should tell you something about the way I feel about the Setons,' said Isabel contemptuously.

Alex pushed long fingers through the silky dark hair that lay smoothly against his head. 'I don't want to fight with you, Isabel.'

'Then go away.'

'Is that what you want?'

'Is it what I want?' Isabel uttered a scornful laugh. 'How can you doubt it?'

'You won't even consider being reasonable?'

'How reasonable was your uncle?' she spat angrily. 'How reasonable was Chris?'

'So it is a vendetta,' said Alex flatly. 'Of course. I knew it all along.'

'You know nothing!'

Isabel trembled and, unable to bear his eyes upon her any longer, she turned away, walking stiffly towards the windows, and staring out at the park, which had seemed so friendly just a few minutes before. Oh God, she thought painfully, pushing one hand underneath her hair and massaging the taut muscles at the back of her neck. Here she was, fighting with him again. She had determined not to let him get the better of her but, as usual, she had lost control of the argument. He would never believe her now, if she insisted it was not a personal matter. So far as he was concerned, she was still fretting because Chris had divorced her.

'So I'll tell my uncle there's no chance of his regaining the shares, shall I?' Alex enquired now, and Isabel tensed. Then, when she made no immediate effort to reply, he spoke again, this time from right behind her, and she realised he had crossed the room without her being aware of it.

'You're a fool, you know,' he said harshly, but for once there was no trace of censure in his voice. 'The shares can't mean anything to you, and Robert would pay dearly to have them back again. With what he would give you, you could live in luxury for the rest of your life!'

Steeling herself, Isabel turned. 'Is that what you'd do?'

They were only a few inches apart now, and although it wasn't easy to be as close as this to him, she sensed it was equally as unwelcome to him.

'I—yes. I guess so,' he said, and she could see the pulse hammering away at the taut curve of his jaw. He swallowed. 'You could at least give it serious consideration. You could even start your own agency, instead of working for that creep, Ferry.'

Isabel put her hands down to support herself against the wooden sill. 'You said you hardly knew him,' she reminded him obliquely, and Alex took an impatient breath.

'My association with Jason Ferry is not in question here,' he retorted tersely. 'Look, can't we just forget the past and concentrate on the present? You may be making a living, but you're not exactly affluent, are you? I mean—this apartment is very nice, I'm sure, but you could do better.'

Isabel resented this statement, but right now, she was prepared to overlook it. She sensed that once again the tables had turned and, for all his brusqueness, Alex was just as aware of her as she was of him.

'Do you still live in the same apartment, Alex?' she enquired softly, conscious that her nipples had hardened during their exchange, and were now perfectly outlined against the brushed cotton of her track suit. He had noticed them, too, she was almost sure of it, though he took care to keep his gaze levelled on her face.

'Where I live is nothing to do with you,' he responded curtly, and her lips parted at this further evidence of his frustration. 'Isabel, I'm not trying to trick you. I just want you to think what you'll be giving up, and for what? The opportunity to thwart my uncle's plans for the company? He's made a pretty good job of Denby's without your help. It was on the verge of collapse when he took over. Without him, my grandmother wouldn't have had any shares to leave you. Or do you want to be responsible for the company's decline, is that it? If so, have you thought of all the innocent people who'll lose their jobs if you succeed?'

Isabel shifted a little uneasily now. 'You know, you really should use your law degree, Alex,' she said, forcing a mocking tone. 'You'd be such an asset in the courtroom. You can argue so convincingly.'

Alex held her eyes with his. 'Have I convinced you?'

Isabel swayed. 'About what?' she asked provokingly.

'About the shares,' replied Alex grimly. 'You knew what I meant. Well? What's your answer?'

Isabel lifted her shoulders. 'I'm—thinking about it,' she said, and as if noticing a speck of dust on his collar, she stretched out her hand and brushed the fine cloth.

'What the hell do you think you're doing?' he snarled, grasping her wrist and forcing her hand away from him, and her eyes widened in pained reproof.

'You're hurting me!'

'I could,' he said savagely. 'Don't tempt me!'

'Do I?' she probed artlessly, rubbing her bruised wrist, and Alex swore.

'Do you what?'

'Tempt you?' she responded, enjoying his aggravation, and without answering her, Alex turned away.

'I suggest you inform my uncle of your decision,' he declared grimly, walking towards the door, and without giving herself time to consider the advisability of what she was about to do, Isabel went after him.

Brushing past him, she reached the door before he did, and pressing her shoulders back against the panels, she faced him, as if she had some hope of delaying him by brute force.

'What's the matter, Alex?' she taunted. 'Daren't you wait for my answer yourself?'

'Don't be stupid, Isabel.' Alex halted some distance from her. 'Get out of my way!'

'Make me,' she urged, and it was only later that she realised how reckless her invitation had been.

But at the time, the uncontrollable desire to humiliate him as he had humiliated her in the past was too strong to resist. Instead of moving out of his way, she moved towards him, and he was compelled to restrain her.

'*Isabel!*' He said her name on a note of desperation, and taking advantage of his momentary weakness, she evaded his grasp, and reaching up, let her tongue touch the taut skin covering his jaw.

He stiffened then, his hands seeking a hold on her upper arms and propelling her away from him. And

Isabel let him, content with the progress she had made so far in proving he was not as indifferent to her as he had pretended. She had heard his quickened breathing, and the scent of heated flesh that filled her nostrils was not just her own. That musky fragrance she could smell came from Alex's skin, and she inhaled it deeply, savouring her success.

However, if she had not been congratulating herself so prematurely, she might have noticed the moment when Alex's reactions changed. As it was, the dangerous gleam that entered his eyes went unobserved, and she was still considering what her next move should be when the hands which had been forcing her away from him suddenly changed their tactics. One moment she was fighting his urge to be rid of her, and the next she was fighting an entirely different battle.

'So that's what you want,' he said harshly, jerking her towards him again. 'Well—why should I object?' And before she could summon a protest, he had captured her mouth with his.

But only for a moment. Arching her back, she was able to break that offensive contact, but in so doing, she had to step backwards again. Which was not the most sensible thing to do, she realised at once, when she came up against the unyielding panels of the door. Now she had no way of avoiding him, and as she flailed wildly at his chest, he ground his mouth against hers again with evident satisfaction.

She clenched her teeth and struggled to force her knee between his legs, but he gave her no opportunity to thwart him. Instead, the weight of his body pinned her to the door, freeing his hands to encircle her throat with ever-increasing menace.

She tried to bite him, but she couldn't, and the sudden relaxing of her jaw enabled his tongue to slide between her lips. His stance shifted as the moist warmth of his invasion penetrated deep into the hot cavern of her mouth. His choking grip on her throat eased, and the hands which had previously abused her flesh now took on a sensuous appeal. It was as if he had sensed her own weakening resistance, and his hungry mouth took sustenance from her involuntary response.

With her breathing constricted by his continued assault, all Isabel could feel and taste and smell was Alex. No matter how she fought the insidious flame he was kindling inside her, his forced proximity was making her overwhelmingly aware of how easy it would be to submit. She wanted to fight him; she wanted to escape the very real threat he posed to her independence. But the truth was, the longer he held her, the less strength she had to resist him, and his physical superiority rendered all her efforts useless.

She felt his hands move away from her throat, over the quivering width of her shoulders, and down to grip her forearms just above her elbows. But this time, he didn't push her away. Instead, he brought her closer, arching her body against his and drawing her arms around his waist. And all the time, his mouth continued to devour hers, inciting her participation. No matter how she tried to sustain her resentment against him, he was gradually succeeding, forcing her to meet his need and coaxing her tongue into his mouth.

The heat of his skin through the thin silk of his shirt burned her flesh, fusing them together, and his mouth left her lips to seek the delicate contours of her cheeks. His hands brushed her breasts, taut beneath the cotton, his palms rubbing briefly over the nipples, before moving down to her waist. Her body sagged against the door behind her as one hard thigh was thrust between hers. The powerful muscles probed her womanly softness, and then his hands slid behind her back to cup the rounded curves of her bottom. She was brought even closer, the throbbing maleness between his legs pressing hard against her stomach.

'Oh, God,' he muttered, squeezing her urgently against him. 'I'd forgotten how good you were!'

It was the tormented self-derision in his voice that got to her. It wasn't so much what he said, although that was damning enough. It was the harsh reminder in his tones that he had not instigated this that brought her to her senses. Instead of controlling the situation, she was being controlled and, taking advantage of his sexually-induced weakness, she tore herself out of his arms.

'Get out!'

She practically screamed the words at him, but although Alex was still at the mercy of his senses, he was not incoherent. 'It's a bit late for that, isn't it?' he enquired, fixing her with a lazily mocking gaze. He was making no attempt to hide his arousal from her, and when he ran his fingers down the length of his zip, she actually shuddered.

'I said—get out!' she repeated grimly, uncaring of what interpretation he might put upon it. He was still dangerously attractive to her, and it was taking all her strength to maintain her composure.

'Very well.' Alex took a deep breath and straightened his spine. Then, mocking her attempts to belittle him, he added, 'Did you come to a decision about the shares?'

'You—you bastard!'

'Is that a yes or a no?'

Isabel quivered. 'God—how I hate you, Alex!'

'Well, I guess that's a no,' he remarked, walking indolently towards the door. 'I'll pass your message on.'

She struggled to find a suitable rejoinder while he released the security locks she had set earlier, but it was useless. There was nothing she could say which would give her any satisfaction whatsoever, and when the door banged behind him, she was left with the unpleasant awareness that once again he had made a fool of her.

CHAPTER FIVE

ISABEL stepped into a slim-fitting navy skirt, and searched for the zip. It didn't help when she caught the hem of her cream silk shirt in the fastener, and she was swearing softly to herself when Lauren Bishop entered the dressing-room.

'Temper, temper,' she reproved lightly, kicking off the high heels she was wearing and bending to massage her aching feet. 'You've told him now, and he's accepted it. Think positively, Isabel. Helen, for one, is delighted to be going to Madrid in your place. Jason will get over it. You know he always does.'

Isabel sighed. 'But I told him last week that there was a board meeting on Thursday. He can't have forgotten. Jason doesn't forget things like that.'

'Perhaps he hoped you'd give it a miss,' said Lauren carelessly, leaning towards the mirror to examine her complexion. 'Do you think this foundation really suits me? Maxine says it does, but I'm not so sure.'

'Maxine says what Jason wants her to say,' said Isabel tensely, in no mood to spare the other girl's feelings. 'And how can I give the meeting a miss? I have to be there to know what's going on.'

Lauren sighed, and turned to rest her hips against the vanity unit. She was a tall girl, too, and although she was much darker than Isabel, they could wear the same colours quite successfully. They were not close friends; Isabel's attitude did not encourage close friendships. But they were compatible, and whenever they travelled abroad, they generally shared a room.

Now, Lauren shook her head. 'Why is it so important to you to actually attend?' she asked. 'I mean, you can always get a report of the meeting, can't you? Don't they take minutes or something?

Isabel sighed. 'Yes, they take minutes.'

'There you are then.'

'But I want to be there. It's—important to me to be there. It's what Lady Denby would have wanted.'

'Lady Denby,' echoed Lauren, nodding. 'She's the old lady who left you the shares, isn't she?'

'That's right.' Isabel bit her lip, and then added reluctantly, 'She was my ex-husband's grandmother.'

'Ah.' Lauren made a gesture of understanding. 'How unique!'

'Unique?'

'Yes.' Lauren regarded her wryly. 'Most in-laws do not leave their granddaughters-in-law legacies. Much less ones who are divorced from their grandsons.'

'Oh!' Isabel felt herself colouring. 'No—well, Vinnie and I were friends, you see.'

'Vinnie?'

'Lady Denby.'

'I see.' Lauren moved her shoulders as if she didn't really. 'So, you'll see your ex-husband on Thursday then.'

Isabel hesitated. 'I expect so,' she said at last. That was one eventuality she was not looking forward to.

'Is that why Jason is so peeved about it?' queried Lauren shrewdly, and at Isabel's startled look, she added, 'We all know how he feels about you, Isabel. He's not exactly made a secret of it.'

'Oh.' Isabel shook her head. 'I don't know. I hope not. I like Jason but——'

'—but he's not your ex-husband, hmm?'

'No!' Isabel was vehement. 'No, it's nothing like that. There's no question of Chris and I—that is, well—it was a mistake. Our marriage, I mean. It should never have happened. I—I was young—and flattered, and——' she bent her head to locate her shoes, '——it seemed a good idea at the time.'

Lauren frowned. 'How long were you married?'

'Two years.'

Isabel was offhand now, but Lauren was intrigued. 'So what happened? Was there someone else?'

Isabel straightened. It was to avoid questions like these that she had kept herself aloof. 'Someone else?' she asked, in her most distant voice, and Lauren sighed.

'There was a divorce,' she reminded her ruefully. 'OK,' she could see Isabel didn't want to talk about it, 'forget I asked. For a moment there, I forgot who I was talking to.' She turned away. 'I guess I'd better get changed.'

Isabel picked up her shoulder-bag and then regarded the other girl's back with some misgivings. The temptation to confide in Lauren was appealing, but the habit of keeping her own counsel was hard to break. In any case, much as she liked Lauren, the other girl was not known for her discretion, and Isabel had no desire for her private affairs to become common knowledge throughout the agency. So, with a casual 'Have a good trip!' she left the studio, deliberately using the back entrance to avoid another confrontation with Jason.

She was free now—for a week anyway, she reflected gratefully. On Wednesday, Jason, Lauren, Helen Rogers and two of the other girls were flying to Madrid on the photographic assignment Isabel had had to refuse. They would be away for five days at least, and it was an important break for Helen, the youngest member of the party. It was Isabel's turning down of this opportunity which had been the cause of her quarrel with Jason that afternoon. But Isabel had refused to be intimidated by his threats. If she lost her prime rating with the agency, then so be it. She was determined to attend the meeting of the board of Denby Industries, and she had warned Jason of that fact ten days ago.

Even so, she didn't like quarrelling with him. Two years after the divorce, she had been grateful for his faith in her ability. A period of withdrawal, followed by eighteen months of working at dead-end jobs, had almost convinced her she would never be lucky enough to work as a model again, but an interview with Jason had set her fears at rest. He had seen the potential, which had barely flourished at the time of her marriage, and with his skill and guidance, she had overtaken her youthful promise. That was why it was so hard to disappoint him. That was why she hoped their relationship was not going to become a problem.

Thinking now about Thursday's board meeting, Isabel realised she had less than two days to read all the literature she could find about both Denby Industries and Mattley Pharmaceuticals. So far, her knowledge of both was sadly limited, but she intended to remedy that without delay. She had to admit, her decision to thwart Robert Seton's proposal to take over the smaller company had been made without much thought, and only recently had she realised she might have to face questions about her opposition. In all honesty, all she had really intended was to show Robert Seton that she was determined to make life difficult for *him*. Until Alex brought the subject up, she hadn't even considered what might happen to the employees. All the same, she couldn't believe that blocking the take-over would make any critical difference to Mattley Pharmaceuticals. From what she'd read in the Press, large conglomerates often put in bids for small companies, much against those companies' wishes. Perhaps she was doing the board of Mattley Pharmaceuticals a favour. Considering the alternatives, she certainly hoped so.

Nevertheless, thinking about Alex certainly rekindled her faith in what she was doing. Since he had walked out of her apartment, she had suffered agonies of self-reproach, berating herself time and again for allowing what had happened to happen. She had been so sure she could handle him, so sure she could keep herself aloof from the insidious pleasure of his lovemaking. Maybe if she hadn't made him so angry he would not have attacked her so savagely. If she had only contented herself with the success she had had, instead of taunting him so recklessly, until he had completely lost his head.

And he *had* lost his head, she reflected smugly, with some satisfaction, as she drove her second-hand Mini from the studio in Greek Street to her apartment in Dorset Place. Even he could not deny that. And not for the first time, she remembered, as the unwilling memories refused to be dismissed. If it hadn't been for Alex, she probably would never have married Chris. But pride was an uneasy bedfellow, and she had had her share, the same as anybody else.

And she had been flattered when Chris Seton showed such interest in her. They had met at a media party. She had been there representing the agency for which she had then worked, while Chris had come along with a model from a rival agency. It had been quite exciting to find herself the object of his attentions, particularly when one of the Press photographers advised her who he was. Even in those days, the heir to Denby Industries was considered one of the most eligible bachelors around, and Isabel was too young to be anything but impressed.

Even so, Chris had proved to be an entertaining companion, and, in spite of warnings from friends, she had begun accepting his invitations. She hadn't been afraid of falling in love with him. Her years in the children's home had taught her not to give her affections too freely, and although she had liked Chris, she hadn't meant to take him seriously. But that was before she met his father—and his cousin, Alex—and from that moment on, she had been running for her life . . .

The library did not yield much information about Mattley Pharmaceuticals. There was plenty of literature about Denby Industries, and its parent company, Denby Textiles, but the smaller concern warranted only a brief résumé in business directories, with no details at all about the number of employees or their plans for development. The directors' names were given, and she did contemplate contacting one of them and asking their opinion. But she could hardly ask a complete stranger to give her details of his company's policy, particularly as the merger might well be to his advantage.

What she was grateful for was the fact that the board meeting would take place in Denby Industries' London office. The company's headquarters were just off the Strand in a tall, skyscraper building with its name carved above the smoked-glass doors. Robert Seton, she knew, had his suite of offices on the penthouse floor, and the boardroom opened from them, with deliberate precision.

By Thursday morning, Isabel was half wishing she had decided to sell the shares. She could have saved herself so much soul-searching, she thought impatiently, pouring herself a glass of orange juice in lieu of breakfast. What was she going to gain by putting herself through this ordeal? Perhaps Vinnie had expected her to sell the shares. Maybe it had been her way of ensuring she was given some compensation at last.

But, somehow, Isabel knew the old lady had expected more than that. If she had wanted her to inherit a substantial sum of money, she would have arranged her will that way. No, for some reason best known to herself, Vinnie had wanted her to maintain her connection with the company. And if there was an ulterior motive, no doubt it would expose itself in time.

Isabel dressed with especial care for the meeting. She did have a momentary aberration, when she considered wearing something so outrageously provocative that the other board members would be too shocked to concentrate on what they were doing, but the inclination passed. Behaving outrageously would simply prove to Robert Seton that she was incapable of making a rational judgement, and give him the ideal opportunity to belittle her to the board. To succeed in the task she had set herself, she must first convince her peers of her sincerity. And to do that, she must not give her adversary any reason to undermine her efforts.

With this in mind, she chose a slim-fitting skirt suit in fine, beige-flecked wool, with only a rather modest slit at the back. She teamed it with an amber-coloured silk shirt and a matching tie. The severe cut of the suit was exactly what she was aiming for, and if it served to accentuate her femininity, so much the better. High-heeled bronze pumps completed the outfit, and with her hair strictly confined in a tapering knot, she was pleased with the image she had created. All the same, her hand shook a little as she followed the downward sweep of her cheekbones with a beige blusher. She still had to face Chris and his father and, for all her brave pronouncements, she was definitely apprehensive.

She took a taxi to the meeting, deciding she could not face the harassment of driving in the city this morning. A uniformed doorman opened the swing-door at her approach, and then she was inside the Denby Building, facing a bank of steel-clad lifts, like a prisoner about to serve a sentence. Stop panicking, she told herself fiercely, stepping into the first lift that opened. What have you got to lose? None of them can hurt you now.

The lift remained empty until the tenth floor when two young secretaries joined her. But they paid her scant attention, evidently absorbed with some gossip of their own making, and not until Alex's name was mentioned did Isabel feel a sense of unease.

'Well, I've heard he divorced her because she was having an affair with his cousin,' one of the girls was saying as they entered the cubicle. Then, observing Isabel's presence, she lowered her voice accordingly. 'You know who I mean, Tracy. You've seen him. Alex Seton!'

'Really!' The other girl's eyes widened, as Isabel absorbed what they were saying with hastily concealed disbelief. 'Do you think it's true?'

'I don't know.' Her companion grimaced expressively. 'But I wouldn't mind having an affair with him myself. It's a pity he's not Mr Seton's son. Imagine looking like that, and owning all this!'

'Well . . . Mr Chris isn't so bad,' murmured Tracy, hugging the pile of files she was clutching to her. 'And he does say hello, if you meet him in the building. He's not stand-offish or anything. He's really rather sweet.'

'But he's no Mel Gibson, is he?' exclaimed the first girl drily, and then, realising she had allowed her voice to rise again, she added, barely audibly, 'Besides, I've heard——'

But what she had heard, Isabel was doomed not to hear. The lift doors had opened at the fifteenth floor, and the two girls stepped out. Which was just as well, she thought tensely, catching sight of her own slightly flushed features in the mirrored panel opposite. She had had little difficulty in identifying herself as the guilty divorcee they were discussing, and while it was easy to dismiss their words as gossip, it was disturbing to realise that she was once again the target for careless talk.

The lift reached the eighteenth floor only seconds later, and Isabel wished she had had the sense to stop it at the floor below. She could have done with a few more minutes to compose herself. As it was, someone was waiting to get in, and she was obliged to step out into the reception area bordering Robert Seton's penthouse suite of offices.

Any possible excuse she might have made to give herself time to recover had to be rejected when she was recognised. The plump little receptionist who vetted all visitors to Mr Seton's office identified Isabel at once, and coming round her desk, she gave her a friendly smile.

'Mrs Seton!' she exclaimed, ignoring the fact that Isabel and her ex-husband had been divorced for almost two years. 'It's lovely to see you again. How are you? You're looking well.'

Isabel took a deep breath and went to meet her. 'It's *Miss* Ashley,' she corrected her lightly, not wanting to be reminded of her reasons for being here. 'And it's good to see you, too, Susan. Still working hard, I see.'

'As ever,' agreed Susan Lightfoot, giving a rueful shrug. 'We can't all lead exciting lives like you, Mrs—*Miss* Ashley. I see your picture in newspapers and magazines all the time. It must be lovely to be famous. But, I'm afraid, that's not for me.'

Isabel smiled, aware that Mrs Lightfoot was not as ingenuous as she appeared. She had been with Robert Seton too long to harbour any love for his ex-daughter-in-law, and although her comments seemed innocuous enough, there was an underlying note of disapproval running through them.

'Can I get you some coffee?' the woman asked now, inviting Isabel to take a seat while she informed her employer of her arrival, but Isabel demurred.

'Wouldn't it be easier if I went straight through to the boardroom?' she suggested, her fingers unconsciously tightening about her handbag. 'I am expected.'

'Oh, yes, I know.' Susan Lightfoot was not dismayed. 'But the other members of the board haven't arrived yet, and Mr Seton is busy just now.'

Isabel expelled her breath evenly. 'I think I'd prefer to wait in the boardroom,' she insisted, refusing to be kept waiting here like some interviewee. She wondered what Lady Denby would have done in such a circumstance, and then sighed. Vinnie had not been the kind of person you kept waiting. No doubt if she was here, her son-in-law would have rushed to meet her.

Susan looked taken aback but, short of interrupting her employer while he was dictating, there was little she could do. Besides, Isabel could see her arguing with herself, what possible harm could there be in allowing the newest member of the board to familiarise herself with her surroundings? It wasn't as if there were any confidential papers lying around.

'Very well,' she said at last, and indicating that Isabel should follow her, she led the way along the thickly carpeted corridor. Isabel knew the way for herself, but she allowed Mrs Lightfoot this particular indulgence, stiffening automatically when they passed the door to Robert Seton's office. His voice, as he dictated to his secretary, penetrated even those solid walls, and she mentally steeled herself for the confrontation to come.

The boardroom was large, but not excessively so. The long rectangular table was set about with fourteen ladder-backed chairs, and at each place there was a spotless white blotter, with a jotting pad and a ballpoint pen for making notes.

'I'll let Mr Seton know you're here,' Susan declared as she departed, her voice decidedly frosty now. How not to make friends and influence people, thought Isabel wryly, as the door closed behind her. But if she let someone like Susan intimidate her, what chance would she have with Robert Seton himself?

Putting down her handbag on the table, Isabel controlled the stirrings of panic that gripped her by strolling the length of the room. It was quite a pleasant room, and with a watery sun streaming through the windows, it was not too formidable. The walls were mostly bare, though there was a portrait of Robert Seton at one end of the room. Isabel guessed it was situated above the chairman's position, so that even if he wasn't present at a meeting, his presence could still be felt.

Apart from the portrait, which Isabel considered to be a rather flattering likeness, there was a cabinet displaying the various awards for industry Denby's had accumulated over the past thirty years. Since Robert Seton became chairman of Denby Industries, thought Isabel contemptuously. There was no evidence here that the company had existed at all before the 1950s, and without that earlier nucleus, there would have been no company for the Setons to manage.

To one side of the room, a polished cabinet supported a coffee-maker and a dozen or more porcelain cups and saucers. Cream and sugar resided in matching porcelain containers, and a huge jug of Cona coffee simmered on its stand. Evidently, this was for the use of the board members, Isabel decided and suddenly feeling the need for sustenance, she poured herself a cup.

She was sipping the hot black liquid when the door behind her opened again, and turning with the cup in her hand, she saw her ex-husband standing in the aperture. She didn't know who was the most surprised, herself or Chris. But evidently Mrs Lightfoot had not been around to warn him that their unwelcome visitor had arrived.

And yet, surprisingly enough, Isabel was not as disconcerted by his appearance as she had expected. Somehow, he had never seemed as much to blame as his father and Alex, and although she had once despised him, she could not say she hated him.

'Didn't Susan tell you I was here?' she asked now, as he hovered in the doorway, clearly undecided on his course of action, and Chris shook his head.

'She wasn't at her desk,' he said, making a decision and advancing into the room. 'I—er—see you're having coffee. I could do with some of that myself.'

'White? With two spoons of sugar?' suggested Isabel, picking up the coffee-pot as he closed the door behind him, and Chris nodded.

'You remembered!' he exclaimed, and then his fair skin suffused with colour. 'I mean—well, it's good to see you again, Isabel. I've often wondered how you were doing, but I guessed from what Vinnie told us that you wouldn't welcome my asking.'

Isabel shrugged. It was difficult to sustain any animosity towards him. 'It's all water under the bridge, Chris,' she said, adding sugar to his cup. 'We each have our own lives to lead. Isn't that what Vinnie would have said?'

Chris took the cup she offered him with a rueful laugh. 'Well, anyway,' he added, 'you look jolly fantastic! The pictures I've seen of you don't do you justice. If you don't mind me saying so, of course.'

Isabel's expression was ironic. 'Why should I mind?' She smiled. 'You've gained a little weight yourself.'

'Haven't I just!' Chris grimaced. 'You don't have to tell me. It's the bane of my life!'

'Not so much a cherub; more a satyr!' remarked

Isabel lightly, reminding him of a joke they had once shared, and Chris groaned.

'I guess what I need is a good woman to keep me on the straight and narrow,' he joked, without thinking, but Isabel's smile disappeared.

'Do you?' she countered, meeting his eyes directly, and then, seeing the uncertainty there, she quickly looked away.

'I say—let's not get into all that,' Chris protested following her over to the windows, and standing beside her as she looked down on the panorama of the city far below. 'Dammit, Isabel, you know I'm not my own master. Never have been. God——' he swore '—I wish I were more like Alex! At least he knows what he wants out of life!'

'Don't say that.' Isabel looked up at him unwillingly, and then shook her head. 'Don't *ever* compare yourself unfavourably to Alex! At least you can't be blamed for what you are. Alex is completely without conscience!'

'But I thought you admired Alex.'

'I know what you thought, and I let you go on thinking it.' Isabel sighed. 'But I wanted out of this family, Chris. I had to get out or lose whatever self-respect I had left.'

'Bravo!'

The mocking salute and the smattering of applause that went with it brought Isabel round with a start. She had been so wrapped up in what she was saying, she had half forgotten where she was. And, in those few moments, Robert Seton had come through the connecting door from his office, and was now standing watching them with narrow-eyed malevolence.

But it was not the chairman of Denby Industries who held Isabel's attention. Even as she steeled herself to face his cold antagonism, another man came into the room behind him. Tall and dark, dressed in a lightweight business suit that complemented his tanned complexion, he moved easily to stand beside his uncle, and seeing them together, Isabel thought how similar they were.

'You don't mind if Alex joins the meeting, do you, Isabel?' Robert Seton inquired, coming towards her, his hand outstretched. His initial hostility at finding his son and his son's ex-wife together had melted in the heat of his success in confusing her, and now his palm closed about her cold hand with unconcealed satisfaction.

Isabel withdrew her fingers immediately however, clasping the hand he had touched inside the other, as if his touch had burned her. He was totally unscrupulous, she thought angrily, annoyed with herself for allowing him any advantage. The only way she could hurt Robert Seton was through his company. All other avenues had been closed to her.

Alex made no attempt to greet her, other than a faint raising of his eyebrows. Instead, he went and helped himself to some coffee, surveying the other occupants of the room with mild insouciance. Like Robert Seton, he was completely in control of his actions, and Isabel wondered if he had told his uncle about their confrontation at her flat. It she had believed that by relating that particular incident to Robert Seton she could gain some advantage, she would have done so. But she was very much afraid she would only make a fool of herself, and in spite of her antipathy towards Alex, she was not prepared to take that risk.

'So—isn't this nice?' Robert remarked, giving his son an encouraging pat on the back. 'Together again after all this time. I hope Vinnie can see us. She's certainly got what she wanted.'

Isabel took a deep breath, and then, ignoring the faintly anxious look on Chris's face, she said, 'I wonder if she'd be so happy if she knew how you'd tried to thwart her wishes, Mr Seton.' And, encouraged by the calmness of her tone, she added, 'I'm so sorry I had to refuse your generous offer for the shares she left me. But I felt I owed it to Lady Denby to abide by her decision.'

Robert's face darkened. 'Don't try to fool me!' he snapped. 'We all know how you were able to twist the old lady round your finger! You care nothing for Denby Industries. You're only interested in yourself. And whatever her doctors say, no one will ever convince me Vinnie knew what she was doing when she left her shares to you. My God, she must have had a brainstorm! You're not even *family!*'

Isabel's face was burning now, and before she could find words to repudiate his accusation, Chris chimed in. 'Don't upset yourself, Father!' he exclaimed, moving closer to his parent, as if to demonstrate his support. 'Isabel isn't going to change her mind and sell you the shares if you persist in railing at her. You should try a little psychology. That's what I'd try to do.'

Isabel's lips curled. 'Is that why you've been so nice to me, Chris?' she enquired, stung by the way he had apparently changed sides. 'I should have known you had a motive. You always hedged your bets.'

'I don't think any of us is going to achieve anything by indulging in pointless argument,' inserted Alex abruptly, setting his coffee cup aside and pushing his hands into his pockets. 'Whatever our individual feelings might be, my grandmother did choose to leave the shares to Isabel, and instead of wasting time debating the point, we should be trying to convince her that the Mattley deal would be providential to all concerned.'

CHAPTER SIX

'WELL—we did it!' declared Robert Seton triumphantly, entering his office some time later, and flinging himself delightedly into his chair. 'Alex, my boy, you're a genius! I've said it before and I'll say it again, and I insist that you let me buy you dinner this evening.'

'Yes, Alex, you did awfully well,' echoed his cousin, following them into the office. 'You really had her tied up in knots. By the time it came to the vote, she hadn't a leg to stand on!'

'I merely explained what it would mean to the staff of Mattley Pharmaceuticals if the merger folded,' said Alex flatly, not enjoying his sudden notoriety, but his uncle wouldn't let it rest there.

'It was *how* you told her, Alex,' he said, reaching for a cigar and rolling it experimentally beside his ear. 'Chris is right. She was all tied up in knots. She knew if she'd opposed it then, she'd have had the shareholders to contend with.'

'Well, perhaps if you'd taken the time to explain the situation to her, you'd never have reached an impasse,' retorted Alex, flexing his shoulder muscles wearily. 'It seems to me there's been a lack of communication on both sides. When it came to the crunch, she saw reason.'

'And do you think she'd have listened to me?' demanded Robert Seton forcefully, abandoning his relaxed position and swinging himself forward in his chair. 'Dammit, man, we both—that is, the three of us,' in deference to his son, he included Chris, 'know it was your eloquence that swung it. Don't belittle your achievement, Alex. You saw what had to be done, and you did it. And, if you caused her some bad moments in the process, so much the better.'

Alex pushed his hands into the waistline pockets of his trousers. 'What is that supposed to mean, exactly?'

'Dad's only pointing out that Isabel started this fight, not us,' exclaimed Chris, defending his parent, and Alex's mouth compressed.

'As I understand it, we set the wheels in motion when we tried to buy back the shares,' he returned, with abrasive logic. 'Perhaps if we hadn't shown our hand so openly, the question of whether or not the Mattley deal should go through wouldn't have become an item.'

'You don't believe that!' Chris gave a scornful gasp. 'My God, you were as peeved as any of us when Grandmother's will was announced! And after what she tried to do to you——'

'Just stop there, will you?' said Alex quietly, the moderation of his tone in no way detracting from its menace. 'You weren't exactly showing total disinterest when your father and I interrupted you earlier. What were you saying to her then, I wonder? She seemed to think she might have had your support.'

'That's not true!' Chris was looking hot under the collar now, and he moved about the room restlessly, searching for a suitable rejoinder. 'She—Isabel, that is—she was trying to enlist my help. Of course, I explained where my obligations lay; that naturally I supported Father's stand on the shares, and so on. But that didn't stop her making up to me. In fact, if you and Dad hadn't come in as you did, who knows what might have——'

'That's a lie!'

Before he could finish what he was saying, Alex's hand shot out and grasped a rough handful of his cousin's shirt front. Chris's neatly tied cravat was pulled out of his collar, and his face suffused with colour at the sudden constriction in his breathing. Alex's grip was lethal, and in seconds Chris was gasping for air.

'For pity's sake, Alex!' Robert left his seat to circle the desk and prise the two men apart.' 'Why are you so touchy about what Chris says about that woman? Dammit, she's caused nothing but trouble ever since she became involved with this family! You can't expect Chris to be tactful. Not after what she did to him!'

Alex's jaw was hard. 'I'm sorry,' he muttered, smoothing a hand through his hair and turning away. 'I guess I'm just sick of this whole damn business!'

'Aren't we all?' sniffed his cousin, his hands shaking as he struggled to put his clothes to rights. 'There's no need to take your frustration out on me! Just because you're stung that Vinnie didn't leave those shares to you!'

Alex turned then, but his uncle was between them. 'That will do!' he exclaimed angrily. 'Chris, you'll take back that remark or you'll pay your own bills in future. Alex, we're all in something of a state at the moment. Let's cool it, shall we? And I still haven't had your answer about dinner this evening.'

Alex took a deep breath. 'I'm afraid I can't make it, Uncle,' he said, forcing a note of regret into his voice. 'I've—er—I've got a client to see at eight-thirty. I'm sorry, we'll have to make it some other time.'

'Then how about coming down to Nazeby at the weekend?' suggested Robert eagerly. 'You didn't make it last weekend, so how about this week instead? I'm not expecting any visitors. There'll just be ourselves. It would give us a chance to play a round of golf.

Maybe even take the boat out, if the weather's good.'

Alex sighed. 'I don't know . . .'

'What about me?' Chris demanded peevishly. 'Am I invited, too? Or is this just a tête-à-tête?'

'Don't be such an ass!' His father rounded on him impatiently. 'Nazeby is your home, isn't it? When have you ever not been welcome there?' He breathed heavily. 'But, as I recall it, you told me you were going to Newcastle; to the races. Or have you changed your mind about that, too?'

'What do you mean—*too?*' Chris blustered. 'Am I to understand you believe Alex's version of my conversation with Isabel, not mine?'

Robert shook his head. 'I didn't say that.'

'Not likely.'

'Look, I've got to go,' said Alex abruptly, not prepared to get involved in any more argument. 'I'll ring you later about this weekend, Uncle. If I can get away, I'll let you know.'

He felt a definite sense of relief when he came out of the Denby building. The clouds which had hung around earlier that morning had all cleared away and, like his mood, the sky was considerably lighter. It was warm, too, the first really seasonable warmth of the summer, and he decided to walk to his office instead of taking a taxi, as usual.

Half-way there, however, he was beginning to regret his enthusiasm. Walking gave him far too much time to think, and the avenue his thoughts were taking was not one he preferred. He didn't want to think about the morning's meeting; he didn't want to think about his feelings, when he had seen Chris and Isabel together; but most of all, he didn't want to think about Isabel herself, and how defeated she had appeared at the end of his cross-examination. She herself had said, just recently, that his skills as a barrister were being wasted. Well, perhaps they were. But that was no reason to feel guilty because he had used his courtroom logic to make her look a fool.

He sighed, looking bleakly about him, trying to find something to divert his troubled intellect. But the young women in their summer dresses, and the older ones, pushing toddlers in their chairs, only reminded him of what might have been, and how devastated he had been when he had first met Isabel. How many years was it now since he first saw her at Nazeby? Five? Six, maybe? Long enough, certainly, for him to have forgotten that first meeting; long enough to throw off the shackles of the past and put what had happened behind him.

The fact that that first glimpse of his cousin's future wife was still as sharply etched in his mind as ever caused him no small sense of irritation. He wanted to forget it—and her—but circumstances just kept getting in the way. Of course, until Vinnie died, it had been just a rather annoying memory, which raised its head from time to time, but which mostly he could keep under control. Since the divorce, it had become progressively easier to keep such thoughts at bay, and although he had kept himself informed of Isabel's whereabouts, and what she was doing, if ever he felt himself softening he had had only to think of Chris.

Vinnie's contact with her had made this easier, although his grandmother had never discussed Isabel with him, except in the most impersonal terms. Nevertheless, he was aware of their regular meetings, and if ever he felt the urge to update his mental dossier, it had been a simple matter to ask a perfectly innocent question.

His grandmother's death had changed many things, not least Isabel's status within the family. By leaving her the shares, Vinnie had successfully involved her grandson's ex-wife in Denby—and Seton—affairs, for years to come. She had made a mockery of Alex's determination never to see Isabel again, and locked the door, once and for all, on those halcyon days when he hadn't thought about her at all.

Now, he was uncomfortably aware that he was thinking about her far too much. If he hadn't felt the need to see her again after that disturbing scene at the flat, he would never have allowed his uncle to persuade him to attend the meeting that morning. He was quite capable of refusing his uncles's requests, and he had known at the time that by giving in to Robert, he was actually giving in to himself. But he had wanted to see her again. He had had an uncontrollable urge to go there and convince himself that what had happened between them couldn't happen again. And then, Robert had opened the door into the boardroom. Alex's blood still pounded in his temples when he remembered the scene they had interrupted. Isabel and Chris, standing closely together, deep in conversation, their nearness so reminiscent of that day at Nazeby, when Alex had come upon them in the library . . .

It had been a summer day then, too, only there had been a storm earlier in the day, and the air was still damp and thundery when Alex drove down from London. He had been in a good mood, he remembered. His interview with Storey and Heathcliffe had gone well, and he'd had every expectation of being appointed to their staff. An expectation which had later proved conclusive, when Arnold Heathcliffe had called him with the news that he had got the job.

He had walked into the house, which he had always regarded as his home, looking for either his uncle or his grandmother, with whom to share the news of his appointment. But instead of finding Robert, or his grandmother, in the library, he had found Chris and

his new girlfriend, the importunate young woman his
uncle had spent the last six weeks complaining about.

Alex had convinced himself that it had been because
of his uncle's professed dislike of the girl that he
himself had felt such an immediate aversion to the
scene that confronted him. Seeing her there, with his
cousin, should not have affected him at all; but it had.
He had known a sudden, and totally unfamiliar, surge
of animosity towards both of them, and the feeling
was so powerful, he had found it difficult to be polite.

Looking back, he doubted Chris had noticed
anything amiss. His cousin had never been particularly
perceptive, and he had been so eager to introduce
Isabel to Alex, he had apparently overlooked his
reluctance.

To be honest, Alex had to admit that Isabel was
nothing like what he had expected. After hearing his
uncle's derogatory remarks about her success as a
fashion model, he had been prepared to meet either a
busty blonde or a hard-faced brunette. That Isabel
was neither was immediately obvious. She was tall,
and slim, and the colour of her hair defied description.
It was a tumbling mass of dark red curls, shorter than
she wore it now, but decidedly feminine. Her skin was
flawless, a combination of apricot cream and smooth
alabaster. Her mouth was wide, her nose prominent,
but attractive none the less; and her eyes were a hazy,
smoky-grey, with long, curling lashes tipped with gold.
And when she spoke, her voice was soft and musical,
and just a little husky. Chris was evidently infatuated
with her, and Alex couldn't exactly blame him.

His own reactions were less easy to diagnose, but,
in the days and weeks that followed, when it became
apparent that Chris was determined to marry the girl,
he found himself taking Robert's side in any argument.
For some reason, the idea of his cousin being married

to Isabel disturbed him more than he cared to admit, and if he had been able to change Chris's mind, he would have done so without hesitation.

But for once, Chris was digging in his heels and refusing to listen to either his father or Alex. He was in love, or so he said, and if his father chose to cut him off without a penny, he still intended to make Isabel his wife.

Vinnie, Alex's grandmother, was less unequivocal in her views. She like Isabel. She liked her very much. But, surprisingly, she did not actively encourage the marriage, even though, when it happened, she did give them her blessing.

Eventually, Robert Seton had given in. For all his faults, he did care deeply for his only offspring, and the wedding date was set for the autumn. Alex thought his uncle had become resigned to the prospect of becoming a grandfather in the fullness of time, and only Alex was left to accept the inevitable.

Then, one morning at the beginning of October, Alex received a telephone call from Chris. Could he do him a favour? he asked. He had arranged to come up to London that afternoon and pick Isabel up from the studio, but something had come up. An old schoolfriend had arrived unexpectedly at Nazeby, and Chris didn't like to turn him away without a meal. As it was Friday, and Alex was coming down for the weekend anyway, could he collect Isabel from the studio and give her a lift to Nazeby? He'd be eternally grateful, and it would save him an embarrassing scene.

Alex had no choice but to agree. What excuse could he have given, after all? He had arranged to spend the weekend at Nazeby, primarily so that the local vicar could arrange a rehearsal of the wedding. As Alex was to be best man, he had to attend, so there was no way he could invent a prior engagement.

Isabel was waiting outside the studio when he arrived. Evidently, she had been prepared for his arrival, for she showed no surprise when the black Porsche he had then been driving rolled to a halt beside her. Without allowing him the courtesy of getting out and assisting her into the car, she opened the door herself and slipped into the seat beside him. The overnight bag she was carrying was wedged between her knees and, reaching for the seat-belt, she gave him a polite smile.

'Thank you,' she said, straightening her shoulders against the back of the seat. 'I hope you don't mind this imposition.'

Alex was tempted to say that it would be all the same if he did; but he didn't. It was a good two-hour drive to Nazeby, and for all his antipathy towards her, he disliked the notion of starting the journey with a row.

Instead, he dismissed her gratitude with casual indifference, making some innocuous remark about the state of the traffic, to set their relationship on an even footing.

Yet, for all his apparent negligence, Alex was aware of the young woman sitting beside him with every fibre of his being. Although his impression of her by the roadside and getting into his car had been necessarily brief, he knew how she looked and what she was wearing. Surprisingly enough, she had not dressed formally for the journey. Alex guessed the thigh-length, collarless T-shirt dress and mauve tights, were her usual attire to and from the studios. Even her face was scrubbed clean of make-up so that the pearly radiance of her skin was unblemished. Only her hair appeared a contradiction. Someone, the hairdresser at the studio possibly, had threaded the fiery strands into dozens of small braids. Each braid was fastened with tiny ceramic beads, and when she moved her head too quickly, the beads chinked together. It was not an unpleasant sound, but it was unusual, and the first couple of times it happened, Alex found his eyes drawn to its source.

'Um—Chris is entertaining an old schoolfriend, isn't he?' she queried, after Alex had negotiated the traffic in central London. Like him, she was obviously endeavouring to forget their differences, for the journey, at least, and Alex made an effort to respond in equal vein.

'So I believe,' he said, immediately aware that his tone was not as cordial as hers. 'Chris has a lot of friends from his days at Haveringham.'

'Haveringham.' Isabel picked up on his last word. 'That's a public school, isn't it? I seem to remember hearing the name, but I don't know where it is.'

'It's in Buckinghamshire,' replied Alex evenly. 'It's quite a beautiful part of England. Do you know that part of the country at all? Or is London more to your taste?'

He realised his final question was decidedly patronising, but he couldn't help it. The more he spoke to her, the stronger was the urge to try and belittle her. He didn't know why that was. He only knew that her indifference infuriated him.

'No. I don't know Buckinghamshire,' she responded honestly. 'But London hasn't always been my home. I was born in Lincolnshire, as a matter of fact. It wasn't until I started working that I actually came to London.'

Alex absorbed this news with reluctant attention. Somehow, he had assumed she had always lived in the city. His assessment of her character had been so total, it was disconcerting to realise there were facets of it he had overlooked.

'What part of Lincolnshire?' he asked now, assuring himself his interest was purely circumstantial, and Isabel gave him a sideways glance.

'I'm not sure,' she admitted ruefully. 'I was brought up in a children's home, you see. I never knew my parents. Only that my mother abandoned me, when I was a few days old.'

Alex was amazed. No wonder Chris had glossed over the fact that Isabel's parents were dead and unable to attend the wedding. If Robert Seton had known that the girl was an orphan, he might well have decided to call Chris's bluff.

'Are you shocked?' she asked now, and Alex struggled to put his thoughts in order.

'Surprised,' he conceded, after a moment. Then, compulsively, 'Didn't you ever try to find out who your parents were?'

Isabel shook her head. 'No.' she paused. 'I decided that if my mother was the kind of person to abandon her own daughter, I didn't really want to know her.'

They were travelling along the M3 now, and Alex had to concentrate on overtaking a stream of slow-moving lorries at that moment, so it was several minutes before he said, 'And your father? Didn't you ever try to trace him?'

Isabel sighed. 'He probably didn't even know of my existence,' she replied. 'Eighteen years ago, people were a lot less liberal-minded than they are today. My mother may have kept my birth a secret. Is it fair now to resurrect a mistake?'

Alex lifted his shoulders. 'You're very philosophical.'

'Just practical,' she amended quietly. And then, with a little splaying of her hands, she gave a low laugh. 'I don't know why I'm telling you all this. What is it they say when they're arresting someone? "Anything you say will be taken down, and may be used in

evidence against you?" Is that what you're planning
to do? Tell your Uncle? Give him yet another reason
to try and prevent this marriage?'

Alex cast her a cooling glance. 'If Chris hasn't
chosen to tell him, why should I?'

'Because you're your uncle's favourite.' Isabel spoke
without prejudice. 'Oh, you may not be his son and
heir, but you're the one he depends on, aren't you?
You're the one who supports him, who shares his
opinion of me.'

Alex's mouth compressed. 'Which is?'

'What?' Isabel was momentarily confused.

'My opinion of you. What is it?'

'Oh——' She bent her head now, and the tiny beads
chinked against the vulnerable curve of her neck. 'You
don't like me. You never have. Well—the feeling's
mutual. So don't bother to deny it.'

Alex's hands clenched on the wheel. 'You know
nothing about me.'

'Yes, I do.' She drew a steadying breath, and looked
up at him. 'You haven't exactly hidden your feelings.
You think I'm marrying Chris because he's got lots of
money. You despise my profession; and you criticise
how I look.'

Alex's breathing was less than steady now. 'You
don't have a *profession!*' he retorted at last. 'Taking
your clothes off in front of a camera is hardly
meaningful employment——'

'I don't take my clothes off!' Isabel was indignant.

'You would, if the price was right,' returned Alex
without sympathy, and she glared at him impotently,
restrained from physical retaliation by his concentration on the traffic.

Thereafter, there was silence for a while. Isabel flung
herself round in her seat, so that she was facing away
from him, her knees nudging the door handle, and

Alex tried to take some interest in his driving, which
usually gave him satisfaction. But, for all his determination to ignore her, his eyes were irresistably drawn
to the long, slender fingers, balled into fists on her
knees, and the smooth shapely curve of her thigh,
exposed to some advantage by the sheer tights she
was wearing. The shortness of her skirt was disturbingly provocative, although he doubted if she was
aware of it. She wore her clothes with the same
careless elegance with which she moved. She was
naturally graceful, that much he had to grant her, and
the sexuality of her movements owed more to his
sensitivities than to hers.

They left the motorway after Winchester, turning
on to a narrower, two-laned road, and driving deep
into the Hampshire countryside. They passed through
villages, sleeping in the shadows of early evening, tiny
hamlets some of them, with only a church and a petrol
pump to mark their passing.

Alex knew his way well. There was a busier, major
road he could have taken to reach his destination, but
her preferred the quieter route. Besides, at this hour
on a Friday afternoon, all the major roads were
crammed with commuter traffic, and inhaling someone
else's exhaust fumes was not the way he liked to start
his weekend.

ISabel had evidently noticed their detour, however
and judging by the way she was reading the road signs
they passed she was no doubt wondering where he
was taking her. Knowing Chris's penchant for taking
the shortest route between any two points, he doubted
his cousin had brought her this way. His lips twitched.
Perhaps she was afraid he might be abducting her for
his uncle; or planning to murder her, and dump her
body in some remote corner of the county.

'It's only about twenty miles now,' he remarked, at

last, compelled, for reasons he didn't care to admit,
to reassure her, and Isabel turned her smoky eyes his
way.

'Is it?'

'I don't lie,' he assured her crisply, slowing as they
approached a *Give Way* sign. 'This way may be a few
miles further, but at least we're not hampered by slow-
moving vehicles. And,' he appended almost defensively, 'It's a much more scenic route.'

Isabel shrugged. 'I wasn't complaining, was I?'

Alex's blood rose. 'Is it too much to expect that
you might speak civilly——'

'Civilly!' Isabel hardly let him finish the word, her
eyes fixed on his face in raw contempt. 'After what
you've said to me?' You arrogant—bastard! If it
wasn't for the fact that Chris thinks you're wonderful,
I'd never speak to you again!'

Alex's foot hit the brake almost instinctively. His
anger was almost choking him, and without hesitation
he swung the car on to the grassy verge at the side of
the road, uncaring of the fact that the waving fronds
of ragwort could be hiding a ditch or worse. He was
lucky. The Porsche's tyres skidded a little bit on the
grass which had been dampened earlier in the day by
a thunderstorm, but apart from a few bumps, the car
came safely to a halt.

Then he turned towards her, his eyes blazing
furiously, saying the first thing that came into his head
to prevent himself from physically attacking her. 'If
you feel like that, I suggest you find your own way to
Nazeby!' he snarled, gripping the wheel as he'd like to
grip her neck. 'Go on! Get out! I'm sure you'll find
someone more to your liking to give you a lift!'

Isabel blanched. 'You don't mean that.' She glanced
about her and he saw the muscles of her throat flex
as she swallowed. 'I don't even know where we are.'

'We're approximately nineteen miles from Nazeby,' said Alex harshly. 'Exactly one mile further than we were when I gave you our situation. Is the prospect daunting? It shouldn't be for someone of your doubtful—talents!'

Isabel caught her breath. 'You'd do this, wouldn't you?'

'You'd better believe it.'

She sniffed. 'And what will you tell Chris?'

Alex shrugged. 'I may not *tell* Chris anything. I might just decide to waive my role in this fiasco of a wedding, and drive straight back to London.'

'You wouldn't do that.' She stared at him.

'Wouldn't I?'

Alex returned her stare without flinching, and as if he had just pushed her too far, Isabel acquiesced. 'All right,' she said, a disturbingly flat note in her voice now. 'All right. I'll take my chance.' She shook her head. 'There are such things as buses; and trains. I don't need your help to get to Nazeby.'

Thrusting open her door, she threw her overnight bag on to the verge and started after it. She really expected him to abandon her here, Alex realised, and suddenly he knew that for all his simmering resentment, he couldn't do it. What *would* Chris say? he asked himself bitterly; but it wasn't just his cousin's reactions that were causing him to have second thoughts. He couldn't leave her here, at the mercy of every tramp and sexual pervert that might come her way. Besides, the sky was still very overcast, evening was approaching, and if a storm erupted, there were too many trees around for safety.

'Forget it!' he said abruptly, putting out his hand and grasping her shoulder, preventing her from following her bag out of the car. But now, she turned on him.

'Let go of me,' she commanded, in an icy voice, though her eyes sparked fire. 'Don't you think because you're having an attack of conscience, you can manipulate me at will. I didn't ask you to give me a lift. Chris insisted on it. And, fool that I was, I thought you might actually be prepared to make friends at last. But I was wrong. I should have realised you were too much like your uncle to have a charitable thought in your head!'

Alex's mouth hardened. 'I said, forget it,' he repeated harshly. 'Now, cut out the dramatics and pick up your bag. We still have several miles ahead of us, and I want a shower before supper.'

'I'm not stopping you,' said Isabel carelessly, but she was making no attempt to reach out and pick up her bag, and with a sigh of impatience, Alex was forced to push open his own door to walk round and get it himself.

However, as soon as he released his hold on Isabel, she was out of the car in a flash and, as he first of all lunged after her, and then, finding himself baulked by the gear console, thrust his legs out of the car and came to his feet, she snatched up her bag and scrambled through a gap in the hedge into the field beyond.

'Isabel!' he yelled, his frustration knowing no bounds as he plunged after her. 'For God's sake, what the hell do you think you're doing?'

She was a hundred yards ahead of him when he emerged from the hedge, his hair almost torn from his scalp by a wayward briar. Looking down at his jacket, he saw that it too had been raked by the prickly bushes, and the cuffs of his trousers were already damp from the wet grass. When he got his hands on her . . . he promised himself savagely. But threats were not going to bring her back, and with a violent oath he went after her.

Although she had a head start, his shoes were flat-heeled and he had a longer stride. Besides, she had accidentally stumbled into the boggy surrounds of a swollen pond, and while the herd of cows that occupied the field lifted their heads in mild curiosity, Isabel's steps were dogged with cold mud. She flailed about for several seconds, like a swimmer who has suddenly discovered he's wearing cement shoes, and then she over-balanced, sinking to her knees in a morass of dirt.

Alex reached her just as she was using her hands to lever herself to her feet again, and for all his anger with her, he couldn't prevent the errant lifting of his mouth. She looked so pathetic somehow, her knees and feel all caked with mud. And funny, too; a kind of cruel retribution.

'Don't move,' he said, as she endeavoured to lift her feet out of the squelch. 'You may lose your balance again. Here,' he took some papers, a pen and his wallet out of his jacket pocket and tossed the expensive garment down on the earth between them. 'Step on to that, and come this way. 'It's dry enough where I'm standing.'

Isabel gasped. 'But your jacket!'

'I have another,' he informed her drily. 'Just do as I say. Or do you like standing in mud? If so, I'll leave you to it.'

Isabel cast him a resigned glance. 'Oh, all right,' she said wearily, lifting one foot and depositing it, not without some reluctance, on the fine silk lining of the jacket. Then, gaining courage, she lifted the other, and seconds later she was on the comparatively dry grass beside him. 'Thank you.'

Alex shook his head. 'You look a mess.'

'I know.' She looked down at herself ruefully. 'What can I do?' Then, looking up at him. 'What am I going to tell Chris?'

'What am *I* going to tell Chris?' amended Alex drily. 'We're going to have to think of something. But first of all, I suggest we do something about your hands and legs.'

'Can we?' Isabel was doubtful, and Alex found himself grinning.

'I guess so. It may have slipped your notice, but this pond adjoins a stream. Over there. With a bit of luck, the water in the stream will be clean. Cold, perhaps, but clean.'

It was. With an absence of affectation, Isabel peeled off her tights and washed them in the stream while Alex did his best to clean her shoes. Grass and dock leaves soon had the plain purple pumps looking outwardly as good as new. The lining inside remained stained, but once they were on her feet, this discrepancy would not be visible.

With her hands and feet washed clean of the mud, Isabel rose to her feet to face her rescuer. 'I'll put these in my bag,' she said, indicating the damp tights in her hand. She shivered. 'Is it very badly stained? I tried to keep it out of the mud as best I could.'

'I've brushed it down, and I guess when it's dry it'll be as good as new,' said Alex, handing her her shoes, but hanging on to the bag. 'Right. Are we ready to go? Or are you still intent on hiking to Nazeby?'

Isabel's lips twitched. 'What do you think?'

Alex felt his senses stir. 'I think we should get back to the car before someone steals that,' he replied, his tone a little cooler than it might have been because of his unexpected arousal. 'After you. And take care where you put your feet!'

Isabel carried her shoes to the car, walking easily in her bare feet. Without heels, she seemed smaller, more vulnerable somehow, and Alex had to remind himself

of who she was as his antagonism gave way to other
emotions. Her bare legs were disturbingly beautiful,
long and slender, and far too accessible below her
short skirt. He found himself staring at the rounded
curve of her rear as she scrambled back through the
hedge, and the unmistakable tightness of his trousers
betrayed his callow reaction. It was years since any
woman had had such an effect on him, and he swung
round the car irritably to avoid her observation.

This time, he stowed her case in the boot of the car
realising, as he did so, that had he done that in the
beginning, none of this might have happened. She
could hardly have gone charging off across the fields,
leaving him in possession of her belongings. Without
her purse, her clothes, she would not have felt such
independence, and he would not be suffering now
from the discomfiting effects of his frustration.

'Where's your jacket?' she enquired, as she slipped
into the seat beside him, and Alex glanced over his
shoulder.

'In the boot, with your bag,' he replied, waiting for
her to close the door so that they could be on their
way. He was eager now to reach their destination.
Eager, too, to escape the knowledge that had eluded
him for so long.

'Will it clean?' she persisted, examining her shoes
before putting her feet into them. She gave him a
rueful smile. 'You'd better send me the bill.'

'Perhaps I will.' Alex was curt, but he couldn't help
it. For Christ's sake, he fretted, why didn't she shut
the bloody door? Every second they remained here,
his control over the situation decreased.

'I've always liked these shoes,' she said instead,
surveying them affectionately, like some remarkable
find she'd made. 'I got them in Venice at Easter. Have
you ever been to Venice? Oh, yes, I suppose you must

have. Chris says you've travelled quite a lot.'

Alex sighed. 'Aren't you cold?'

'A little bit. Why?'

'Then why don't you close the door? So we can get moving.'

Isabel looked surprised. 'Oh—sorry.' She reached for the armrest. 'I'll just put my shoes on first. Then I can see what I'm doing.'

Afterwards Alex cursed himself for his impatience. He could have waited, while she bent and slid the offending shoes on to her feet, but he didn't. Instead, as she bent to accomplish her task, he leaned across her to reach the door, and when she came up suddenly, his arm was trapped behind her.

He never knew who was the most surprised: himself, for being caught that way, or Isabel, when she found his face only inches from hers. But, in either case, the result was the same, and for a heart-shuddering moment, neither of them moved. Alex found he was breathing more quickly than his exertions had warranted and, his eyes falling from Isabel's flushed, startled face to the steady rise and fall of her lungs, discovered a similar reaction in her. As he watched, the tenor of her breathing accelerated, and the rounded breasts beneath her dress swelled against the cloth. Her nipples hardened, creating little aureoles of darkness beneath the brushed cotton, and Alex's lips parted involuntarily, tempted beyond measure to discover how they would feel beneath his mouth.

Isabel spoke first, her voice several shades higher than it normally was, dragging his eyes away from her breasts and back to her face. 'No, Alex,' she got out chokily, but he could tell from the way she said his name that she was as aroused as he was.

'Why not?' he demanded, the arm behind her drawing her inexorably nearer, his hand sliding beneath her arm to touch the warm swell of her breast.

'Because we can't,' she articulated unevenly, but Alex was scarcely listening to her. The feel of her breast beneath his hand was so incredibly good, he couldn't think of anything else, and when her soft lips opened to rebuke him, his mouth took possession of hers.

She fought him at first, trying to drag her lips away from his, and pushing at his chest with her hands. She would have used her legs, too, had the console not been in the way. But Alex was deaf and blind to her pleas, intent only on satisfying the insatiable urge he had to make her as aware of him as he was of her. And he succeeded, too. Or at least, he thought he did. When she stopped fighting him, when she stopped clenching her teeth together and allowed the hot wet thrust of his tongue to slide between, Alex felt a sense of pleasure he had never felt before. The seductive cavern of her mouth offered boundless sweetness, and when her tongue entwined with his, his senses swam.

He forgot who she was, and why he was bringing her to Nazeby. The idea that she was his cousin's fiancée, and as such, forbidden fruit to him, didn't so much shame him as inflame him. She didn't love Chris, she *couldn't* love Chris, not and kiss him as she was doing. Her hands were no longer resisting him, they were curled quite confidingly against his neck. And when he let his hand trace the shape of her breast beneath the dress, she pressed herself closer, making him catch his breath.

He wanted her. God, how he wanted her! The raw possession of his tongue was no substitute for the sensual delights of imagining her tight muscles closing about his taut manhood. He was aching for her already, and he longed to take her hand and let her feel his need.

But he was very much afraid, if he did so, his control would slip completely. Time enough for that afterwards, he thought. Right now, he had other things on his mind. Thank God, it was getting dark at last. No one would observe them when they made love.

His hand moved lower, caressing the tremulous curve of her stomach, before sliding down to the provocative hem of her skirt. Isabel's legs parted willingly when his hand slipped between them, and he stroked the inner skin of her thigh, as his fingers moved even closer to the moist, scented core of her being. She smelt delicious, all warm and soft and feminine. He had to steel himself not to rush her, and he groaned when her small teeth fastened on his ear . . .

'Isabel . . .' he rasped huskily, burying his face in the hollow of her neck, hearing her beads chink together as his mouth sought the warmth of her flesh . . .

CHAPTER SEVEN

THE SUDDEN tapping on the window at his side of
the car shocked them both. To his relief, as he lifted
his head, Alex saw that the glass had misted over all
round, so that anyone peering through it would have
only a hazy impression of the two people inside. But
then a torch was switched on that penetrated the
condensation, and Alex swiftly turned to press the
button that operated his window.

'Is everything all right, sir?'

Before he could voice a protest, a helmeted
policeman bent to peer through the open window at
them, eyeing the two occupants of the car with a
jaundiced eye. Alex immediately felt about fifteen
again, caught making love in the back of one of his
uncle's Land Rovers. He had driven a Land Rover
about the estate from the age of twelve onwards, and
he clearly remembered his first experience of sex with
the daughter of one of his uncle's tenants. She had
been older than he was, eighteen or nineteen at least,
but more than willing to initiate him into the arts of
sexual pleasure. He had been a willing pupil, too, he
remembered, as Isabel hurriedly straightened her
clothes beside him; but he was not fifteen now, and
Isabel was no easy conquest . . .

'I—perfectly,' he said, realising it would be unwise
to complain. They were parked in a prominent
position, after all, and his car had always attracted
attention. He just hoped the policeman hadn't recognised its registration. All the cars belonging to the
members of the Seton family were licensed with private

plates, and his own was instantly recognisable to anyone who knew him.

'Are you all right, miss?' The policeman had now turned his torch on Isabel, and she shifted nervously.

'I—of course,' she answered. 'Um—I was feeling rather sick, and—and I asked if we could stop. I'm feeling much better now, thank you.'

'Good, good.' The policeman patted the roof of the car as he straightened, evidently satisfied that they were unlikely to corrupt the neighbourhood. 'OK, sir, I won't detain you any longer. Have a good evening, and remember, don't drink and drive.'

'Thanks.'

Alex's response was necessarily brief, but at least his identity was still intact, he reflected with some relief, as he started the car. And, the policeman's intervention had brought him to his senses. God! he thought incredulously. He had actually been considering making love with Isabel in the car! He hadn't made love in a car since he was at university. He must have been temporarily deranged!

Nevertheless, he was no less aware of her now than he had been before, and that knowledge ate him up. What was wrong with him? She was Chris's fiancée, for Christ's sake! Was he out of his mind?

And what about Isabel? What was she thinking? he wondered. After all, he added, struggling to justify himself, she had been as much to blame as he was. She hadn't exactly had hysterics when he touched her. On the contrary, after that first perfunctory protest, she had encouraged him, inviting him to take liberties with her, and responding with a passion he would not have believed her capable of.

His hands tightened on the wheel. Why the hell didn't she say something? She must know how he was feeling. Or was she more experienced in these matters than he was, he asked himself bitterly. Was that why he had overcome her protests so easily? Because he wasn't the first man she had played around with since her engagement?

'Will you tell Chris?' she asked at last, and Alex's lips twisted at the implied anxiety.

'Will you?' he countered, keeping his eyes on the stretch of road ahead, illuminated by his headlights.

'Of course not,' she answered, twisting her hands together in her lap. 'I—it should never have happened.'

'No.' He conceded the point, even though his senses rejected the calm summation. 'I guess it could be pretty inconvenient for you if it came out.'

'And for you,' she countered hotly. Then, 'I didn't ask you to touch me.'

'You didn't put up much resistance,' he retorted, despising himself for his inhumanity, even though he told himself he was within his rights. 'Well, don't worry. I shan't destroy Chris's perfect image of you. I'll let you do that for yourself.'

'Thank you.'

Her response was barely audible, and once again Alex felt a pig for accusing her. But what the hell, he argued silently, she deserved everything he could fling at her. She was beautiful, but she was faithless; alluring, but immoral; desirable, and totally without conscience.

Yet, in spite of his professed contempt for her, that weekend at Nazeby was the worst weekend he had ever spent. Seeing her with Chris, watching as his cousin pawed and fondled her, tore him up, and going through the motions of the wedding service was the purest kind of torment. He didn't love her, he told himself through the long nights, when the thought of her married to Chris plagued his senses, but he did want her. He wanted her so badly, he was almost prepared to destroy his friendship with Chris for ever. He had the distinct suspicion that if he went to her room and took up where they had left off in the car,

Isabel wouldn't exactly repulse him, and this knowledge did not make sleep any easier. He knew his uncle wouldn't blame him. On the contrary, Robert would have been delighted to have an excuse to cancel the wedding. Any inkling that Isabel might not be in love with his son would have caused an immediate confrontation between them, and no amount of persuasion on her part would have saved the day.

But Alex did nothing, and he said nothing, allowing the plans for the wedding to go ahead unchecked. He kept out of the way as much as possible, and eventually the weekend passed. Chris took his fiancée back to London himself, and Alex stayed on an extra day to cool his heated blood. He knew his grandmother was concerned about him, but he couldn't tell Vinnie what was wrong. Instead, he let her draw her own conclusions, no doubt assuming that, like herself, her grandson still had reservations about the following weekend.

Alex eventually went back to London on Tuesday afternoon, and spent the next three days fighting the urge to see Isabel again. But by Friday evening, the day before she was due to be married to his cousin, he had come to the end of his tether. After imbibing rather freely at the pub across the road from his office, he took a taxi to Stanton Street, and climbed the stairs to the second-floor studio flat she shared with two other girls. He was past the stage of caring who saw him, but as luck would have it, Isabel was alone, ironing the creases out of the dress she was to wear on the following day.

She answered the door to his knock, evidently expecting someone other than the slightly inebriated male who was propped against the wall outside. 'Alex!' she exclaimed, and just for a moment he thought he saw a glimmer of relief in her smoky-grey gaze. But then she realised he had been drinking, and with an exclamation of disgust, she would have closed the door to him.

But, in spite of his intoxication, Alex still had possession of his faculties and, discerning what she ~~was about to do the moment before she did it, he~~ moved to put his foot in the doorway, successfully blocking her attempt to shut him out.

'Now—is that any way to greet your future cousin-in-law?' he protested, pressing the heel of his hand against the door as he spoke, and propelling it inward. 'Aren't you going to offer me a drink? In—cel—cele-bration, so to speak.'

His tongue faltered over the word, but he could see she understood him well enough, and his lips twisted bitterly at the knowledge that even now, in shabby jeans and a loose smock, her fiery hair in wild disorder about her shoulders, she was devastatingly attractive. The tight jeans outlined the long, lovely shape of her and, remembering the warm skin beneath the denim, Alex felt a familiar quickening of his senses.

'What do you want, Alex?' she demanded now, making no attempt to fight him over the door. She acknowledged that he was stronger than she was, and would therefore win in any physical confrontation. But her attitude towards him wasn't conciliatory; it was downright contemptuous.

'What do you think I want, Isabel?' he asked, ignoring the scornful sparkle of her eyes. He closed the door behind him and leaned back against it. 'I want you, of course. And you can't deny that you want me.'

'*I? Want you?* You have to be joking!'

The derisive tone of her voice was a set-back, but Alex refused to believe she meant it. 'Am I?' he asked, moving purposefully away from the door, trapping her between a tapestry-covered couch, which had seen better days, and the ironing-board she had been using earlier. 'I don't think so. We both know what we want, and as we appear to be alone, now would seem as good a time as any.'

Isabel summoned an incredulous laugh, but there was no humour in it. 'You're crazy!' she exclaimed. 'And drunk! Go home and take a shower. A cold one, preferably.'

'Don't—make fun of me,' advised Alex harshly, swallowing back the taste of bile which had risen sickeningly into his throat. The awareness that he had drunk more than he should have done was only adding to his frustration, and he shook his head impatiently to clear his muddled brain.

'Go home, Alex,' Isabel said again, trying to move the ironing-board without overturning the iron. 'Please! You don't know what you're doing. Isn't Chris expecting you? Aren't you and he supposed to be having an evening out together?'

If she thought mentioning Chris's name would make him think again, she was mistaken, thought Alex bitterly, his hands reaching for her shoulders. Even the idea of Chris having the right to touch her as he was touching her, fired him with jealousy, and imagining them making love, filled him with disgust.

'Take your hands off me!' she exclaimed, flinching away from his fingers as they moved caressingly over her shoulders. 'Alex, for God's sake! Are you mad?' But he wasn't even listening to her.

Her bones were so narrow and delicate, so close to the surface of her skin that he could feel every hollow between. Her skin itself was soft and supple, like the thickest cream beneath his hands; and her hair brushing his fingers was fine and vital, so full of life and electricity, that he almost expected to feel a shock when he buried his face in its glory.

Oh, God! It was good to be touching her again, so good to feel her warmth against him, and the more she twisted against him, the more aroused he got. His hands slid over her shoulders and down her back, lingering in the curve of her waist before cupping her rounded bottom, and moulding her softness to him.

He lifted his head then, eager to find her mouth with his, eager to taste the sweetness of her tongue with his own. He couldn't ever remember being so excited, not even as a youth, and his growing sense of urgency was only equalled by his desire to prolong the pleasure.

The searing heat of the weight that swung against the side of his neck was devastating. Aside from the fact that it almost knocked him unconscious, the exquisite pain of the burning metal caused him to yell in agony. He didn't remember releasing Isabel, he didn't remember knocking over the ironing-board, as he clapped a protective hand over the burn and staggered back against the door. The first coherent memory he had was of Isabel staring at him in horror, while the tears poured down her face, and then her rushing towards him, desperate to tend his injury.

But Alex was sober now, stone-cold sober, his brain washed clean of any emotion but outrage by the crippling blow of the iron. For that was what it had been. He recognised that fact now; even while his subconscious protested that it really couldn't have been Isabel's hand that lifted it.

But it *had* been her hand. There was no one else there and, as if to certify his belief, she was still holding the offending article as she rushed towards him. She realised what she was doing before she reached him, of course, throwing the erstwhile weapon aside before reaching out to him with trembling hands. She was evidently as shocked by what had happened as he; though not as afflicted, reflected Alex bitterly, gritting his teeth against the pain in his neck; not as afflicted at all.

'Alex—I'm sorry!'

Her distress was palpable, but Alex had no sympathy for her. Indeed, he was wondering how he could have been so stupid as to come here in the first place. Without her air of confidence she was quite a pathetic figure, he reflected contemptuously, and unlike some women who could cry gracefully, Isabel's tears were causing her lids to swell, and the skin around her eyes to become puffy.

'Spare me!' he muttered, wincing as he took his hand away from his neck and a sliver of skin came with it. 'You knew what you were doing, and I guess I should be grateful for it. You were right. I was drunk, bloody drunk, as it happens, or I wouldn't be here in the first place. However——' he turned towards the door, '—you certainly brought me to my senses. Put it down to experience. When a woman comes on to me, I usually try to oblige her.'

After that, the wedding was an anticlimax. Alex remembered going through the motions, as he had done at the rehearsal, without allowing any part of his emotions to become involved. The band-aid on his neck had aroused some comment from his uncle, but a dismissive remark about the razor slipping while he was shaving had successfully balked further enquiries. It was easy enough to let Robert, and Chris, think that he had not been entirely sober when he did it. And Kerry O'Flynn, who had just joined him at his apartment in London, and who had actually attended to the burn when he got home, would never have dreamed of questioning its origins. He was too well versed in diplomacy for that.

If only that had been the end of it, thought Alex now, reaching the building that housed his office with some relief, and pushing open the swing-doors. It should have been the end of it and certainly, so far as

he was concerned, her marriage to his cousin had
severed any connection between them. He might have
been willing to cheat on Chris, so long as he and
Isabel were not actually joined in wedlock, but stealing
his cousin's wife was quite a different matter.

None the less, when they came back from honeymoon, his good intentions had been stretched beyond
measure. Far from looking tanned and relaxed,
contented after four weeks of sunning herself in the
Caribbean, Isabel appeared pale and nervous, and
thinner than he remembered. She hardly ever looked
him in the eye and, instead of gaining in confidence,
if anything she had become tense and withdrawn.

Chris, however, seemed much the same as usual.
Alex's first, treacherous suspicion, that he might be to
blame for Isabel's apparent unhappiness was quickly
dispelled. If anything, Chris was even more attentive
to her as his wife, than he had been as her fiancé, and
it was obvious that if anything was wrong with their
marriage, Isabel must be to blame.

Even so, he was outraged when his uncle confided
in him a few months later that Isabel had suggested
to him privately that the marriage should be dissolved.
Her reasons, Robert said, were that she found life at
Nazeby excessively boring after living in London, and
Chris couldn't please her, no matter how he tried.

'Imagine coming to me!' his uncle had exclaimed
savagely, when he told Alex what had happened. 'The
boy's own father! As if she could expect me to take
sides against my own son!'

But later, when Alex had suggested that perhaps a
separation might be the best thing for all concerned,
his uncle had been adamant that that was not feasible.
'I don't want the girl going back to London, telling
all her friends that Chris is to blame,' he averred
strongly. 'No, that's not the way, Alex. We'll have to
think of something else.'

Alex had sometimes wondered why Isabel hadn't just walked out when she had first wanted to do so. Chris and his father could hardly keep her at Nazeby by force. But, apparently, according to Robert, she was holding out for a marriage settlement, something his uncle was not prepared to give to someone who had used his son so cold-bloodedly.

'There's no question about it,' he said to Alex, during one of their interminable discussions on the subject. 'She only married Chris for what she hoped to get out if it. I wouldn't care, but the boy's still as besotted as ever. He's begged me not to do anything to hurt her, and God help me, I don't know what to do!'

And then, providentially, the situation had resolved itself without his uncle having to do anything about it. Remembering this now, Alex could feel again the savagery he had felt when Robert had informed him of Isabel's actions. He hadn't wanted to believe it then, but now he was quite resigned to her betrayal. All the same, the memory still had the power to scrape across his senses, grating on his nerves, like a scar that wouldn't heal. He never had met the man in question. He had only known that he was some associate of Chris's, who had spent time at Nazeby, ostensibly recuperating from an illness. In those days, he had avoided Nazeby whenever possible, making excuses for his absence in the complicated demands of his work. He had seen his uncle often enough in London, and whenever Chris was in town, they had a meal together. But he hadn't wanted to see Isabel, in case the knowledge she and Chris were having problems overcame his resolution. He was still attracted to her, he had acknowledged that. And the fact that she was unhappy was a constant aggravation. But her defection with Jarrold Palmer had proved the ultimate deterrent. The man had done him a favour. By the time she appealed to him for help, he had had no feeling left for her.

But that was then, and this was now, he reminded himself grimly, entering Diana Laurence's office with a scowl on his face. And however distasteful the truth might seem to him, seeing Isabel again today had not convinced him of his immunity. In all honesty, he had hated himself for destroying her arguments, as he had done in the boardroom, and however justifiable his case had been, he had felt an utter bastard for making her look small. And she had looked small as she had gathered the documents she had brought together, and submitted to the will of the majority. But she hadn't avoided his eyes when the meeting was concluded, and the dignity he had seen in hers had torn him to the quick. That was why he had been so angry with Chris, and his uncle for that matter, when they had been gloating over their success. He had felt like the Judas goat, used to bait the trap; the treacherous pawn in his uncle's hands, sealing the fate of the queen.

'I gather the meeting did not go well,' murmured his secretary now, taking her cue from his expression, and Alex had to bite back the angry retort that sprang to his lips.

'As a matter of fact, the meeting was extremely successful,' he replied evenly, striding towards the door to his office. 'Are you going to lunch now, Diana? You can if you like. I shan't be needing you.'

'All right.' Diana pushed back her chair and stood up, but curiosity was getting the better of her, he could see it, and he was not surprised when she added a little appendage to her earlier remark. 'So—your uncle has got control of Mattley Pharmaceuticals, after all.'

'After all,' agreed Alex ironically, opening his door and giving her a mocking glance. 'Doesn't he always?' he remarked, rhetorically, and disappeared inside before she could take him up on it.

But although he could close his office door, he could not close his mind to thoughts of Isabel. Even after swallowing a rather stiff Scotch from the supply he kept in his office for the use of clients—something he never did at lunch time—he was still tormented by her image as he had seen her last. What was she thinking of him? he wondered. She probably despised him for doing Robert's job for him. She had always chided him for being his uncle's lackey, and this latest incident would only have strengthened her belief.

So why did he care? he asked himself, angrily, walking across to the windows and staring out at the sunlit streets below him. However pathetic she had seemed today, she was still the same Isabel who had led him on and then rejected him; cheated on her husband, and then appealed to him to take her part. She was completely without scruple, and if he wanted to keep his sanity, he should banish her from his thoughts.

The sound of the phone ringing behind him interrupted his mood. He waited for a moment, expecting Diana to answer it, and then, when she didn't, he recalled he had told her to go to lunch. Evidently, she had switched the line through to his office when she went out. Why else would it be ringing? he asked himself impatiently, realising that his attention had been totally distracted.

'Yes? Seton speaking,' he said curtly, picking up the receiver, and then knew a sudden craving that it might be Isabel.

But the light tones that answered him were nothing like hers, and although they were feminine, there was no similarity. 'Alex? Alex, darling, is that you? I thought you were going to ring me. Haven't you forgiven me yet?'

Alex's disappointment was instant, and acute, but

he managed to overcome the bitter disillusionment that gripped him. 'Penny,' he said, managing to infuse a trace of warmth into his voice. 'What a surprise! I expected you'd be out of the country.'

'I was,' she replied, the quickly disguised censure in her voice revealing her frustration. 'I just got back from Cairo last night, but you hadn't left a message with my answering service, and I was worried. We are going to see one another again, aren't we, Alex? You can't really intend that we go our separate ways.'

Alex took a deep breath. His initial inclination was to offer his apologies, and get off the phone as quickly as possible. He wasn't in the mood for Penny's recriminations, and getting involved with her again was not the most sensible thing to do.

But then, he anticipated the evening ahead, with nothing more demanding on his schedule than calling up some other female, with possibly less attraction for him than Penny had right now, and thought again. Maybe this was what he needed, he told himself grimly. A night spent in Penny's demanding company, and he would be fairly exhausted by the morning. One thing was sure, with her or without her, he was unlikely to get much sleep, and at least she cared for him, or said she did . . .

CHAPTER EIGHT

IT RAINED on Saturday morning and Isabel, standing in the bay window of her living-room, drinking her morning cup of coffee, wondered what the weather was like in Madrid. No doubt hot and sunny, she reflected gloomily. Certainly warmer than it was in London, and with the added bonus of being able to go swimming in the hotel pool. She guessed Lauren and Helen, and the other two girls who were on the assignment, were having a marvellous time. Lots of sun, the chance to wear beautiful clothes, and the happy awareness that they were being paid for it as well.

She sighed. Well, it was her own fault she wasn't with them. Jason had been furious when she insisted on staying in England. She knew he had been close to firing her when she refused to change her mind. But pragmatism, and perhaps his affection for her, had won the day, and eventually, he had agreed to her absence, albeit with bad grace.

And now she was wondering why she had bothered to risk her job, and her friendship with Jason, so that Alex could make a fool of her once again. The board meeting had been a fiasco, at least so far as she was concerned. All her fine schemes to thwart Robert Seton had come to nothing. From the minute Alex began delineating the reasons why Mattley Pharmaceuticals needed this merger with Denby Industries, Isabel had known she was fighting a losing battle. The smaller company was apparently in debt; it had gambled much of its resources on the research into a

new, and supposedly, miracle cure for arthritis, only
to have its development arrested by the findings of a
government agency, investigating drug abuse. One of
the ingredients of the capsule they were developing
had been found to be habit-forming, and all research
using Mirafen had been halted. The company needed
immediate financial assistance, or almost five hundred
employees, many of them research chemists, would
lose their jobs. Ally to this the fact that Denby was in
the market for a research laboratory, for its developing chemical industry, and Isabel was left with no
argument. Her own unqualified contention that the
smaller firm's independence was being undermined by
the proposed take-over simply wasn't credible, and
she forbore from voicing it. Instead, when the vote
was taken, she acquiesced, and had had to suffer the
ignominy of aiding in Robert Seton's undisguised
triumph.

It had been a sobering experience, finding herself
outflanked and outmanoeuvred, though she couldn't
in all honesty say that Alex had taken any satisfaction
in his victory. He had merely been stating the facts
and, surrounded by the other members of the board,
who had all supported the motion, she had been
unable to think of any reasonable objection.

But her defeat, if that was what it was, had left her
feeling totally deflated. Somehow, she had built herself
up for a confrontation that had never happened, and
now she had an awful feeling of anticlimax. She should
have gone with Jason, she reflected glumly. She should
have known that she would only be wasting her time
trying to balk Robert Seton. What chance did she
have against the might of a conglomerate? None at
all, even had her case been genuine. But it hadn't; and
she'd achieved absolutely nothing.

She turned away from the window dejectedly,
surveying the room behind her without satisfaction.

What was she going to do today? What *could* she do?
There was always housework, of course, but as she
paid a daily woman to come in twice a week to keep
the place tidy, there was nothing spoiling. She could
go out for a walk, although the rain seemed to put a
question mark on the advisability of that. So—what?
The hairdresser? *Shopping?* She pulled a wry face. She
had to eat, so probably that was the most sensible
suggestion. She would go up into the West End and
buy some pâté at Fortnum and Masons. She deserved
some compensation for giving up the trip to Madrid.
And, at least, she could afford it! The income which,
her solicitor had informed her, would be earned by
the shares she held in Denby Industries meant she
need never work again, if she didn't want to. She
could live in luxury for the rest of her life. Was that
what Vinnie had intended?

Thinking of Lady Denby brought her thoughts full
circle and, depositing her empty cup in the kitchen,
she went into her bedroom and flung herself on to the
unmade bed. 'What a tangled web you've left behind,
Vinnie,' she announced to the empty room, and then
rolled on to her stomach to rest her head on her
folded arms.

What had the old lady been thinking of, leaving the
shares to her? she wondered for the umpteenth time.
It wasn't as if Vinnie had nurtured any hopes that she
and Chris might get back together again. On the
contrary, his grandmother had helped her to leave
Nazeby and had supported her financially until she
could find a job and support herself. Of course, she
had paid the old lady back; every penny. But that still
didn't explain her generosity now.

Isabel sighed. The two years she had spent at
Nazeby would have been pretty bleak without Vinnie's
friendship. She had been the only real ally she had
had in that household, although it had taken her some

time to discover it. Robert Seton had never liked her. He had never wanted her to marry Chris, and he had made no secret of the fact. Chris himself she had thought to be her friend, as well as her husband, but he had ultimately betrayed her. And Alex . . . Alex . . .

She swallowed. Her relationship with Chris's cousin had never been a simple one. From the moment Alex had come upon her and Chris in the library, he had been an enigma to her. She never knew why he had taken such an instinctive dislike to her, but he had, and he had taken pains to avoid being in her company. The fact that he had become a dominant force in her life had troubled her a lot. She hadn't wanted to feel so conscious of him whenever he was around, particularly when his own hostility towards her was so acute. But in this her senses betrayed her, and right from the start she had been aware of an unwilling attraction towards him.

She had had no suspicion that he saw her as anything more than an annoying intruder until the afternoon he had given her a ride to Nazeby. And even then, their initial conversation had given her no clue to his real character. Oh, Chris had told her that his cousin had had dozens of girlfriends, and that he was immensely attractive to women, but in spite of her own attraction to him, Isabel had seen no evidence that Alex Seton possessed any more feelings than his Uncle Robert. She had thought him a cold man, who probably used women to satisfy his baser needs, without ever becoming emotionally involved himself. She had always found him distant and sarcastic, and she had naturally assumed that he would never relax with her.

And his manner at the start of that journey had reinforced this opinion. He had been both distant and mocking, though he had shown some compassion when she had told him about her parentage. She didn't know why she had confided in him. In all honesty, she hadn't even told Chris the whole story and, with hindsight, it seemed the height of foolishness to have exposed her possible illegitimacy to Alex. But it was done and, so far as she knew, he had never betrayed her to his uncle.

But that was a small thing compared to what had happened after. And then it had been her objections to his rudeness that had precipitated the argument. And she had had justification, she reflected, remembering what he had said to her. But, even then, she had acted totally on impulse when she ran away from him.

If she had stopped to think, she would have realised how foolhardy she was being by taking off like that. If Alex had taken her at her word and driven off and left her, she dreaded to think what might have happened, and that nameless prospect had haunted her for many nights to come.

But at the time, she had not been thinking reasonably, and remembering how Alex had forced his way through a bramble hedge to follow her brought a smile to her lips even now. It was such an unusual sight: the immaculate Alexander Seton, with his hair all tangled, and threads of mohair hanging from his jacket. If she hadn't been in such a sorry state herself, she would have burst out laughing. But at least she had discovered he was human, that he had humour. She had glimpsed the man behind the mask, and when he smiled, her heart had skipped a beat.

He had been so nice about it, she recalled, rolling on to her back and gazing blankly up at the scrolled ceiling. He hadn't lost his temper, or been scathing, as she had naturally expected. He had actually thrown down his jacket, so that she could get out of the bog, and then cleaned her shoes up for her, so that no one would ever have guessed they had once been caked with mud.

But then, when they got back to the car, everything had gone wrong. Instead of capitalising on his good humour, she had made him impatient with her again. She hadn't realised he was so eager to get going until he reached past her to slam the door. Then, when she had sat up and trapped his arm, the outcome had been inevitable.

Or that was how it had seemed. When he had touched her, when the strong hard length of his fingers had closed about her breast, she had felt powerless to stop him. Oh, she had made some preliminary protest, trying to fight him when he pulled her into his arms, clamping her lips together in an effort to repulse him. But it had all been useless. She hadn't really wanted him to stop, and somehow he had known it, and when his mouth took possession of hers, she had responded with an urgency that frightened her. Chris had never made her feel like that; he had never kissed her like that, thrusting his hot tongue into her mouth, until she had almost swooned from the pleasure he was giving her.

But still, it wasn't enough. She had wanted more. She had wanted *him;* and the barrier presented by their clothes had seemed an insurmountable complication. She had known he wanted to make love to her, too. The feverish invasion of his hands had been just a sensual foretaste of how it could be between them, and when they had been disturbed, Isabel could have cried with frustration.

After that, nothing was the same any more. By the time the policeman had finished his inspection, Isabel had been made to feel like some cheap tramp, only worthy of jumping in the back of a car, and Alex had reverted to the cold, detached stranger she was used to dealing with.

She had had a bad moment, when they were on their way again, when she had wondered if what had happened had not been a deliberate set-up, devised by Robert Seton to prove to his son she was no better than she should be. But when she had asked Alex if he intended to tell Chris, he had denied it, and to her knowledge he never had.

But that weekend at Nazeby had been difficult for both of them. Until then, she had had no real doubts about her relationship with Chris, and attending the rehearsal of the wedding, she had realised it was a little late to have second thoughts. Besides, Chris had been so sweet to her in those days, and she had succeeded in convincing herself that what had happened with Alex had been a momentary aberration.

So confident was she that her feelings for Alex were purely sexual, that when he came to the flat where she was living, the night before the wedding, she had had no hesitation about turning him away. In any case, Alex himself had been drunk and abusive, and not until he tried to touch her was she in any danger of giving in to him.

But then, he had touched her, and she had been terrified that if he succeeded in kissing her, she would not be able to resist him. Once she was married, she had told herself desperately, she would not feel this weakness towards him; once she and Chris had consummated their relationship, she would no longer feel this shameful need for a man who clearly only wanted her as his mistress.

In those days, Chris's reticence about making love to her had seemed endearingly old-fashioned, and she had always felt that her own willingness to respect his wishes until after the wedding was perfectly natural.

That was why her attraction to his cousin was so contemptible, and as soon as Alex pulled her against him and she felt the exciting thrust of his arousal, she had acted purely on instinct. She had to get away from him, she had to escape him, before the prospect of surrendering to his naked passion became too desirable to resist.

She had used the iron without thinking, never dreaming that its weight would make up for any lack of strength on her part. But when he let out that howl of pain and staggered back against the door, she had been almost frantic with horror, and if he had let her tend him then, it might have been quite a different story.

Of course, she had gone ahead with the wedding. Pride was a strange bedfellow, and it was pride as much as anything that got her to the altar. She had no intention of letting Robert Seton think his disapproval had discouraged her, and besides, she wanted to prove to Alex that she had chosen the better man.

Isabel shook her head now. How stupid she had been! Just how stupid, she had learned on her wedding night. By the time she and Chris came back from honeymoon, she had been drawn and nervous, and miserably aware that she had locked herself into a marriage that was no marriage at all.

She had tried to end it as soon as they were back in England. Unable to appeal to Chris, she had gone to his father and begged him to let her have the marriage annulled, but he had been incensed that she should dare to bring such a problem to him. She was lying, he said. Chris was perfectly normal; he was his son; and no two-bit stripper was going to make his son a laughing-stock.

He had threatened her, too, telling her that if she tried to leave Nazeby, he would personally see to it that she never worked again. And she believed him. Robert Seton did not make empty threats. His competitors in business had learned that often enough.

Chris used to delight in relating his father's exploits to her, but she had never dreamt that ruthless determination would ever be turned against her. She had been shocked, and frightened. She had only been eighteen, after all, and without any money of her own, she was helpless.

She considered calling his bluff and running away anyway, but somehow the opportunity never presented itself. Besides, the pride that had got her into this situation asserted itself sufficiently to enable her to try and make the marriage work. Chris was still Chris, after all, and in his way he still loved her. Or so she thought.

She had been weak; she had realised that afterwards. She had let Robert Seton manipulate her, without making any real fight for her independence. She had let the freedom from money worries, the beauty of her surroundings and her affection for Chris seduce her into a state of near-inertia, and only when she saw Alex did she feel like the coward she really was.

She had made excuses for herself, of course. Anyone who had been brought up in the austerity of a children's home could appreciate the luxury of having a room of her own, in what was undoubtedly one of the finest country houses in England. She had the chance to buy as many clothes as she liked, so long as she charged them to Chris's account, naturally; and the food that was served at Nazeby would make even a connoisseur's mouth water. Materially, she had everything she had ever wanted, and if the relationship between her and her father-in-law had never achieved its earlier tolerance, at least she had been able to put his threats to the furthest recesses of her mind.

And Vinnie had been there to smooth her passage. For some reason, Lady Denby had taken her under her wing, and although Isabel had never made the mistake of confiding in her while she was married to Chris, somehow the old lady had guessed that all was not as it should be.

Looking back, those two years at Nazeby had assumed a little of the substance of a dream. They had never seemed entirely real, even when she was living them, and she had learned exactly how unreal her marriage was when she found Chris with Jerrold Palmer.

She shivered, rolling on to her stomach again and digging her nails into the bedspread. That, she supposed, had been the worst moment of those two years; worse even than the shock she had had when she was served with divorce papers citing Jerrold Palmer as *her* co-respondent.

Her immediate thought had been, how had Robert Seton persuaded Palmer to participate in such a deception? But, the answer had been equally as swiftly supplied. Evidently, Jerrold Palmer had as little desire as Chris to have his sexual aberrations aired in public, and their joint testimony against her was totally damning.

Oh, she had been staggered that Chris's father should sink to such depths to protect his son, but she should have known that where his family's name was concerned, Robert Seton was implacable. *If there's no defence, attack!* she had read somewhere, and Robert Seton certainly used this as his motto. She was to be sacrificed, and from Robert Seton's point of view, he was accomplishing a dual achievement. Chris would emerge as an innocent bystander, while anything she said would be negated by her presumed bitterness at being found out. He had wanted rid of her long enough, goodness knows. Only the fear of what she might betray had forced him to keep her at Nazeby.

Of course, she had appealed to Chris to change his mind, begging him to tell the truth and exonerate her.

He could have a divorce, she said. The marriage could be annulled any time he wanted it. He had only to say the word.

But Chris had refused to speak to her. She guessed his father had given him his instructions, and a week after the papers were served, he had taken himself off to the continent, leaving her no forwarding address, and effectively abandoning her to her fate. Even Vinnie wasn't there to help her. She was in Australia, visiting an old friend in Melbourne, whose address again Isabel did not know. Besides, events were moving so swiftly, by the time she got back to England, it would be much too late for her to do anything.

Which left only one person she could turn to—Alex. He was the only person she knew with sufficient influence—and resources—to plead her case. She had little money of her own. She had never liked to ask Chris for any, and as most of her needs had been satisfied by a credit card, she had used her small savings to cover any personal expenses. Only now did she realise how advantageous her position was to Robert Seton. Without money she was helpless, and he must have known it.

For days after the idea of approaching Alex had come into her mind, she had thought of little else. Pacing the empty rooms at Nazeby, she had persuaded herself that if he knew the truth, he would be sympathetic. She had always loved Nazeby, but during those long, anxious days, she had grown to hate it, realising Robert had left her there to appreciate how powerless she was against the might of the Seton organisation.

Nevertheless, the notion to contact Alex took root, and with it, the realisation that a doctor's examination might disprove Chris's lies. Surely if she told Alex the truth, he would help her. Even after all that had happened between them, she trusted him. He was his uncle's protégé, that was true, but he had always had a mind of his own.

She went up to London the next day, driving the Audi estate car, which had always been at her disposal. No one tried to stop her. Robert Seton had given her six weeks to find somewhere else to live, and she guessed the staff at Nazeby imagined she was house-hunting.

She had never been to the apartment Alex occupied at that time, but she knew it was in a tower block near Hyde Park, which wasn't hard to find. She had chosen to come on a Saturday morning, in the hope that she might find him at home. The idea of approaching him at his office had seemed too formal. Besides, she had had no wish for any member of his staff to feel obliged to report her visit to his uncle.

She had left Nazeby early, and it was barely nine-thirty when she pushed through the smoked-glass doors of Romsey Court. She knew, from what Chris had told her, that Alex's apartment was on the fifteenth floor, but what she had not bargained for was the fact that the building was patrolled by a highly efficient security staff.

A man in a grey uniform vetted all visitors to the apartments from a steel and plate-glass desk, set to one side of the foyer, and Isabel felt like an intruder as his features took on an inquiring expression.

'Um—I'd like to go up to Mr Seton's apartment,' she explained, approaching the desk as he rose to his feet to face her. 'Mr *Alex* Seton. At 1504.'

The man studied her intently for a moment, and then inclined his head. 'Very well,' he said, indicating the lifts. 'Go ahead. I'll inform Mr Seton's butler that a visitor is on her way up.'

'Thank you.'

Isabel supposed it could have been worse. The man could have asked her name, and she was not at all convinced that under those circumstances, Alex would have agreed to see her. Instead, the officer had apparently decided she was harmless. Either that, or Alex's butler was a force to be reckoned with.

The diminutive Irishman who opened the door of Alex's apartment at her ring was neither huge nor intimidating. But he was evidently surprised to see her, and once again Isabel was obliged to state her business.

'I—er—I'd like to see Alex,' she said, unquestionably daunted by another unfriendly face. If she'd known how difficult it was going to be to see him, she probably wouldn't have come.

'And is Mr Seton expecting you, miss?' enquired the man, with the smug air of one who already knows the answer to his question, and Isabel sighed.

'It's *Mrs,* actually,' she said. 'Mrs *Seton!* And no, he's not expecting me, but I think he'll see me all the same.'

It was amusing to watch his dawning comprehension, or it would have been if Isabel had felt less tense. As it was, she waited impatiently for some recognition, wishing deep inside her there had been some other way.

'Would that be Mrs—*Christopher* Seton?' the Irishman appended, after a moment, his brogue thickening as his thoughts occupied themselves with this new development.

'Just—Mrs Seton will do,' Isabel averred flatly, glancing beyond him into a living-room that seemed filled with light. 'May I come in? I gather Alex is at home.'

Kerry O'Flynn, as she later learned his name to be, stepped back abruptly. 'Sure, why not?' he agreed, clearly too uncertain of her relationship with his employer to keep her standing there while he went to inform his master of her arrival. 'Come forward, won't you? I'll let Mr Seton know you're here. I think he's awake. I took him his breakfast quite a while ago.'

'He's still in bed?' exclaimed Isabel, stepping inside on to a polished wood-blocked floor, and the Irishman nodded as he closed the door behind her.

'Ah, the man was working half the night, wasn't he?' he declared, without really requiring a reply. 'Now, if you'll wait here, Mrs Seton, I'll see what's going on.'

Isabel saw immediately why the huge living-room of the apartment seemed so bright. Because the apartment was on the corner of the building, two walls of plate-glass windows gave an uninterrupted view of the park nearby. Reinforced double glazing cut out all intrusive sounds from the street below, and the long, slanting blinds could be turned to take advantage of the light.

The room itself was just as luxurious as she had expected, although the colour scheme was surprisingly subdued. A thick Oriental rug occupied most of the floor space, while two enormous sofas faced one another across the width of a lacquered coffee-table. A modern desk, with a tubular, cushioned chair beside it, was set beneath one of the windows, and the walls were hung with groups of etchings, mostly Oriental again in design. It was a comfortable, uncluttered room, with the minimum amount of ornamentation. Yet there were some attractive pieces adorning the stereo unit and the bookshelves, solid carvings of jade and crystal, that blended well with the other appointments.

Isabel was admiring a cut-glass figurine when she became aware that she was no longer alone. She turned, half expecting to find the butler, ready to make his apologies, and instead found Alex, dark and intensely disturbing, and evidently not pleased to see her. In a knee-length navy blue bathrobe and little else, he looked grim and unapproachable, and Isabel, who hadn't seen him in months, felt a treacherous surge of emotion.

'Oh—Alex!' she said, moistening her lips and setting the figurine she was holding back on its shelf. 'Er—thank you for seeing me.'

'I don't have much choice, as you're here!' he remarked, without expression. 'What do you want, Isabel? Chris is not here. And I don't have his address, if that's what you're thinking.'

Isabel took a deep breath. 'I didn't come here to ask where Chris was.' She paused to control the tremor in her voice, and then went on, 'Believe it or not, I don't care where he is; or who he's with, for that matter. I—I came to see you. I should have done so long ago.'

Alex's dark brows descended. 'Really?'

'Yes, really.' Isabel took a step towards him. 'Oh, Alex, why did you let me marry Chris? Why didn't you stop me, when you had the chance?'

'When *I* had the chance?' Alex's brows arched now in apparent disbelief. 'Isabel, your reasons for marrying my cousin were nothing to do with me. And I couldn't have stopped you. I wouldn't have wanted to.'

'That's not true!' Isabel bit her lips frustratedly. 'I assure you——'

'Oh, for once in your life, be honest, can't you?' she cried. 'You *could* have stopped me. You know it, and I know it. But we both behaved stupidly, and now—and now I'm paying the price!'

Alex gave her a scathing look. 'I understood it was Chris who was paying the price, as you put it,' he remarked bleakly. 'I hope you're not trying to blame me for this—affair you've been having with Jerrold Palmer——'

'I haven't been having an affair with Jerrold Palmer!' Isabel interrupted him desperately. 'Alex—that was

Chris! Not me! Your uncle devised the whole thing. To frame me, and to protect his precious son!'

Alex stared at her scornfully. 'You mean, Chris made the whole thing up?' He shook his head. 'I don't believe it!'

'No, that's not what I meant——'

'So, he didn't make it up?'

'No! That is—Alex, you don't understand!'

'Well, that's the truest thing you've said since you got here,' he agreed harshly. 'I think you'd better go, Isabel. You and I have nothing to say to one another.'

Isabel moved her head from side to side, unwilling and unable to believe that Alex wouldn't even listen to her. 'Please,' she begged. 'You've got to believe me. I haven't done anything!'

'You're wasting your time, Isabel.' Alex's mouth had hardened. 'You forget—I know you! I know what an unscrupulous creature you are. Anyone who could behave as you did on the eve of her wedding——'

'That wasn't my fault!'

'Then whose fault was it?'

'You came to where I lived, Alex!'

'Because I'd found out what you were really like, and would have done anything to protect Chris——'

'No!'

'Yes.' He was inflexible. 'My God! And you had the audacity to come to me to get you out of this mess you've got yourself into. I don't know how you had the nerve——'

'Alex——'

'—Just because I didn't tell Chris what a randy little bitch you were first time around is no reason for you to believe I'd defend you now. Christ, I don't know how he's put up with you for so long. I saw through you, right from the start. And if one man wasn't enough for you you should have had the decency to get out, instead of making a fool of Chris with one of his own friends!'

Isabel flung herself at him then. A combination of pain and anguish and bitter disappointment had balled in her stomach, and she needed to expunge at least a bit of it or go out of her mind.

'You—you brute!' she sobbed, all thought of explaining how a doctor's testimony might clear her name going out of her head. All she could think was that Alex was her enemy, and that, far from supporting her innocence, he actually believed what Chris had told him.

Alex was unprepared for her initial attack, and her nails raked his chest in the opened 'V' of his bathrobe, and her knee almost made contact with that most vulnerable part of his anatomy before he was able to control her. But quick reflexes, and a superior strength, rapidly quelled the effectiveness of her assault, and Isabel was reduced to swearing at him as his hands imprisoned hers at her sides.

'Bastard!' she mumbled impotently, as the fight went out of her and, as hot tears overspilled her eyes, Alex stifled an expletive and released her.

'I think you'd better go.'

Isabel turned away, drawing a hand across her eyes as she did so. She couldn't bear to look at him, not just then, and the knowledge that he despised her, too, was the final humiliation.

She never remembered how she got back to Nazeby. She must have driven there, because the Audi was back in the garage the next morning, when she loaded her few belongings into it. She took only those things she had brought to Nazeby. All the expensive suits and dresses she had bought since her marriage to Chris, she left hanging in the wardrobes.

After making arrangements for the car's return with the housekeeper, she drove away from Nazeby for the last time. A week later, she found a room in a house in Bayswater, and an allowance from the social services tided her over until she found a job.

And there she stayed until Lady Denby returned from Australia and discovered what had happened in her absence. Of course, the old lady had come to see her, and in spite of Isabel's reluctance to accept anything from the family, she had insisted on finding her a small flat. The two-roomed apartment in Earl's Court was not exactly what Lady Denby had wanted her to have, but Isabel had insisted it was all she was going to be able to afford, and Vinnie had respected her wishes.

Isabel sighed now. Chris's grandmother had never asked any questions. She had never mentioned Chris's name in connection with the divorce, or queried Isabel's association with Jerrold Palmer. She had allowed Isabel to tell her, only if *she* wanted, and it was many months before Isabel had confessed that she had not been the guilty party.

Even then, she remembered, she had been wary of making any claims against her ex-husband. After the way his father and his cousin had reacted, she had been half afraid his grandmother wouldn't believe her story either. But Vinnie had made no judgement either way, and when the whole truth was revealed, she had merely put her arms around Isabel and comforted her in the only way she knew how. It wasn't until Vinnie's solicitors had contacted her after her death that Isabel had appreciated the full extent of Lady Denby's faith in her, and the gift of the shares now seemed the final exculpation. Was that why she needed so desperately to hang on to them? Because they represented the fact that someone had believed in her?

CHAPTER NINE

ISABEL was folding the hems of soft, tan leather pants into fringed cream boots when the intercom buzzed. Frowning, she finished putting on the second boot, and then went to lift the receiver. She couldn't imagine who it might be, unless Jason had cut short his trip to Spain. But, remembering how angry he had been with her before he went away, she didn't think that was likely.

'Yes?'

'Isabel?'

It was Alex's voice, and her stomach gave a sickening little lurch. *Alex?* What did he want? After her painful reminiscences earlier, he was the last person she wanted to see.

Swallowing, she kept her voice as expressionless as possible, 'Yes. What do you want, Alex?'

'Can I come up?'

Isabel almost gasped. 'I don't think that's a very good idea,' she replied distantly. 'If it's something to do with the shares, I suggest you contact my solicitor——'

'It's nothing to do with the shares,' he interrupted her harshly. 'I want to talk to you. Preferably not standing in the pouring rain.'

Isabel hesitated. 'If it's about the board meeting——'

'I've told you, it's nothing to do with Denby's!' He sighed. 'Please.'

Isabel's lips parted. Alex, saying *please!* Now that was really something. Besides, she was curious to know what had brought him here on a *Saturday* morning. It seemed out of character, somehow.

'I—all right,' she said at last, coming to a decision. She pressed a button. 'Push the door. It's open.'

She had unlocked her door by the time he had climbed the stairs, leaving it ajar so that she could take up a position in the window bay. With the light behind her, she had a momentary advantage, although, as it was such a dull day, the advantage was very small.

Alex reached the door and opened it tentatively. Then, glimpsing her across the room, he stepped inside and closed the door behind him. The brief time it took him to secure the latch gave Isabel a chance to look at him unobserved, and in spite of her determination to be cool and detached, it was still unnerving to have him there.

He had evidently had to walk after leaving his car, and his dark hair was damp and moulded to his scalp. Its wetness accentuated the fact that he needed a haircut, and where it brushed his collar, it curled upwards with irrepressible vitality. He was wearing black trousers and a matching black suede jerkin, both of which were smudged with water, but it was his lean face that held her attention, and the disturbingly black eyes that he now turned in her direction.

'Isabel,' he acknowledged, by way of a greeting, unzipping his jacket and shaking drops of rain-water from his wrists. 'What a morning!'

'Miserable, isn't it?' Isabel took her cue from him. 'I was just about to go shopping, but I'm not looking forward to it.'

'I wouldn't if I were you,' Alex put in wryly. 'The West End is clogged with traffic, and you can't find a parking-space to save your life.'

Isabel shrugged. 'I was going to take a taxi.'

'Ah.' Alex nodded. 'And is it essential?'

'The shopping?' And after gaining his acquiescence, 'I have to eat.'

Alex inclined his head. 'I see.' Then, startling her, he added, 'You could eat with me.'

'With you?' The words were out before she could prevent them, and she saw his instinctive withdrawal at her incredulous words.

'Even bastards eat,' he remarked drily, and to her surprise she saw a hint of colour invading his cheeks.

'I—well——' His behaviour had disconcerted her. Whatever reason he had had for coming here, she would never have believed it was to invite her for a *meal!* 'I don't know what to say.'

Alex shrugged now and, noticing that the trickling dampness from his hair was invading his neck, Isabel crossed the room to her bedroom, emerging a few moments later with an apricot-coloured hand-towel. 'Here,' she said, handing it to him. 'You'd better take off your coat.'

'Thanks.' Alex did as he was bidden, and Isabel dragged her eyes away from the evidence of taut muscle silhouetted beneath the silk of his pale blue shirt. As he towelled his hair dry, she cupped her elbows in her hands and turned to face the rain-swept view of the park outside. Anything rather than look at him, she thought tensely. She had been a fool to think she still hated him. If she ever had, it was long ago now. Although she might deny it, her feelings came from a vastly different source.

'Well?'

He spoke again then and, swinging round to face him, Isabel found he had put his jacket on again. However, with his hair ruffled by its towelling and his eyelashes still glinting with a few errant drops of rain-water, he was distractingly approachable. Too approachable, she acknowledged tautly. She was used

to seeing his public face; his private one was much
too human.

Swallowing, she assumed an expression of smiling
inconsequence. 'I—can't believe you came here on a
wet Saturday morning, just to invite me out to lunch,'
she declared lightly, relieved to find she sounded
infinitely more confident that she felt. If he knew how
the thought of having lunch with him was chewing
her up, he wouldn't doubt that sooner or later he'd
persuade her to sell the shares.

'I didn't,' he said now, in answer to her remark,
and she kept the smile glued to her face by an immense
effort of will. She should have known, she thought
bitterly. Every day was a working day to someone like
Alex Seton. He would use any means that were necessary to get into her apartment, but once he was there,
he had no reason to sustain the act.

Swallowing again, she bit back her disappointment.
'Well, then, I suggest——' she began harshly, but he
interrupted her before she could finish.

'I came to apologise,' he said, astounding her
completely. 'What I did on Thursday morning
was—unprofessional. I should have had the relevant
papers delivered to you in advance of the meeting, so
that you could have been prepared for what was said.
But instead, I took Robert's line, and put you on the
spot. There's no excuse for it, but I wanted you to
know I've felt bloody bad about it ever since!'

Isabel was glad the window was behind her, as her
hands sought the sill for support. She had thought she
had heard everything when he asked to be allowed to
come up. But this—this was totally out of character,
and her brain worked desperately, trying to ascertain
some reason for his apparent change of heart.

'So,' he said at last, 'the least I can do is offer to
buy you lunch. Will you accept?'

Isabel made a helpless gesture. 'Did your uncle send you here——'

'No.'

'This isn't some new ploy to gain my confidence or something?'

'No.' Alex's denial was adamant. 'Believe it or not, but coming here was all my own idea. My uncle wouldn't approve, I can assure you.'

Isabel could believe it. She imagined Robert Seton would likely blow his top if he discovered his favourite nephew had been fraternising with the 'enemy'.

Now, she shook her head. 'Well, I—I'm grateful for your honesty, and—and I appreciate your taking the trouble to come here and tell me how you feel. But—there's really no need to take me to lunch——'

Alex's lips thinned. 'No *need*,' he agreed flatly. 'But it's what I'd like to do, anyway.'

Isabel licked her lips. 'Why?'

'I've told you.'

'To make amends?'

'Yes.'

'And I've told you there's no need.' She gathered all her composure and faced him squarely. 'I wouldn't like to put you out.'

The dark eyes were intense. 'And if it's what I want?'

Isabel caught her breath. 'I find that hard to believe.'

'Do you?' He breathed evenly. 'Well—that's still no reason for you to refuse me.'

Isabel shifted awkwardly. 'Alex——'

'Isabel?'

She pressed her lips together. 'You don't even like me!' she protested.

'I don't like myself much either,' he commented drily. 'But the fact remains, we both have to eat, and I see no real reason why we shouldn't do it together. Do you?'

Isabel could think of several, not least her own unwilling attraction towards him, that was being strained to its limits by his proximity. But still, she reflected weakly, there was probably less danger in having lunch with him in some restaurant than in arguing with him in the intimacy of her living-room. And she had already had one example of how that could end.

'All right,' she agreed at last, inwardly despising herself for her weakness. 'I'll have lunch with you: But afterwards——'

'Let's take one step at a time, shall we?' he suggested, the faintest suggestion of a frown marring his dark good looks. 'OK. Shall we go?'

Isabel hesitated. The flat-heeled boots and leather trousers had seemed suitable attire for tramping round the shops, but they were less appropriate for the kind of restaurant Alex probably patronised. Her hair, too, plaited into a braid that fell just below her shoulders, had been secured for convenience, rather than style, and only the cream silk shirt seemed acceptable.

'You look fine to me,' Alex inserted suddenly, and she realised he had guessed what she was thinking. 'Go on. Put on a coat or something. Just to keep your shoulders dry.'

In fact, Isabel paused long enough to apply a touch of mascara to her lashes, and a beige eyeshadow to her lids. With her exotic colouring, she needed little make-up, and the result was pleasing even to herself.

'I'm ready,' she said, emerging from her bedroom to find Alex occupying the position she had occupied earlier. Tying the belt of her dark green raincoat about her waist, she looked at him almost shyly, realising as he walked towards the door that this was the first time he had actually invited her company.

The Ferrari was parked a few yards along the street and, bidding Isabel wait under cover of the porch,

Alex sprinted towards it. Within seconds, he had unlocked the doors and climbed inside, starting the engine almost instantly, and reversing back to where she was waiting.

Isabel left her sanctuary as he pushed open the nearside door and, as she coiled herself into the seat beside him, she was uncomfortably reminded of the last time they had driven together.

'All right?' he asked, his eyes softer now, and distractingly gentle. She had never known Alex to be gentle, and the experience was unnerving. Oh, God, she thought, clamping her lips together, on no account must she make a fool of herself again!

As he had said, the roads were all jammed with traffic, everyone reverting to personal transport to avoid the discomfort of waiting for buses in the rain. Trying to drive into central London was a nightmare, but after realising that Alex had the situation under control, she sat back to enjoy the experience of driving in a car that attracted all eyes, even in the rain.

'An English summer,' she murmured ruefully, as they ground to a halt once again. 'I should have gone to Spain, after all.'

'Spain?' Alex glanced her way.

'Madrid, actually,' she conceded. 'I was supposed to be part of a shoot Jason's doing there.'

Alex frowned. 'So why aren't you?'

Isabel grimaced. 'Would you believe—the board meeting?'

There was silence for a while, and then Alex said incredulously, 'You gave up a trip to Spain to attend the board meeting?'

'That's right.' She shrugged. 'Stupid, wasn't it? Jason was really mad!'

Alex negotiated the next set of traffic lights, and then said tersely, 'You and Ferry—you spend a lot of time together?'

Isabel looked his way. 'Some,' she admitted cautiously. 'We're—friends. He's been very kind to me. I owe him a lot.'

'How much?'

It was an odd question, but Isabel took it at its face value. 'He took a chance and employed me, when no one else would,' she replied evenly. 'The agency I worked for before I—before I was married, wouldn't even consider me. They prefer—younger models. Not mid-twenties divorcees, who've forgotten how to move their bodies.'

Alex made a curious sound. 'Do you forget?'

'Oh, yes.' Isabel was serious. 'A good model is the result of good training. You can't walk in off the street and do it.'

Alex's glance was faintly mocking. 'It's a profession, then?'

'As I once told you,' she reminded him swiftly, and then relaxed. He wasn't baiting her today. He was being incredibly nice, as a matter of fact. Too nice, she warned herself fiercely. What was it they said about the smile on the face of the tiger?

It wasn't until they were crossing the Hammersmith Bridge that Isabel realised they were not going into the West End after all. Until then, she had been prepared to concede the fact that Alex probably knew his way around London better than she did. Besides, the rain made aliens of the most familiar sights, and only the river remained the same, whatever the state of the weather.

'Where are we going?' she asked, her voice not quite as sharp as it might have been had she not suspected he was taking her to some surburban road-house. 'We seem to be leaving the city behind.'

'We are.' Alex cast her a reassuring look. 'So, tell me, what would you be doing now, if you were in Madrid?'

Isabel bit her lip. The temptation to demand an answer to her question was compelling, but she didn't want to spoil their tenuous harmony. 'Oh—working, I suppose,' she conceded, lifting her shoulders in a careless gesture. 'I'd probably be too hot, but I'd be looking forward to a swim later. That's one of the advantages of staying at an hotel. They always have a pool, and we—that is, the other girls and I—usually take full advantage of it.'

'And Ferry?' inserted Alex softly. 'Does he join you?'

Isabel hesitated. 'Sometimes.'

'Most times?'

'Just—sometimes,' she said, turning to look out of the window. 'Where are we?'

'Are you in love with him?' Alex asked beside her, and his words brought her round to face him.

'No!'

'Are you sure?'

'Of course I'm sure.' She felt the hot colour invade her cheeks none the less. 'In any case, that's my business. Isn't it?'

Alex shrugged. 'What time is it?' he asked then, changing the subject completely, and she fumed.

'It's a quarter past twelve,' she said, glancing at her watch automatically, before staring rather ostentatiously at the clock on the console. 'Isn't it?'

'So it is.' His lips twitched. 'We should be there in time for a late meal, anyway.'

The interchange with the M3 was looming, and Isabel felt a sudden hollowing of her stomach. This was the way to Nazeby, she realised sickly. Oh, God, he must be taking her to see his uncle! And she had believed him when he said he wanted to apologise.

'Stop the car,' she said abruptly, gripping the strap of her shoulder-bag and mentally cursing herself for being so gullible. Why was she always so weak where

Alex was concerned? She already knew the answer, but that didn't make it any less unpalatable.

The Ferrari didn't slow its pace however, and she was not so foolish as to attempt to open the door at speed. She was no stuntwoman; her appearance earned her her living. If she leapt out now and broke a limb, her career would be in tatters.

'Alex, please,' she said, despising herself for begging him, but totally incapable of facing the prospect of meeting Robert Seton again on his own ground. 'Don't do this to me!' she pleaded, torturing the strap of her bag, and he shook his head impatiently as they ran down on to the motorway.

'Where do you think I'm taking you?' he asked, as the Ferrari picked up even more speed, and Isabel slumped in her seat.

'Nazeby,' she said dully, wondering why she didn't hate him now, when she had every reason for doing so. 'I'm right, aren't I? That is where we're headed. God, why did I believe you, when you said you wanted to apologise!'

Alex's lips twisted. ' "Oh, ye of little faith"!' he quoted wryly, settling more comfortably in his seat. 'Why do you think I'm taking you to Nazeby? So that Uncle Robert can capitalise on his victory?'

Isabel sniffed. 'Something like that. What does it matter? Anyway, I shan't get out of the car; so you'll have to bring me back.'

Alex made an amused sound. 'And if I tell you we have the place to ourselves? That Uncle Robert is in South America, and apart from Mrs Cowie and the other servants, the place is unoccupied. What then?'

Isabel gasped. 'You're not serious!'

'Why not?'

'Because—because—well, why there?'

Alex shrugged. 'To erase a bad memory, perhaps,' he remarked softly. 'Nazeby's not so bad; it's just the

people in it. And,' his lips parted to reveal a lazy
smile, 'there's always the pool. As I remember, you
used to use it more than any of us.'

Isabel stared at him. 'How did you know that?'

'I used to watch you, on those rare occasions I was
compelled to spend some time at the house. You know
the partition that adjoins the conservatory is made of
one-way glass? I could see you, but you couldn't see
me.'

Isabel blinked. 'But why would you want to—watch
me?'

'Voyeurism, what else?' he retorted, suddenly
brusque. 'Look, it's a bit late now, but you will come,
won't you? I phoned Mrs Cowie while you were
getting ready, and she's expecting us.'

It was still raining when they reached the gates that
gave access to the Denby estate, but not so heavily
now. Instead, a drifting mist wreathed itself around
the trunks of the trees in the park, rising from the
earth that was still warm from the previous days of
sun.

Nazeby itself nestled in its fold of the downs, lush
now with the promise of high summer. There were
foals in the paddocks that ran down to the river, and
an abundance of blossom in the hedges that marked
the boundary of the gardens.

Mrs Cowie, the housekeeper, opened the door as
the Ferrari crunched to a halt on the gravelled forecourt. If she was surprised—or even shocked—to see
the ex-wife of the son of the house, who had left here
under a cloud, with her employer's nephew, she was
too polite to show it. Instead, she offered a suitable
greeting before excusing herself about her duties, and
Alex led Isabel into the hall with obvious satisfaction.

'Why are you doing this?' she asked, in a low voice,

as they stood together in the panelled entrance hall, and Alex smiled.

'Why don't you take off your coat and freshen up?' he suggested, instead of giving her a reply. 'You know where everything is, so make yourself at home. I'm going to change these clothes. They feel decidedly damp.'

Isabel caught her lower lip between her teeth, still barely convinced that they were alone. But when he went ahead of her, up the curving arc of the carpeted staircase, to stand looking down at her from the galleried landing, she eventually subdued her fears and followed him, shivering at the memories the simple act evoked.

'Use this room,' Alex said, opening a door along one of the carpeted corridors, which ran in either direction from the head of the stairs, and reluctantly, Isabel stepped inside. It was one of the guest rooms, an attractive apartment, hung with ivory silk and cream damask; it was the room she had used in those traumatic days before she left Nazeby. And as such, no threat to her troubled sensitivities.

'I won't be long,' he added, as she walked slowly across the carpet, to stand gazing absently from the windows. 'Take off your coat. It's warm enough in here.'

But when he came back, Isabel was still standing by the window, and he came across the room towards her, dark and disturbing, in a lime-green polo shirt, and cotton shorts. 'No point in getting dressed, if we're going swimming,' he remarked, as her eyes widened. 'Don't worry. We'll find a bathing-suit for you. There's quite a selection in one of the changing-rooms downstairs. Uncle Robert always thinks of everything when he entertains guests.'

'Yes.'

Isabel's response was mildly ironic, and Alex

grimaced. 'OK, OK, I won't mention his name again. Now,' he took hold of the belt at her waist and tugged it loose, 'are you going to relax?'

Isabel's breathing had quickened at this unexpected, and decidedly proprietory, display of familiarity. She was not used to Alex touching her, not any part of her, and the brush of his fingers against her waist was much too close for comfort.

'I—I want to wash my hands,' she said abruptly, slipping off the coat, and dropping it on the floor. 'I'll—I'll see you downstairs. Just give me a few minutes.'

'As you wish.' Alex bent and picked up her coat and deposited it on the bed. 'I'll be waiting in the conservatory. I thought we could eat there, and anticipate our swim.'

Although Isabel washed her hands twice, they were still sweating when she went downstairs again. She told herself it was being in this house again, with all its hateful memories, but it wasn't true. Nazeby had always soothed her spirit, even in those terrible weeks following her discovery of Chris and Jerrold Palmer in the stables. It was only at the end that she had come to hate it. But that was because it had symbolised her helplessness. With hindsight, she could see that the house had not been to blame.

The conservatory adjoined the morning-room, and at this time of year, it was like an indoor garden. Hanging baskets, spilling over with fuchsias and geraniums, were suspended from every beam, while tubs and troughs of every kind of flowering blossom rioted in vivid colour across the Italian tiles.

Mrs Cowie had prepared them a cold buffet, and this occupied a side-table. A mosaic of meats and salads was artistically arranged around a whole dressed lobster, with dishes of fruit and cream to complete the meal. A circular glass-topped table had been laid for

two, and beside it, a chilled bottle of hock rested in
an ice bucket. It was a display made to fit its surroundings, and Isabel, who had forgotten how cosseted life
could be, pressed a nervous hand to her throat. It was
all too disturbingly familiar—and yet, not familiar at
all.

The solarium adjoined the conservatory. Sliding
glass screens could be rolled back to open up the
whole area, and the pool itself could be either outdoor
or indoor, according to the weather. At present, the
screens between the pool-house and the conservatory
were rolled back but, because of the weather, the pool
itself was enclosed by glass walls. There was something
rather satisfying about being able to swim whatever
the temperature was outside, and Isabel remembered
how much she had missed the privilege when she was
dogging the agencies, looking for work.

As she hovered by the table in the conservatory,
Alex emerged from one of the dressing-rooms that
adjoined the pool, and when he saw her, he grinned.
'I was just checking that we had a swimsuit to fit you,'
he called, circling the pool and climbing the two stone
steps that led into the conservatory. 'Do you want to
swim now, or later?'

Isabel moistened her lips. 'Oh—later, I think,' she
ventured awkwardly, daunted by the prospect of taking
off her clothes in front of Alex. Her skin was so pale
compared to the darkness of his, the long, powerful
legs exposed by his shorts revealing he did not spend
all his time in his office. Besides, he had never seen
her in a swimsuit before—with her knowledge, that is.
Those occasions when he said he had watched her
swimming didn't count. She had been unaware of his
observation.

'OK,' Alex agreed now, and picking up the bottle
of wine, he filled their two glasses. 'Here,' he said,
handing one of the delicate flutes to her. 'To better

times, hmm? Drink it. I think you'll like it.

Isabel did as she was told, the chilled mouthful she took spreading deliciously over her palate. 'It's lovely,' she said, in answer to his look of enquiry. 'This is lovely,' she added, using the colourful buffet to drag her eyes from his. 'Mrs Cowie has gone to a lot of trouble. Did—did she know who you were bringing?'

Alex took another taste of his wine, and then inclined his head. 'Yes, she knew. And no, she didn't make any comment,' he appended lazily. 'I don't need anyone's approval to bring you here. This is my home, too. I invite who I like.'

Isabel looked down into her glass. 'And if your uncle had been here?' she queried, and he gave her a wry smile.

'*You* wouldn't have come,' he replied, setting his glass down on the table. 'At least, only on sufferance. But if you had been willing, I dare say he'd have survived.'

Isabel sighed. 'Alex——'

'Why don't we eat?' he suggested, taking her glass from her and turning her towards the buffet table. 'Help yourself to anything you like. Mrs Cowie will only grumble if we don't do her efforts justice.'

CHAPTER TEN

IN ALL honesty, Isabel wasn't very hungry. Her appetite had always been dependent upon her disposition and, in spite of Alex's efforts to relax her, she was still extremely tense. Even the careless touch of his hand at her elbow set her nerves jumping, and it was difficult to behave casually when she was so aware of him.

Two glasses of wine later, she felt much better. She had eaten some of the wafer-thin Italian ham with a slice of melon, and gorged herself on a plate of raspberries and whipped cream, even laughing when Alex wiped a smear of cream from her lip with his finger and then licked it. She felt relaxed and absurdly happy, and only when one of the maids came to clear and recognised her did she remember where she was and what she was doing.

'Alex,' she probed softly, when the maid had departed again with their dirty plates. 'Why? Why here? You know your uncle won't approve, whatever you say to the contrary.'

'I think we should take a sauna,' said Alex, without answering her, pushing back his chair and getting to his feet. 'I turned on the heater earlier, so it should be pretty hot by now.'

Isabel looked up at him and shook her head. 'A sauna!' she echoed. 'Straight after your meal!'

'No better way to cleanse your body of all that alcohol,' he responded, grinning. 'Aren't you going to join me? There's plenty of room.'

Isabel shook her head. 'I don't think so.'

'Why not?'

'Well . . . ' She moved her shoulders. 'It's too humid already.'

'OK. We'll swim then,' he declared easily. 'The water's fairly cool. Now, don't tell me you need time to digest your lunch. You didn't eat enough to warrant the effort.'

Isabel bit her lip. 'All right. If that's what you want.'

'I thought it was what you wanted,' Alex reminded her drily. 'I seem to remember something about a hotel pool . . . '

Isabel sighed. 'All right. All right.' She got to her feet. 'Which dressing-room should I use?'

'Whichever you like,' he replied carelessly. 'I left the swimsuits in the first one, but as I don't need one, you can choose another if you like.'

Isabel grimaced. 'Why should I do that?'

'I don't know.' Alex gave her a considering look. 'You might think I had an ulterior motive for that, too. Perhaps I've got a peep-hole in the wall of that changing-room, hmm?'

Isabel had to smile at that. 'I won't be long,' she said and, leaving him, she crossed the room and descended the few steps into the pool area.

The pool itself was just short of Olympic size, with diving-boards and a water-slide, as well as yards and yards of pale green tiles. In consequence, the water looked smooth and inviting, and deliciously transparent.

The changing-rooms were comfortably equipped, and spacious. Each compartment had its own shower and vanity unit, and the pine-panelled walls gave the illusion of being in a cabin. Alex had left the selection of bathing-suits on the vanity table and, looking through them, Isabel realised they were all far more revealing than anything she might have chosen for herself. Still, she reflected, she hadn't bought a swimsuit for over a year, and the ones she had back at her apartment were probably out of date.

She eventually chose a one-piece *maillot,* that was mainly black, with inserts of blue and amber. It was the least vivid of all the swimsuits, but the amount of thigh exposed by its cut-away leg-line caused her some embarrassment as she walked out to find Alex.

He was already in the water. He had shed his polo shirt and was presently perfecting a slow crawl from one end of the pool to the other. But, as if some sixth sense had alerted him to her presence, he lifted his head and saw her and, abandoning his efforts, he swam swiftly towards her.

'What's wrong?' he asked, as her hands hovered protectively at the backs of her thighs, and Isabel cast her doubts aside.

'Nothing,' she said, as he folded his arms on the pool-side at her feet, realising she was only drawing attention to herself by behaving coyly. 'What's it like?'

'Come and find out,' he said, holding out his hand towards her, but she had more sense than to take it.

'In my own time,' she insisted, sitting down on the edge of the pool and dipping her feet into the water. 'God, it's freezing! I thought you said it was only fairly cool.'

'It is—once you're in,' he replied, turning on to his back and spreading his arms wide. 'Come on. It's beautiful!'

Overhead, a watery sun was trying to penetrate the low-hanging clouds, and the pool took on a glittering opacity. Luxury, indeed, she thought ruefully, finding it difficult to believe she was really here. Had she once taken all this for granted? Maybe if she'd been married to Alex, it wouldn't have seemed just a compensation.

Slipping off the rim of the pool, she allowed herself to slide down into the water. It was deeper than she remembered, easily four feet, even at this, the shallow end. Further along, where the water-slide and the diving-boards were situated, it was almost ten feet.

She was catching her breath when Alex swam back to her and, ignoring her efforts to evade him, he grabbed her hand and pulled her after him towards the middle of the pool. Pretty soon, she was out of her depth and compelled to swim or pull both of them down, and she panted indignantly as the chill of the water penetrated her skin.

'Are you trying to drown me?' she exclaimed, when he released her, and she was forced to tread water to keep afloat.

'You forget—I've seen you swimming,' he retorted, unmoved by her protests. 'Now—isn't this good? Much better than languishing in some stuffy restaurant all afternoon.'

Isabel sighed. 'Is that why——'

'Just enjoy it,' he overrode her insistently. 'No one's going to hurt you here. Not while I'm around, anyway. OK?'

It was difficult to do anything else but enjoy herself, with Alex doing everything in his power to help her. Chris had never used the pool much, and even when they were on their honeymoon, he had much preferred to sit at the pool-side bar, drinking daiquiris, to splashing about in the water. But Alex was different. He was an excellent swimmer, for one thing, and he evidently enjoyed the water as much as she did. So much so that the short dip she had envisaged lasted over an hour.

When she finally protested that she was too tired to swim any more and climbed out on to the side, her legs felt like jelly, and she flopped down on a padded air-bed, uncaring of what she looked like. After squeezing the moisture out of her braid, she rested back on her elbows, drawing up one leg in innocent

provocation and tilting back her head to rest her
aching muscles.

'You're out of condition,' Alex remarked, his
shadow blotting out the shaft of sunlight in which she
was lying. Opening her eyes, she saw he had vaulted
out of the pool and was standing looking down at
her, the shorts he had worn to swim in moulded to
his thighs. 'You notice I don't say out of shape,' he
added lazily. 'That wouldn't be true. You always were
a beautiful woman, Isabel. On that score, Chris and I
were always in total agreement.'

Isabel's inertia fled. It was the first time he had
brought Chris's name into their conversation, and
whether it had been deliberate or not, it had
immediately destroyed her mood.

She sat up. 'I think I'd better get dressed,' she said,
preparing to get up, but Alex's hand on her shoulder
held her where she was.

'Not yet,' he said, hooking another of the cushioned
air-beds towards them. Then, dropping down on to it,
he faced her steadily. 'We have to talk.'

'To talk?' In spite of the water she had swallowed
in the pool, Isabel's mouth felt suddenly dry. 'I don't
think we have anything to talk about, Alex.'

'That's not the impression you've been giving me,'
he remarked softly. 'You wanted to know why I
brought you here. Don't you want me to tell you?'

Isabel lifted her shoulder to escape his touch, and
he withdrew his hand at once, sitting cross-legged on
the air bed beside her, apparently indifferent to the
water trickling down his chest from his wet hair.

'I—thought you said it was to erase an unpleasant
memory,' she countered tautly. Her lips twisted. 'Don't
tell me it was to try and effect a reconciliation between
me and Chris.'

'Why would I want to do that?' Alex was sardonic.
'I'm not that benevolent. Chris had his chance, and

he blew it. I don't intend to do the same.'

Isabel swallowed. 'I don't know what you mean.'

'Oh, I think you do.' His eyes were disturbingly intent. 'In fact, I think you recognised it right from the beginning. You know, they say hatred is akin to love——'

'No!' Her heart palpitating wildly, Isabel tore her gaze away from his and scrambled to her feet. 'I don't have to listen to this. I'm going to get dressed.'

'Scared?' he queried, as she started towards the dressing-room, and because she resented his ability to see right through her, she halted.

'Not—scared,' she contradicted huskily. 'Amazed, perhaps. I never thought I'd see the impassive Mr Alex Seton reduced to speaking in clichés!'

His lips twitched, and turning, he rested back on his elbows to look up at her. 'I'm not impassive, Isabel,' he informed her wryly. 'Impatient, perhaps; frustrated, certainly. But not impassive. Not where you're concerned.'

She gasped. 'I don't believe this!'

'What don't you believe?'

'I don't believe you're saying what you're saying. Heavens, two days ago, you practically used court-room brutality to make me look a fool!'

'Not a fool,' he corrected her quietly. 'Just—ignorant of the facts, that's all. And I did apologise.'

'And that makes it right?'

'No.' He abandoned his lazy stance and sat up. 'It just attempts to explain the—ambivalence of my position.'

Isabel shook her head. 'Is that how you square your conscience?' she enquired scornfully. 'By calling your position ambivalent?'

Alex sighed, and with a lithe movement, he got to his feet. 'I couldn't—square my conscience, as you put it, even if I wanted to,' he said, a little more forcefully.

'And this isn't getting us anywhere——'

'Us?' she snorted.

'Yes, us,' he insisted, stepping off the air-bed and coming towards her. 'Isabel, you know what I'm talking about.'

Isabel took a step backward. 'No, I don't.'

'Yes, you do.' He considered his words before adding, 'Ever since I came to your apartment that first time, I haven't been able to touch another woman.'

Isabel's lips parted. 'And is that supposed to mean something?' she demanded. 'My God! Are you blaming me because you're temporarily impotent?'

Alex closed his eyes for a moment, and when he opened them again, she had put at least another three feet between them. 'Don't be crude, Isabel,' he said wearily. 'It doesn't suit you.'

'Well . . . ' She moved her shoulders nervously. 'What do you expect? Sympathy?'

Alex's mouth compressed. 'OK, OK.' He gave a careless shrug and turned away, 'If that's the way you want it, go ahead. Get dressed. I'll take a shower, and drive you back to town.'

'Wait!' The word sprang from her lips before she could prevent it, and although Alex hesitated, eventually he turned to look at her again.

'Well?'

Isabel licked her lips. 'Why—why did you invite me to have lunch with you?'

His brows arched. 'Do you really want to know, or are you getting ready with some other clever retort?'

She tried to control her breathing. 'I—really want to know.'

Alex stepped towards her. 'Because, in spite of everything I've said and done, you were right all along. I do want you. I think I always did.'

Isabel trembled. 'You mean—you mean——'

'I mean,' said Alex, removing the space between

them, 'that ever since I came into the library here and found you with Chris, my feelings for you have never been ambivalent.'

Isabel shook her head, the wet braid sending a spray of drops across the tiled surround of the pool. 'But you hated me!' she protested.

'I said my feelings had never been ambivalent,' Alex reminded her softly, stroking damp strands of hair from her forehead with his thumbs. 'I did hate you then; because you were marrying Chris. I hated him, too, but that I could control.'

Isabel blinked, looking up at him disbelievingly. 'And—and that evening you drove me down from London——'

'I think you know how I felt then,' he muttered, bending his head to touch her bare shoulder with his tongue. 'If that policeman hadn't interrupted us, I'd have taken you there and then.'

Isabel quivered. 'I wish you had,' she whispered fervently, as he drew her into his arms, and Alex said, 'So do I,' against the parted sweetness of her lips.

His kiss was firm and gentle, as Alex rediscovered the contours of her mouth, a sensuous benediction to the altar of her beauty. There was no rush, no haste, no hurried need to satisfy the senses. Just a sensual awakening to the delights that they might share. Even the hands that caressed her waist made no overt attempts to disconcert her. Alex was quite content to explore her lips, her cheeks, the fluttering femininity of her lashes, and the scented hollow behind her ear with his tongue, so that by the time he found her mouth again, she was aching for much more.

This time, when he kissed her, she responded, urgently, winding her arms around his neck and pressing herself against him. It was marvellous feeling his hard body close to hers, and not until her breasts encountered a certain roughness did she realise he had pushed the strapless bodice of her swimsuit down to her waist.

'What—what if someone comes?' she stammered huskily, as his hands slid from her waist to find the swollen fullness of her breasts, and Alex's lips twisted.

'I don't particularly care,' he said honestly, lowering his lips to take one rose-tipped nipple into his mouth. 'But relax,' he added, as she jerked beneath his hands, 'no one will come.' He smiled. 'They wouldn't dare.'

'Are you sure?' she fretted, shifting her weight from one foot to the other, and with another lazy nod, Alex sought her mouth again.

'I'm sure,' he told her, cupping her face between his hands and rubbing his forehead against hers. 'Besides, we've got nothing to be ashamed of. You're not married this time.'

In spite of the lethargy that Alex's kisses were inducing in her, Isabel heard his careless words quite succinctly. 'This—this time?' she echoed blankly. 'Why—this time? I wasn't married when——'

'Forget it.'

Alex didn't want to talk right then, but Isabel's brain was clearing with every second that passed. 'When, Alex?' she pressed him urgently. 'When did we ever do this before? I was never unfaithful to Chris, ever! You know that. Don't you?'

Alex allowed her to escape only to arm's length. 'Well, not with me,' he conceded softly, his thumbs caressing her shoulder. 'Darling, it really doesn't mat——'

'It matters to me!' she exclaimed, and now she tore herself out of his grasp. 'You—you still believe it, don't you? You still believe I had an affair with Jerrold Palmer.'

Alex's shoulders sagged. 'Isabel, we don't have to talk about this——'

'We do!'

'Why?' He sighed. 'Look, I'm prepared to accept that you and Chris were not compatible. And, knowing how I feel about you, I'm even prepared to admit that, being the passionate woman you are, you needed someone else——'

'How big of you!' Isabel caught back the sob that trembled on her words. Alex still didn't believe her. He never had. He was prepared to make her his mistress believing she and Jerrold Palmer had been lovers!

'Isabel, Isabel . . . ' Alex was trying to reason with her. 'Don't you see! It doesn't matter to me. God, why do you think I stayed away from Nazeby so much after you and Chris were married? I knew you two weren't happy, and I was afraid that if I spent any time with you, I might destroy us both!'

Isabel was struggling to pull the *maillot* over her breasts. 'And I suppose I destroyed myself?' she choked, her fingers shaking so much she could hardly do anything, and with an oath of impatience, Alex stepped towards her.

'Here,' he said roughly, 'let me!' But Isabel was too strung up to let him touch her again.

'Keep back,' she said, jerking violently away from him, and as she did so, her foot slipped, and she pitched backwards into the water.

In normal circumstances, the fact of falling into the pool would have meant little. But in her present state, her hands shaking, and her breathing shallow, she was in no condition to weather the body-blow of the water. Instead, she gulped as the air was knocked out of her, and felt a stinging pain as water surged into her lungs.

She thought she must have lost consciousness, for she remembered little of the next fifteen minutes. She had a vague recollection of Alex hauling her out on to the pool-side and applying pressure on her back to clear her lungs, but it all had a dream-like quality.

Her first real coherency came when she was lowered on to the silky coolness of a bedspread, and the softness of a mattress eased the bruises from the pool-room floor.

She blinked and looked around her as another weight was deposited on the bed at her side, and she breathed a little less easily when she discovered that it was Alex.

'Wh—where am I?' The honey-brown walls and gold silk draperies were not familiar.

Alex grimaced. 'On a bed,' he said, and she noticed that he had shed his wet shorts in favour of a pair of cotton trousers. But his chest was still bare, and he looked distractingly handsome.

'I know that,' she said, feeling her throat ache a little when she swallowed. 'But whose bed? This isn't the room I was in before.'

'It's my bed, actually,' he informed her flatly. 'But don't worry, I'm not planning my revenge. I just thought you'd prefer not to have what happened broadcast. So I brought you up here to recuperate . . .'

Isabel caught her breath. 'But I'm wet.'

'Yes, you are.' He shrugged. 'I didn't think you'd approve if I changed your clothes.'

'I wouldn't.' Isabel propped herself up on her elbows and looked about her. 'Why didn't you put me on a towel? This swimsuit is going to ruin the bedspread.'

'I didn't want to,' said Alex honestly, smoothing the satin spread with a lazy hand. 'I wanted to see how you looked against my pillows. Putting you on a towel would have spoiled the whole effect.'

Isabel had never heard anything so erotic in her life, and in spite of the recklessness in doing so, she couldn't prevent herself from asking 'And?' in a voice husky with emotion.

Alex's dark eyes appraised her. 'I'd have preferred

you naked,' he said, with devastating candour, and
before she could escape, he had bent his head and
covered her mouth with his own.

It was not like his other kisses. This time, there was
a feverish urgency in his lips, and the tongue that
fought its way into her mouth was hot and sensual.
He wasn't just kissing her, she realised, he was giving
a fair impression of what it would be like if he
possessed her, and her protests wilted beneath the
hungry pressure of his mouth.

She lifted her hands to fasten them in the still-damp
thickness of his hair, determined to force his head
away from her; but she couldn't do it. Instead, her
hands slid compulsively round his neck, curling into
the silky hair at his nape, sliding up against his scalp
and pulling him down on top of her.

She managed a shaky 'Alex!' when she felt his
fingers in the bodice of her swimsuit, forcing it down
to her hips, but he didn't stop. This time, he pushed
the offending garment down to her ankles, following
its progress with his lips so that she was incapable of
resisting him.

Naked now, she gave herself up to the sensual
pleasure of his lovemaking. She was deaf and blind to
the dangers in what she was doing, and any doubts
she had were submerged by the simple needs he was
creating inside her. No one had ever kissed her, and
caressed her, and aroused her, as Alex was doing, and
what had always seemed so wrong with her emotions
suddenly seemed so right.

There seemed no part of her body he hadn't touched,
and although she knew he was on the bed beside her
now, she was hardly aware that he was naked, too.
Only the length of his legs rough against hers, alerted
her to their intimacy, but her mind was spinning so
dizzily with his kisses, she had no sense of inhibition.

'You're beautiful!' he groaned, burying his face

between her breasts, before cupping their fullness in his hands and suckling them urgently. Her nipples swelled and hardened beneath his searching tongue, and she knew a sense of wonder at her own body's fulfilment.

When he left her breasts to trail his lips down over her waist and her flat stomach, she dug her nails into his hair as if to stop him, but the erotic caress of his tongue in her navel evoked even more pleasure. He was sensitising every quivering muscle, and when he reached the apex of her thighs, she shuddered convulsively.

'Now—I think . . . ' he said huskily, sliding back over her, the throbbing heat of his arousal hard against her stomach. With infinite tenderness, he parted her legs to slide into her, and seconds before she felt any pain, she knew the sensuous nudge of his manhood against her.

Even then, she felt no urge to draw back, even if he had been prepared to let her. This was what she wanted; this was what she had been made for; and there was no one else but Alex whom she wanted to share it with her.

She realised she should have told him, the minute he thrust himself inside her. She had thought she was ready; that all those books she had read, which had said it could be painful, were exaggerating. But they weren't. She had not realised he was so big, or so powerful. His unguarded invasion tore into her like a knife, and although she tried to stifle her cry, Alex was too experienced to doubt what he had done.

For seconds after he had buried himself inside her, he lay completely still, and as the pain subsided, Isabel began to hope she might get away with it yet. But then, with a groan of anguish, Alex turned her face up to him, and she saw his raw frustration that she had deceived him yet again.

'You should have told me!' he bit out savagely, and although she knew she had tried to explain the truth many times, his total self-derision would not allow her to let him take the blame. Ignoring his instinctive attempt to propel himself up from her, she wound her arms round his neck and dragged him down to her again. With deliberate provocation, she slipped her tongue between his teeth and courted his participation. Then, when his teeth closed upon her tongue, to prevent its seductive dance, she let one hand trail down his back to his buttocks, and he groaned protestingly in his throat as his own needs overwhelmed him.

'Isabel . . . ' he muttered, as she ran one foot lightly up and down his calf, and she arched against him.

'I thought you wanted me,' she whispered, innocently, stroking his nipple with a delicate finger, and he closed his eyes.

'I do. I do!' he acknowledged tormentedly and, giving in to his emotions, he captured her lips with his . . .

CHAPTER ELEVEN

'YOU don't mean this, Isabel!' Jason stared at her disbelievingly, a look of frustration marring his faintly over-indulged features, and Isabel thought how typical it was that he should still assume he knew what was best for her.

'I do,' she insisted now, dropping down on to the chintz-covered sofa, and crossing one long, slender leg over the other. 'Jason, it's no use! I'll never go back to modelling.'

'Don't say that!' Jason sighed, spreading his hands. 'Isabel, when—when this is all over, you're going to feel altogether different, believe me. You'll soon get bored with this—*rustic* existence.'

'I don't think so.'

Isabel turned away from him to stare through the lattice windows of the cottage, out on to the fields that bordered the canal a hundred yards away. Somewhere a farmer was ploughing a furrow, preparing the soil for the winter's planting, and the steady drone of the tractor's engine was soothing. It helped to smooth away the disturbing ripples that Jason's invasion into her life here always created and, thinking of the changing seasons, she was more convinced than ever that this was where she would stay. Perhaps we do retain some remnant of our ancestry, she reflected ruefully. Certainly this corner of Norfolk, that bordered on Lincolnshire, seemed to hold some attachment for her. Or perhaps it was simply the fact that this cottage had been available, and she had leased it, she admitted honestly. And its distance—and inaccessibility—from London *had* suited her purpose.

Jason's nostrils flared. 'Don't you think you're being rather reckless? Something could go wrong. Situated like this—miles from anywhere—what happens if you're taken ill?'

'There is a phone,' said Isabel shortly, indicating the instrument occupying a corner of the window-ledge. But he had voiced a fear she had already experienced. In spite of her assertions of independence, her isolation here was a little daunting to someone used to city life. She wasn't afraid of being ill; she had always been disgustingly healthy, and in the last few weeks, that had not been one of her priorities. But being alone at night still made her nervous, and even the knowledge that the Vicarage was only a few yards away was no compensation in the middle of the night.

'Nevertheless,' Jason exclaimed now, 'sooner or later you're going to have to come back to town.' He made an impatient gesture. 'Won't you have to attend the Denby board meetings, at least sometimes?'

Isabel bent her head. 'As a matter of fact, I'm thinking of selling the shares.'

'Selling them!' Jason was astounded. 'After what you said!'

'I know, I know.' Isabel lifted her shoulders. 'But I don't want to see any of the Setons ever again, and by selling the shares, I can guarantee that.'

Jason snorted. 'You're a fool!'

'Maybe.'

'Robert Seton won't thank you for it.'

'I don't expect him to.'

'But you do intend giving him first option on the shares.'

'Probably.'

Jason shook his head. 'You're crazy! Put them on the open market. Let him bid for them, like anyone else.'

'I don't think Vinnie would have wanted that.'

'Vinnie!' Jason was scathing. 'I suppose you realise your precious Vinnie is responsible for everything that's happened. If she hadn't involved you in the company in the first place, you'd never have seen Alex Seton again.'

Isabel got to her feet now, a slim, defensive figure in her long suede skirt and loose-sleeved shirt. 'I'd really rather not talk about it,' she said, crossing the low-beamed room and disappearing into the adjoining kitchenette. 'Do you want some coffee? I'm afraid I've got nothing stronger.'

Jason seethed, but there was nothing he could do. Isabel had made up her mind, and he knew of old that nothing he said would change it.

'No,' he said now, pushing his hands into the pockets of his corded jacket. 'No, I've got to go. I've left some things at the hotel in Spalding, and I want to collect them before driving back to town.'

'Oh.' Isabel came to the door of the kitchen again, her slim hand resting against the frame. 'Well—thanks for coming.'

'My pleasure.' But Jason was ironic. 'Look after yourself, Isabel. Remember, if you change your mind, I'm just at the other end of the line.'

She kissed him then, going towards him and pressing her lips against his cheek. 'Thanks,' she murmured, her hand lingering against his lapel. 'I wish—I wish things could have been different.'

Jason grimaced. 'Yes. So do I,' he averred, putting her firmly from him. 'I'll be in touch. *Ciao!*'

She watched him drive away, the wheels of his Mercedes sending up a cloud of dust from the dry track. It was weeks since there had been any prolonged rain, and the lane from the cottage down to the main road was cracked and powdery. July had been a wet month, but both August and September had been dry, and now, at the beginning of October, the farmers were beginning to grumble about the drought.

Still, she reflected, glancing up at the overcast sky, perhaps their wishes were soon going to be granted. It certainly looked thundery, the clouds hanging on the horizon just lightly tinged with yellow.

Shrugging off the oppressive thought of an impending storm, Isabel went back into the cottage and closed the door. Then, she leaned back against its gnarled panels, acknowledging, somewhat ruefully, that Jason was unlikely to come again.

Since she had come to live at the cottage, he had visited her several times, always hoping, she knew, that time and isolation would bring her to her senses. But after today, after learning what she had had to tell him, he seemed finally convinced, and although she was relieved, she couldn't help a pang of remorse. He had been a good friend; better than she deserved. And maybe she would have second thoughts when the next six months were over.

But right now, the idea of going back to London, of possibly running into Alex again, and him learning what had happened, seemed no alternative at all. If things had been different; if she had still been seeing Alex, the situation might have had endless possibilities. But they weren't, and she wasn't and, thanks to Jason's co-operation, her secret would remain her own.

Leaving the door, she crossed the room to the fireplace, and added another log to those already smouldering there. The day wasn't exactly cold, but the cottage walls were thick, and even on the hottest day, a fire was not out of place. Besides, it heated the water, and although the plumbing was primitive, she intended to take a bath that evening.

She was feeling hungry, too, and, discovering it was half-past four, she decided to make herself some tea.

These days she felt hungry at the oddest times, and because she had only herself to please, she generally kept country hours.

She got most of her provisions in the village, only driving into Spalding when it was absolutely necessary. She knew the local people were curious about her, but she managed to keep herself to herself. The only person she had had a long conversation with was the Vicar, although she had confided in the doctor that she did have private means. If only to reassure her neighbours that she was not a fugitive criminal, she had excused herself afterwards. But the truth was, she didn't want anyone feeling sorry for her. A hangover from her childhood, no doubt, but important none the less.

She went for a walk after her tea. She did a lot of walking these days, and she was considering getting a dog. As well as the companionship it would offer, it would give her a reason for going out. A woman walking alone attracted all sorts of undesirable comments. Still, since coming to Norfolk, she had tackled her own housework again, and the idea of having an animal shedding hairs all over the furniture was not appealing. Maybe later, she decided, when she decided to buy a house.

It was almost dark by the time she got back, and she locked the door behind her, and quickly drew the curtains. It was another of her foibles that she never turned on the lights until the curtains were drawn. Living in the city had made her super-cautious.

However, with the curtains drawn against the night, and a low rumble of thunder echoing across the marshes, it was cosy in the cottage. She poked the fire into flame and turned on her radio, and then went out to the kitchen to prepare her bath.

It was one of the vagaries of the cottage that the bathroom was downstairs. Someone, a previous tenant she guessed, had turned what used to be a larder into a bathroom, and although the pipes were efficient, the floor was made of stone. It was nothing like the luxurious whirlpool bath she had at her apartment, and she tried not to think of what it would be like in winter as she rapidly shed her clothes.

Soaking in the claw-edged tub, though, she could forget her surroundings. The warmth, the sudsy depth of the water, was like a womb, cocooning her against the world outside. As her womb was cocooning Alex's baby, she acknowledged painfully. How strange it was that although she never wanted to see the child's father again, she already loved the scrap of humanity growing inside her.

She sighed. Jason's appearances always coincided with thoughts like these. Or rather, his arrival triggered memories she would rather forget. After all, the first time he had come, she had half expected Alex to be with him. But each succeeding visit had taught her the futility of that.

If only she knew what Alex had been thinking when he had left for South America. Was it only coincidence that he had left the day after their visit to Nazeby? And why had he gone to South America anyway? It wasn't as if he had any connection with his uncle's business there.

She had racked her brains to try and find a solution, but she had never found one. All she knew was that Alex had gone away without seeing her again, and that although she had waited almost three weeks for him to get in touch with her, he hadn't.

She shook her head. She had thought—she had *really* thought that discovering she had never slept with any other man would prove to Alex that Chris had been lying. It *must* have proved it; and to begin with, she had believed he had gone to South America to confront his uncle with that proof. But as the days and weeks went by, without any further communication from him, she had to accept the inevitable: that although Alex had wanted her, her innocence didn't mean a thing.

And after all, he had virtually told her that, when he was kissing her down at the pool. Her outrage that he should have believed she had had an affair with Jerrold Palmer hadn't meant a thing to him. He had only been interested in her body, and although he hadn't liked the idea of her taking a lover at the time, the fact that that was all over—as he saw it—cancelled out any further recriminations.

She shook her head. She should have realised what he was like then, she acknowledged now. She should have known he was too much like his uncle to suddenly change character. He had wanted her, and he had had her—by fair means or foul—and once that was accomplished, he had no further interest.

A lump formed in her throat at the realisation that she would never see him again. No matter how determined she was not to let the memories hurt her, they always did, but with each succeeding day, she was becoming stronger. This time, she had even restrained herself from asking Jason if he had seen him. He had told her so many times, she had at last accepted the truth.

Alex had gone away, because it was the simplest method of severing any connection between them. He must have known that after that passionate interlude at Nazeby, she would want to see him again, and simply to leave the country saved a dozen bland excuses.

She sighed. Even now, there were occasions when she found it hard to believe that he had not got as much out of that afternoon as she had. He had seemed so sincere at the time, and the fervour of their lovemaking had lasted well into the evening. It was true, they had not talked much, but Isabel had been content that there would be time enough for talking afterwards. Just then, she had more important needs to be satisfied, and she had found herself insatiable when it came to loving him.

They had made love several times, and in between they had slept in each other's arms. They had only stirred to love again, and that first unfortunate experience had been erased by the ecstasy that came after. Alex was so good at it, she fretted now, feeling the familiar ache in the pit of her stomach that always came with thoughts of him. After her experiences with Chris, she had half believed herself to be frigid, but with Alex she had reached the heights again and again.

They had explored one another's bodies with a thoroughness she could hardly believe now. Alex had been totally without inhibition, letting her do with him as she willed. And she had lost all modesty beneath the possessive touch of his hands.

It was Mrs Cowie who had eventually disturbed them, knocking on Alex's door and asking if he was staying to dinner. Isabel had waited, hoping he would say they were staying the night, but he didn't. 'We'll have dinner back in town,' he had called to the housekeeper carelessly, and then had taken Isabel once again, with the woman's retreating footsteps still audible to their ears.

The journey back to town had been a strain for both of them. Isabel had not known what to say to bridge the gulf between their physical compatibility and their mental discord. It was difficult to imagine herself bringing up the subject of marriage, and it was equally illogical to avoid what must be said.

And then, when they got back to her apartment, when she was steeling herself to invite him in and get the whole thing over, she discovered Jason was waiting for her. He had finished the shoot earlier than planned, he said, and feeling sorry for her for having missed the trip, he had come to take her out to dinner. He had been waiting around for over an hour, he added, convinced that sooner or later she would turn up. Isabel had had no choice but to invite him in in consequence, and Alex had simply left her, with hardly a word of farewell.

His message the next day was left on her answering machine. It was short and almost lethal in its ability to shock. He was leaving for Rio de Janeiro on the morning flight. He'd get in touch with her on his return.

Of course, he hadn't. Although she had known he must be back in London, he had made no attempt to contact her, and she had been too proud to contact him. One week went by, then two; and by the third she was already suspecting what had proved to be the case. That crazy spate of lovemaking had left her pregnant: after six desperate years she was going to have a baby.

That was when she had decided to go away. At first, she hadn't told Jason why; just that she and Alex had had a brief relationship that had gone sour, and that she needed some time to be alone.

And he had been surprisingly co-operative. She suspected he didn't approve of her associating with any member of her ex-husband's family, and he probably thought a few weeks' holiday would be enough to solve her problem. He had had no idea that finding this cottage on the borders of Lincolnshire would prove so attractive. But by the end of August, he had discovered her intention to give up modelling and, since then, his enthusiasm had evaporated.

She hadn't told him about the baby until today; and only then because he still refused to believe that she was serious about giving up her career. Not that he had accepted it entirely, she sighed. He probably

thought that once she had had the baby, she would
rapidly come to her senses. Perhaps she would, she
shrugged, and then ran a tentative hand over the faint
swelling in her belly. But she didn't think so. Her
child was not going to be abandoned by its mother;
not if she had anything to do with it.

She was stepping out of the bath when she heard
the rattle of the letter-box. She started first, and then
relaxed, guessing it was the parish magazine, or some
other circular they were delivering around the village.
But when the noise came again, she realised someone
was there.

Wrapping the towel closely around her, she padded
silently through to the living-room, blessing her
penchant for closing the curtains before putting on
the light. No one could really know she was alone in
the cottage. Not unless they knew her, she added,
wishing that gave her more confidence. She had read
too many stories about lonely women murdered by
people who knew them. What did she really know
about the people in the village? How well did she
really know the Vicar?

'Isabel! Isabel, are you in there?'

The painfully familiar voice turned her knees to
water, and she grasped the back of the sofa weakly,
half inclined to believe she was hallucinating. *Alex!*
Alex couldn't be here! It must be the Vicar, and she
was superimposing Alex's voice over his cultured tones.
That was it. It had to be. Alex didn't even know
where she was.

'Mr—Baynes?' she said faintly, clutching the ends
of the towel to her breasts, and there was a moment's
silence before the voice spoke again.

'No,' it said, 'it's not *Mr Baynes;* it's Alex! For
God's sake, open the door! There's an electric storm
going on out here.'

She hesitated, torn by the desire to keep him waiting

while she put some clothes on, so that she could meet him on equal terms, and an equally strong concern that he might be struck by lightning. It wasn't that she cared for him, of course, she told herself, winding the towel about her. But she wouldn't like to have to call Mr Baynes to remove a dead body from her door-step. He was already curious why a young woman of her age and appearance should choose to bury herself in the wilds of Norfolk. If she had to explain her connection to Alex, she might well find herself head-lining the local newspaper.

'Isabel . . . '

'All right, all right, I'm coming!' she exclaimed, scurrying barefoot across the carpet. Reaching the door, she removed the bolt and turned the key, keeping herself hidden behind it as Alex strode into the cottage.

Closing the door behind him, she was absurdly conscious of her scant attire. It was all very well sitting in the bath, recalling that afternoon at Nazeby, and how intimate with each other they had been then. Now, it was three months since she had seen him, and what had been between them had long since lost its fire.

Alex had paused on the hearth, looking round her small domain with impatient eyes. Clearly, it was not what he had expected. She wondered if he had thought she had bought herself a house resembling his uncle's. With its occasionally smoking chimney and low beams, Marsh Cottage was no one's idea of luxury.

Then he turned to look at her, and she saw to her surprise that he looked tired. But it wasn't just that, she realised, her gaze dropping compulsively down the lean length of his body. He had lost weight, and his black suede trousers and leather jerkin could not hide the fact. How funny, she thought with bitter humour; he had lost it and she had gained it. There was a moral there somewhere, if only she could see it.

'Do I amuse you?' he asked, noticing her tilting lips and misinterpreting their meaning. 'If this is meant to be some kind of joke, do let me in on the punch line!'

Isabel rapidly sobered. 'What are you doing here, Alex?' she asked, straightening away from the door with unconscious hauteur. 'How did you know where to find me? Did you think of asking Jason at last?'

Alex's dark face was sombre. 'At last?' he queried harshly. 'Did I think of asking Ferry at last? It might interest you to know I've asked your photographer friend if he knew where you were on at least half a dozen occasions. But every time I got the same answer: don't ask, because *you* didn't want to see me.'

Isabel blinked. 'No!'

'What do you mean—no?'

'I mean—no, Jason wouldn't do that.'

'Wouldn't do what?' Alex sounded scathing. 'Keep your address from me? Oh, yes, he would. That bastard has it coming, believe me.'

'No, I——' Isabel took a couple of steps towards him, biting her lips. She didn't understand this. Whenever she had asked Jason if he had heard from Alex, he had always said no. And she had believed him. Why wouldn't she? 'Jason . . . ' She stumbled to find the words. 'Are you saying you have asked Jason where I was?'

'In words of one syllable: yes.'

She blinked. 'But—why?'

'Why?' He sounded incredulous. 'Don't you know?'

Isabel stepped back again. 'There's been some mistake.'

'You bet your sweet life there has.' Alex was breathing heavily. 'And when I get my hands on Jason Ferry——'

'Oh, please!' Isabel shook her head. 'Don't talk like that. I—you must have said something to make Jason think you meant to harm me——'

'To harm you!' Alex stared at her savagely. 'My God! I think you've cornered the market on *harming* people! Or should I say one person; this person; *me!*'

Isabel shivered, but she wasn't really cold. She was just finding it incredibly difficult to accept the fact that Alex was standing here in her living-room, and what was more, he was saying that he'd been trying to find her. She dare not go beyond that. She had been hurt too much already.

'Are you cold?' he demanded now, turning to stare frustratedly at the smouldering logs. 'What do you do to get some heat around here? You'd better put some clothes on. This could take some time.'

'My—my dressing-gown's in the bathroom,' she said, unwilling to brave the stone floor again to get it. 'Behind you,' she added, when he looked up the stairs. 'The bathroom's off the kitchen. If you follow the steam, you'll find it.'

Alex hesitated, but then, with an impatient gesture, he strode out to the bathroom. 'Here,' he said, holding the green velour robe out to her. 'Drop the towel. I promise not to look.'

But he did. She knew it. Even though she turned her back, she could feel the penetration of his eyes through her shoulder-blades. And when she slipped her arms into the sleeves and drew it up around her shoulders, she felt him close behind her. The heat of his body was unmistakable.

'Thank you,' she got out at last, tying the belt of the robe about her waist and putting the width of the hearth between them. 'Um—can I get you a cup of coffee? I don't have any alcohol.'

'No?' His lips twisted. 'That's a pity. I could use a drink.'

'Well, then——'

'*Not* coffee,' he assured her grimly. 'Forget it. I can wait.'

Isabel pressed the heels of her hands together. 'If—if Jason didn't tell you where I was, how did you——?'

'I didn't say that,' Alex interrupted her. 'I said I'd asked him half a dozen times where you were and he wouldn't tell me. Today he had no choice. I cornered him in Spalding. I think he knew the game was over.'

Isabel shook her head. 'I don't believe it.'

'Don't? Or won't?'

She sighed. 'Why would he do it?'

'What? Keep me away?' Alex snorted. 'I guess he's jealous. I know the feeling, believe me.'

Isabel gasped. 'But—you went to Brazil!'

'Yes.' Alex nodded. 'The day after we went to Nazeby. Do you think I'd forget that?'

Isabel licked her lips. 'And—and when you came back you said you'd contact me.'

'Yes.'

She gulped. 'Well, you didn't.'

'Didn't what? Come back? I know. I can explain——'

'No——contact me,' she broke in huskily. 'You didn't contact me. I—I waited three weeks for you to ring, but you never did.'

'Not for three weeks, no,' he conceded heavily. 'Not for four, as a matter of fact. It's difficult to be confidential from the other side of the equator.'

Isabel stared at him. 'You mean—you were still in Brazil!'

'As you'd have found out, if you'd cared to ring my office.' Alex shrugged. 'I know I should have written. I did write on two occasions, but I destroyed the letters. I was afraid I'd read too much into our relationship, and no one was going to accuse me of being a fool a second time. When I got back and you'd disappeared, I was half inclined to believe that I'd been right.'

Isabel moistened her lips. 'I don't understand.'

'Well, that makes two of us,' he declared sardonically. 'Do you want me to explain, or am I making another mistake?'

Isabel shook her head. 'Just tell me what happened,' she whispered huskily. 'I want to know.'

'Why don't you sit down?' he said roughly, noticing how she was trembling, and Isabel subsided obediently on to the sofa. In truth, her legs did feel like jelly, and she wasn't sure how much longer they would have held her.

'OK.' Alex unzipped his leather jacket and pushed his hands into the pockets of his trousers. 'You won't like this, but the reason why I didn't ring you was because my uncle begged me not to. And, I thought I owed him that much, in spite of what he'd done.'

Isabel's eyes grew wary. 'You did what your uncle told you?' She swallowed. 'I see.'

'No, you don't see,' said Alex abruptly, squatting down in front of the hearth with a lithe, disturbing grace. 'Whatever you've thought of me in the past, when I flew out to Rio, it was to have it out with Robert Seton. I think I wanted to kill him; until I got there and discovered Chris had almost done it for me.'

Isabel frowned. 'Chris?'

'Yes, Chris,' said Alex, taking one of her hands and holding it between both of his. 'You know that affair with Palmer? The affair *I* accused *you* of having? Well,' he paused, 'Chris had got himself involved with someone in California, someone not as scrupulous as Palmer, someone who had taken pictures, and sent them to his father.'

Isabel caught her breath. 'You mean——'

'I think you know what I mean.' Alex bent his head. 'My uncle was being blackmailed for half a million dollars. The night I arrived in Rio, he had a serious stroke.'

'No!'

'Yes.'

'But there was nothing in the papers, no stories in the Press——'

'No. That was my job,' said Alex grimly. 'No one had to know what was going on or Chris would have become involved. Uncle Robert was scared to death that Chris would find out and exercise his right to take over the running of the company in his absence. Somehow, we managed to disguise his illness as heat exhaustion, until I could get him back to England.'

Isabel hesitated. 'And now? How is he now?'

'Partially paralysed,' said Alex flatly. 'He can speak, but not everyone can understand him. His doctor says he'll probably be confined to a wheelchair for the rest of his life. The trouble is, he's changed his will. Since—since that affair with Chris, he won't even agree to see him. He wants me to take over the running of Denby Industries, and I don't know what to do.'

Isabel gazed at him helplessly. 'Does Chris know?'

'About his father? Or about his father's will?'

'Well—both, I suppose.'

'Yes. He does now.'

'And?'

'Well, to begin with, he was pretty shattered; on both counts. Lately—well, lately, he's accepted it, I guess. In any event, he's considering moving permanently to the States. Apart from the unfortunate experience I mentioned, he likes it over there. He has friends in California, as well as enemies. He'll make out.'

Isabel's eyes were round. 'And the blackmailer? Did you have to pay the money?'

Alex's lips twisted. 'My uncle would have, I think. I contacted the police instead. They're pretty clued-in to cases like that. It was all sorted out with the

minimum amount of publicity. He was a pretty
amateur blackmailer.'

Isabel bit her lip. 'So that—that was why you
couldn't contact me?'

'That was why.' Alex looked at her steadily. 'I knew
you'd think I was all kinds of a heel, but what could
I do? Until I got back to England, it was impossible.
I just consoled myself with the thought that we had
the rest of our lives ahead of us. Then, when I got
back, you'd disappeared.'

'Oh, Alex . . . '

'And that bastard of a photographer wouldn't tell
me where you were. Even today, he screwed me to get
your address.'

'Screwed you?' Isabel blinked. 'I don't understand.
What were you doing in Spalding anyway?'

'Would you believe—looking for you?'

'But——'

'Look, I've rung your apartment a hundred times,
and I knew that creep was still seeing you. So——I
had him followed. My contact said he'd lost him
somewhere in Spalding yesterday. I drove up this
morning and trailed round every estate agency in the
town, showing them your picture. I was sure someone
must remember you. You're not exactly unknown,
you know.'

'I am here,' said Isabel ruefully. 'But when did you
see Jason?'

'About two hours ago. He was coming out of an
hotel with a suitcase. I cornered him, and he made up
some story about checking out a location for a shoot.
I think he realised I was likely to shoot him if he
didn't tell me where you were. Anyway, after an
argument, I agreed to let him submit terms for the
spring catalogue at Denby Textiles, on condition he
gave me your address. And here I am.'

Isabel caught her breath. 'He was interested in that

catalogue, as soon as he found out we were—related,' she exclaimed, and Alex pulled a wry face.

'So? What the hell! It was a small price to pay to find you. Just tell me that you wanted me to find you, and I'll consider it all worthwhile.'

Isabel quivered. 'Oh, Alex,' she breathed, leaning towards him and sliding her arms over his shoulders. 'I wanted you—so much!'

He moved then, subsiding on to the sofa beside her and pulling her hungrily into his arms. 'And I've wanted you,' he muttered, his mouth finding hers. 'I feel as if I've been serving a sentence, and you've just given me my freedom . . . '

It was some time before they spoke again, but when Alex aroused himself sufficiently to stir the logs to flame, Isabel smiled.

'I hope Mr Baynes doesn't come to call this evening,' she murmured, stroking caressing fingers down his spine. 'You're not exactly dressed to meet my neighbours, are you, darling? And I have the feeling he might not approve of what we've just been doing.'

Alex turned from the fire to look down at her. 'Who the hell is Mr Baynes?' he demanded, and her tongue appeared provocatively at his obvious impatience.

'Just the Vicar,' she said, too content to prolong her teasing. 'He's been quite a good friend to me, although I'm sure he thinks I'm in hiding.'

'You were,' Alex reminded her harshly, bending to caress her ear with his lips. 'My God, when I came home from South America, and discovered you'd disappeared, I nearly went out of my mind.'

'Did you?' Isabel looked at him as he lifted his head, sliding her fingers over his nape. 'But that night we drove back from Nazeby, you couldn't wait to get away.'

Alex groaned. 'That night we drove back from

Nazeby, I was too consumed by what had happened.
I couldn't believe I'd been fooled for so long, and if I
seemed remote, you have to remember, you'd thrown
all my schemes for us aside.'

Isabel frowned. 'How?'

'Oh——' Alex sighed. 'After fighting my emotions
for you for over six years, I'd finally decided to tell
you how I felt about you. I was being magnanimous,
you see. I'd managed to convince myself that my
earlier resentment of your relationship with Chris had
been justified by your *affair* with Palmer, but that
whatever had happened in the past, we might still
have a future together. I needed that justification,
don't you see? Without it, I couldn't entirely banish
the thought that I had *wasted* six years; that if I'd
been honest about my feelings right from the start,
you might never have married Chris.'

'Oh, Alex!'

'I know.' His hand curved possessively round her
cheek. 'I've been a fool. I know that now. But that
night I still needed a scapegoat, and Uncle Robert
was it.'

Isabel's lids veiled her eyes. 'He—he knew.'

'I know that, too. Believe me, he didn't come off
lightly. As soon as he was able to speak to me, I
confronted him with it, and he had to admit that you
had begged him to have the marriage annulled.'

Isabel trembled. 'He hates me. He always did.'

'*Hated,*' Alex amended roughly. 'He *hated* you.
Right now, he doesn't hate anybody, and if I turned
up tomorrow with you as my wife, he'd welcome you
with open arms.'

'I doubt that.' Isabel blinked suddenly, and looked
up at him. 'Wh—what did you say?'

Alex's lips curved. 'I said, if I turned up with you
tomorrow, he'd welcome you with open arms.'

Isabel looked puzzled. 'But I thought——' She

licked her lips. 'Well, we'll have to see, won't we?'

Alex's laugh was teasing. 'Does that mean there's a doubt that you'll marry me?' he queried, and her eyes widened.

'Then—you did say——!'

'—that if I introduced you as my wife, my uncle wouldn't object?' He grinned. 'I may have done. Well? Do you want me to kneel?'

Isabel's arms imprisoned him on top of her. 'That won't be necessary,' she said huskily. 'Oh, Alex, I do love you!'

'Is that a yes or a no?' he murmured against her lips, and she hugged him closer.

'It's a yes,' she breathed unsteadily. 'Except—except there is one other thing . . . '

'I know.' Alex drew back to look down at her, and a faint colour invaded her cheeks.

'You know?'

Alex inclined his head. 'You're worried about me becoming chairman of Denby Industries,' he said softly. 'But nothing's definite yet. I told you. I don't know what to do about that. I wanted to talk to you about it, and we'll have plenty of time for that. If you don't want me to have anything to do with it——'

'That's not it.' Isabel broke into his words, expelling her breath on a long sigh. 'That is—well, whether you become chairman of Denby Industries is important, of course, but—there is something else.'

Alex frowned now. 'What else?' He hesitated. 'I've told you, Chris is leaving England——'

'It's not Chris.'

He shook his head. 'Then I don't know——' He looked puzzled. 'Unless you mean your shares. You can keep them——'

Isabel shook her head. 'Oh, Alex, it's not the shares. You can have them back, if you want. I'd already decided to offer them to you.'

'Then, if it's not the company—and it's not Chris —and it's not the shares——' Alex gazed at her uncomprehendingly. 'You're not—ill, or anything. You're not hiding out here, because you thought I wouldn't want you if I knew? Darling, if that's what it is, we can find specialists——'

'I'm not ill.' Isabel allowed herself a broken laugh now. 'Let me tell you! I—I'm pregnant. I'm going to have a baby.'

'A baby!' Alex stared at her now, then his eyes dropped lower, over the rosy fullness of her breasts to the faintly discernible swell of her abdomen. 'Oh, God! A baby! So that's why you hid yourself away up here!'

Isabel nodded. 'It was part of the reason, yes.'

'And the other part?' He was intent.

'You know the other part. Because I loved you, and I couldn't bear to go on seeing you, thinking you didn't love me.'

Alex's eyes darkened. 'Were you going to tell me?'

Isabel shook her head. 'I was afraid you might not have believed it was yours.'

Alex groaned. 'Oh, love—*love!*' He buried his face in the loosened glory of her hair. 'I believe it. I just can't believe I've wasted so many years.'

'Well—perhaps we shouldn't waste any more,' she ventured gently, spreading her palms over the smooth, brown skin of his shoulders, and he agreed.

'Do you think this Mr Baynes of yours would marry us?' he asked, his voice huskily teasing. 'As a newly pregnant father, I'd like you to make an honest man of me as soon as possible!'

Isabel smiled. 'You know, I wonder if Vinnie had any of this in mind when she left me those shares,' she tendered thoughtfully, and Alex drew her closer.

'You know,' he said wryly, 'you could be right. I always thought the old lady was more perceptive than the rest of us.'

TRIAL OF INNOCENCE

TRIAL OF
INNOCENCE

BY
ANNE MATHER

MILLS & BOON LIMITED
Eton House, 18-24 Paradise Road
Richmond, Surrey TW9 1SR

*First published in Great Britain in 1988
by Mills & Boon Limited*

© Anne Mather 1988

*Australian copyright 1988
Philippine copyright 1988
Reprinted 1988
This edition 1992*

ISBN 0 263 77941 6

*Set in Times Roman 10 on 10$\frac{1}{4}$ pt.
19-9208-62194*

Made and printed in Great Britain

CHAPTER ONE

SHE shouldn't have come to the airport. She hadn't wanted to come, goodness knew, but Ben had been so adamant, and she hadn't been able to think of a single legitimate reason why she should not want to meet Stephen's brother after all these years. After all, the rest of the household was in an uproar in anticipation of his return and, after the traumatic events of the past few weeks, she, like them, should have been looking forward to such a happy event. Ben was. In spite of the animosity which had existed between him and his younger son for so long—an animosity which Robyn couldn't help feeling responsible for—he was awaiting Jared's return with an almost painful intensity, looking to his younger son to heal the wounds left by Stephen's death.

For her part, Robyn felt as if she had been living in a vacuum ever since the police inspector arrived to inform them of Stephen's accident. At first, she had experienced a sense of unreality, a lack of belief in what he was saying; and then, an almost shameful feeling of relief that Stephen was dead, that their marriage was over, that never again would she have to suffer the pain and humiliation that Stephen's many defections had caused her.

Of course, his father had known what Stephen was like, but he had been prepared to overlook his elder son's imperfections. He had always loved Stephen best, and although it had angered him when Jared went away, he had not really cared. Perhaps Stephen and his father had been alike, Robyn reflected now. More alike than she knew, anyway. Certainly, Ben's second wife—the mother of his younger son—had not found their marriage tenable. Ben had divorced her for desertion when Jared was only five years old, and although, when she first

5

got to know him, Robyn had sympathised with her father-in-law, her experiences with Stephen had made her wonder whether his father had been as completely innocent as he maintained.

Still, that particular skeleton had never significantly raised its ugly head. Perhaps because he liked her, perhaps because she was the girl he had wanted Stephen to marry, Ben had always been excessively kind to Robyn, and she had to admit, she had come to rely on his support in recent years. In fact, she had sometimes felt that she and Ben had more in common than she and Stephen ever had, and he had certainly done his best to ease the situation between them.

But that was all in the past now. Stephen was dead and, instead of dwelling on his shortcomings, she should be mourning his loss. He had been her husband for the past eight years, after all, and he was Daniel's father. She had to remember that, and forget everything else.

None the less, this duty she had to perform today, this coming to London airport to welcome home the prodigal son, was not one she cherished. On the contrary, she had done everything she could to avoid the responsibility, even to the extent of inventing a headache this morning in the hope that Ben would take pity on her and send someone else in her place.

But he hadn't. He had been adamant. 'One of us should be there, Robyn,' he had said quietly. 'And as I can't...'

The reminder of the stroke which had crippled him three years ago and left Stephen in control of the family business was enough to remind Robyn of her continued dependence on him. For Daniel's sake, she had to go; for Daniel's sake, she had to forget the past.

All the same, she had been in a state of some agitation all the way down on the M1, and she was sure that, had she been driving herself, she would never have found the way to Heathrow. It was just as well that David McCloud, her father-in-law's chauffeur, had been at the wheel, and Robyn had been able to sit back and pretend that her thoughts were as placid as his.

Daniel had wanted to come with her. He was very excited about the arrival of this long-absent uncle, of whom he had latterly heard so much. 'How far away is Australia?' he had asked, not once, but a dozen times, making his grandfather produce an atlas of the world to show him exactly where his father's brother had been living for the past six years. 'But why haven't I ever seen him?' he had persisted to his mother, after his grandfather had failed to produce a satisfactory answer. 'Why has he never come here for a holiday? Saddlebridge is his home, too, isn't it? Grandpa says it is, but he won't say why Uncle Jared went away.'

'It's a long story,' Robyn had replied briskly, hoping Daniel's propensity for asking personal questions was not going to be too much of a problem. It was what came of being the only child in a household of adults, all of whom had their own reasons for spoiling him. He was at times impertinent and precocious, and he was growing up with the impression that he was the most important member of the household. He had needed a father, she thought now. The trouble was, Stephen had been at home so rarely, he had never fulfilled that role.

'I like long stories,' Daniel had protested, when Robyn had proved as unforthcoming as his grandfather. 'Well, if you won't tell me, I'm going to ask Uncle Jared when he gets here. I bet he won't mind talking about it. I bet it's because of some dumb row he had with Grandpa before he went away.'

Yes, entirely too precocious, Robyn reflected bitterly, wondering what she had ever done to deserve this new threat to her peace of mind. She had been a good wife; too good, some people might say, who didn't know her reasons for making herself the kind of wife Stephen had wanted. Some of her friends had thought she was mad to put up with his behaviour, had considered her contention that Daniel needed both his parents to be both untrue and outdated. But Robyn had been determined that Daniel should not be deprived of the heritage that was his, and if she had sometimes wanted to scream with frustration and rebel, thankfully those times had been becoming fewer. After all, she was thirty-two now, no longer a foolish girl to whom the prospect of a loveless marriage offered any fears. She had learned that habit and convenience were far more comfortable bedfellows than the grand passion written about in the kind of books so popular in Saddleford Public Library. In spite of everything, she had made a home for herself at Saddlebridge, and since Ben's incapacitation she had become both his nurse and his confidante. With Stephen's death, she had briefly believed she might have a future, after all. And then Ben had told her he had sent for Jared; that Stephen's death had altered everything; and Robyn had realised how wrong she had been.

Now, standing outside the Customs hall, waiting for the passengers from the Qantas flight to clear Immigration, Robyn steeled herself for the ordeal of facing Jared again after all this time. How long had it been? she wondered, pretending she needed to think about her answer. She knew exactly how long it was since Jared had paid his last visit to Saddlebridge. It was six years and four months, give or take a few days. In the July, just after he had graduated from university. She and Stephen had been married more than two years, and Daniel had been almost eighteen months old.

She caught her lower lip between her teeth and bit, hard. She was doing it again, she thought irritably. Dwelling on the past, and allowing prior events to colour her mood. She had to stop it. Just because her life had altered little since he went away, it was no reason to view this coming meeting with unnecessary trepidation. It was foolish to imagine Jared would not have changed. Heavens, when he went away he had been little more than a boy, with no experience of life to speak of. Now, after six years of being independent, of working at a variety of jobs, from sheep-shearing in New South Wales to working in a hotel in Queensland, he had to have changed out of all recognition. He probably hadn't given a thought to his family for years, and his father's letter must have been a bolt from the blue.

They had learned, from the reply he had sent to his father, that for the past two years he had been working for a firm of financial consultants in Sydney. Evidently, he had grown tired of manual labour, and decided to use the qualifications he had earned at university at last. In any event, he had agreed to come home, although he had made no promises about how long he might stay, and Robyn suspected that taking over his dead brother's position as managing director of Morley Textiles might seem very mundane after the life he was used to.

Or was that just wishful thinking? she asked herself uneasily, aware that, in this instance, her desires conflicted with those of her father-in-law. All the same, although Jared had expressed his grief at the news of his brother's death, he had not mentioned the business at all. And Ben should know that just because he wanted—*expected*—Jared to stay was no reason to assume he would.

Robyn looked around now, wishing McCloud was with her. She felt conspicuously obvious standing here, and she hoped Jared would not think she had arranged this situation. But parking at the airport was not easy, and the chauffeur had suggested it might be simpler if he stayed with the car, so that the effort of hefting Jared's luggage to some distance parking place would not prove a problem.

The passengers from a recently landed transatlantic flight were gradually dispersing, and the first trickle of Australian passengers was beginning to filter through. Watching the smiling, suntanned faces as they were greeted by friends and relatives, Robyn decided she could tell who were from Oz and who were not. Australians looked more relaxed somehow, she thought, watching a middle-aged couple embracing a family group that included two small children, scarcely out of nappies. But then, her sense of satisfaction was ruined by a distinctly mid-western drawl, and that particular attempt at self-distraction was defeated.

Sighing, she slipped the strap of her bag over one shoulder, and thrust her hands into the pockets of her purple corded jacket. Her nerves were stretching by the minute, and, although earlier in the day she had convinced herself she didn't care what she looked like or what Jared might think of her, the continued delay was wearing. Catching a glimpse of her reflection in the glass wall opposite, she saw that the coil of hair at her nape was shedding black strands on to her collar, and that the cup of coffee and the sandwich, which she and McCloud had shared at a motorway service area, had removed all trace of lipstick from her mouth. She looked pale and tired, she thought resignedly, used to her unremarkable features, and seeing no charm in them. She hoped Jared would imagine she was grieving over Stephen's sudden demise. How disgusted he would be if he guessed how difficult it was for her to mourn her husband's passing.

'Hello, Robyn!'

She had not heard him approach, had been too absorbed in her own reflection to notice the tall, lean man, in cream cotton trousers and a dark brown suede jerkin, detach himself from the group of arriving passengers and make his way towards her. Her first intimation that she was no longer alone was when he spoke to her, and she started violently at the amazingly familiar tones.

'Jared!' she got out through dry lips, aware that, for all her preparations, she had not been prepared for this moment. 'Well...how nice to see you. You—you look well. Did you have a good journey?'

'Well...I did,' he mocked gently, setting down the overnight bag he was carrying and glancing round. 'Don't tell me you're all the welcoming party there is. Where's Dad? Didn't he come with you?'

'We—er—we thought it would be too much for him,' Robyn stammered awkwardly, trying not to stare at him too obviously. She had been right in her speculation. He *had* changed. This cool-eyed stranger was nothing like the rebellious youth who had left the country. Recognisable he might be, but familiar he was not.

'Too much for him?' echoed Jared drily, the inflection in his tone evidence of his scepticism. 'That's an original excuse, anyway.' He ran a careless hand over the silky sun-streaked hair that lapped his collar. 'So—you pulled the short straw, hmm? Poor Robyn! I bet this was one duty you could have done without.'

Robyn squared her shoulders, refusing to let him see that he was disconcerting her. 'Not at all,' she replied politely, if not altogether truthfully. 'It's good to see you again, Jared. You've—matured. I'd hardly have recognised you.'

It wasn't true, but he couldn't know that, although his grey-green eyes did register a certain cynicism at her remarks. 'I wasn't a boy when I went away, Robyn,' he said, his eyes shifting to some point beyond her head. 'But you know that, don't you? In spite of your pleas to the contrary.'

Robyn started to say, I don't know what you mean, and then changed it to, 'I don't know—exactly where Mr McCloud is. Is this all your luggage?' She indicated the medium-sized suitcase he had set down at his feet. 'We thought you'd have more.'

'For a week's stay?' Jared shrugged, bending to possess himself of the suitcase once again. 'I travel light, Robyn. I find it's the best way.'

Robyn swallowed. 'A—a *week's* stay?'

'Give or take a day or so. Holidaying in England in winter, when it's summer down under, doesn't exactly appeal to me.'

'Holidaying?' Robyn licked her lips. 'But I thought——'

She broke off abruptly, but Jared raised a speculative eyebrow. 'Yes? You thought—what? That I was staying longer, obviously. Now, why should you think that, I wonder?'

Robyn shook her head. 'Well—well, I assumed——'

'I think this is where I came in,' said Jared briefly. 'Come on. Let's find Mac, shall we? We can talk in the car. I presume you did come down by car, didn't you? Or has the old man invested in a helicopter?'

'I doubt if your father could afford to invest in a helicopter,' retorted Robyn stiffly, walking at his side as they crossed the arrivals lounge to emerge into the cold crisp air of a November morning. For once, the sun was shining, and its brilliance gave the coldly practical airport buildings an unexpected warmth. 'Oh, there's the car.' She raised her arm to wave. 'Mr McCloud! We're over here.'

'Still the same old Roller,' commented Jared satirically, as the chauffeur guided the elderly Rolls-Royce in their direction, but Robyn chose not to bite. He could be as sarcastic as he liked, she told herself fiercely. She wasn't going to defend his father to him. If he wanted to make fun of a sick old man, that was his affair. She would not condone it by making excuses.

David McCloud's welcome more than made up for any lack of enthusiasm on her part. 'It's good to have you back, Jared,' he exclaimed, shaking the younger man's hand warmly with both of his. 'We've missed you, the missus and me. Saddlebridge hasn't been the same since you went away.'

'It's good to see you, Mac,' returned Jared easily, with more warmth in his voice than he had shown thus far. 'How is Janet? And the boys? I guess Jamie must be working by now.'

'Ay, he's teaching in Nottingham just now,' replied Mac, with evident pride, stowing Jared's suitcase in the capacious boot of the car as he spoke. 'Donald's still at school, of course, but we hear he's doing very nicely.'

Jared expressed his admiration as he opened the rear door of the limousine for Robyn to get in. Although she resented the feeling that she was being patronised, Robyn made no demur. It would be less harrowing if Jared sat up front with the chauffeur, even if she had come to regard that position as her own.

However, to her surprise—and consternation—Jared did not take the front seat. Instead, he climbed into the back of the car with her, closing the door and joining her on the worn leather banquette.

'You look as if you're doing very nicely yourself, Jared,' Mac declared, taking his seat behind the wheel. 'Wait until Janet sees that tan. Och, she'll be green with envy!'

Jared leant forward then to make some inaudible comment—inaudible to Robyn, anyway—and both men laughed. Robyn found she was gritting her teeth. She had forgotten how popular Jared had always been with the staff at Saddlebridge; had forgotten his propensity for getting under people's skins—particularly hers.

The amount of traffic waiting to get out of the air-port's perimeter required all McCloud's attention, and Robyn tensed as Jared relaxed beside her. In spite of her unwanted resentment at his evident preference for the chauffeur's company, she was apprehensive of what he might unthinkingly reveal, and although McCloud was occupied, he was not deaf.

'So...' Jared murmured, attracting her attention, 'do you want to talk about it?'

Robyn swallowed. 'Stephen's accident?'

'What else?'

What else, indeed? Robyn licked her lips. 'Didn't your father tell you?'

Jared shrugged, his shoulders depressing the soft leather. 'He wrote that Steve's car went over the bridge at Carnthwaite. Is that all there was to it? When did it happen?'

Robyn shifted a little uncomfortably. 'Surely he told you. It happened six weeks ago——'

'That wasn't what I meant.' Grey-green eyes, shaded by sun-bleached lashes, several shades darker than his hair, narrowed perceptibly. 'What time of *day* did it happen? Dad never said.'

Robyn suspected he knew what the answer must be, and with McCloud sitting up front, hearing every word that was said, she could hardly prevaricate. 'I—it was evening,' she said, hoping he would be satisfied with that. 'Unfortunately, he wasn't found until early the next morning. It was raining pretty heavily. No one saw the car leave the road.'

Jared made a sound of disbelief. 'But surely there must have been some evidence of what had happened. Wasn't the bridge damaged in any way?'

Of course it had been. Aware of McCloud's sympathetic gaze through the rear-view mirror, Robyn strove to avoid the damning revelation that few people used Carnthwaite bridge at one o'clock in the morning.

'It was raining,' she repeated, assuming an interest in a plane that was taking off overhead. 'I expect your father will give you all the details.'

Jared made no comment at this, and for a short time Robyn breathed a little more easily. If she could just get this journey over, she thought encouragingly. Once they reached Saddlebridge, she could at least avoid his presence.

Even so, his silence did promote an awareness of him she would rather not have experienced. While they were talking, she had needed all her concentration to evade his questions, but now that that particular obstacle had been overcome, she was left with her unwelcome sensitivity to his nearness. It was incredible that even after so many years she should still feel that mawkish awareness of something that was long since dead. That particular incident in her past should hold no attraction for her, and she despised herself utterly for allowing it to intrude on what should have been her grief.

All the same, it was impossible not to be conscious of the man beside her. It was natural enough that she should notice the changes in him, and she was quite sure he was not ignorant of his own attraction to the opposite sex. After all, girls had hung around Jared for as long as she could remember. There had always been some girl phoning him up or coming to the house to see him. Even when they were children, when Stephen was fifteen,

Robyn fourteen, and Jared a precocious nine, he had always had some girl in tow—albeit without any effort on his part. Maybe that was why Stephen had resented him so much, and why Ben had always felt the need to protect his elder son.

She sighed. If only it had been that simple. Ben's aversion to his younger son went deeper than that. That was why she had been so shocked when she learned Ben had sent for Jared. It was the last thing she had expected him to do. The last thing she had *wanted* him to do.

But he was here now, and there was nothing she could do about it. After six years of convincing herself that she was unlikely ever to see Jared again, he had come back, and that was something she was going to have to live with.

Catching her breath, she permitted herself a sidelong glance in his direction. To her relief, he was looking out of the window of the car, and she was able to observe him without his knowledge. He hadn't changed that much, not really, she realised tensely. Oh, he was older—weren't they all?—but his features were not that different from when he went away. His face was less angular, perhaps. He had been very thin when he went away, whereas now his features were lean, but not so finely drawn. His skin was darker, too, with the tan McCloud had admired earlier, but the narrow cheekbones and thin-lipped mouth were as she remembered them, and only experience deepened the narrowed penetration of his eyes.

And then he turned his head and looked at her, and her composure fled. Just for an instant, he looked at her without the guarded expression he had worn since he'd got off the plane, and her breathing became constricted. Dear God, she thought in alarm, he hasn't forgotten anything. And that knowledge was more frightening than anything else.

She looked away at once, hoping he had not glimpsed the panic in her eyes, but his next words set her teeth on edge. 'How is Daniel?' he enquired smoothly, his voice devoid of all emotion. 'He must be what? Seven now? Eight?'

'He's seven,' said Robyn quickly, hoping to evade any further questions about Daniel by changing the subject. 'Um—you must be tired. If you want to sleep, don't let me stop you.'

Jared's lips twisted. 'How kind. But I'm fine, really. I slept on the plane. There wasn't much else to do.'

Robyn forced a tight smile. 'I wouldn't know. I've never travelled so far myself.'

'No.' Jared inclined his head. 'No, you wouldn't, would you?'

Robyn swallowed, casting a meaningful glance in the chauffeur's direction. 'I'm probably not the travelling kind.'

'No.' Jared conceded the point. 'You always did like Saddlebridge best.'

Robyn bent her head. 'Saddlebridge is my home. You know that.'

'Do I ever,' jeered Jared mockingly. And then, 'So tell me about yourself, about what you do all day; about Daniel.'

Robyn took a deep breath. 'What can I tell you that you don't already know? Things don't change at Saddlebridge. Not significantly, anyway. Although, since your father had his stroke——'

'His *what*?'

Jared halted her there, a lean brown hand gripping her arm in sudden violence. 'Did you say—stroke?'

'Yes.' Robyn nodded in confusion. 'But you knew——'

'Like hell I did!' he snarled savagely. 'When was this? Before or after Steve's accident?'

Robyn stared at him. 'Be—before, of course,' she stammered blankly. 'Quite a bit before. Er—about three years, I suppose.'

'Three years!' Jared gazed at her, aghast. 'For Christ's sake, why wasn't I told at the time?'

Robyn winced as his strong fingers dug into her flesh, even through the thickness of her sleeve. 'I thought you had been,' she protested faintly. 'Didn't Stephen write to you?'

'Stephen?' Jared's jaw hardened. 'No. Nobody wrote to me. The first communication I had from England was from my father, telling me that Steve was dead.'

Robyn didn't know what to say. 'I—I'm sorry.'

'Yes. So am I.' Jared seemed to realise he was hurting her and abruptly let her go. 'My God! So that was what you meant when you said the old man wasn't fit enough to come to the airport. And I thought he must have had second thoughts about sending for me.'

'Oh, no.' Robin shook her head. 'He—he's looking forward to seeing you. Since—well, since the funeral, he's talked of little else.'

'Really?' Jared did not sound convinced. 'So how is he now?'

'Irascible.' Robyn tried to speak lightly. 'He's—partially paralysed. His speech may be imperfect, but his brain's as sharp as ever.'

Jared frowned. 'And who's running the mill now that—Steve's not around?'

'Um—well, I am,' admitted Robyn unwillingly. 'At least, I deliver your father's orders to Frank Beasley and Maurice Woodhouse.'

'Maurice Woodhouse! Is he still there?' Jared made an evident effort to relax again, lying back in the seat beside her and fixing her with an unnerving stare. 'My God, I'm beginning to understand. That's why I've been summoned to the presence, isn't it? The old man thinks he can persuade me to take Steve's place. The prince is dead, long live the prince, hmm?'

Robyn moistened her lips. 'You'll have to ask him that,' she said, conscious that McCloud could hear every word that was said. He must know she was avoiding a direct answer, but it couldn't be helped. It was up to Ben to put his case himself; not her.

Jared shifted to rest an ankle across his knee, gazing somewhat broodingly at his fingers, plucking at the laces of his suede boot. 'Did you go along with this?' he asked suddenly, and Robyn expelled her breath unsteadily.

'I—um—it was your father's decision, not mine,' she murmured uneasily, wishing she had known he was unaware of his father's condition. Had Ben been aware of his son's ignorance? she wondered frustratedly. Had he banked on the certainty that sooner or later she would betray the truth?

'That's not what I asked,' Jared was saying now, turning cool, calculating eyes in her direction. 'I asked if you went along with it? Did you? *Do* you?'

Robyn put up a nervous hand and looped an untidy strand of hair behind her ear. 'If it's what your father wants...' she murmured awkwardly, and avoided his eyes.

'Is that a yes or a no?'

Robyn sighed. 'Jared, Saddlebridge is as much your home as mine.'

'How diplomatic!' His lips twisted. 'Did you learn that from Steve or my father?'

'Jared——'

'You've not found yourself a wife then, Jared?' McCloud's sudden intervention came as a welcome escape, and Robyn's grateful eyes sought the chauffeur's in the mirror.

'No.' Jared's response was ironic. 'Not yet, Mac. I've not been as lucky as you. The women I choose invariably prefer someone else.'

'The *women* you choose.' McCloud took him up on his words. 'That sounds like there have been quite a number.'

'A few,' agreed Jared carelessly, and Robyn felt a painful tightening of her stomach muscles. Yet, why should it surprise her that Jared had had other women? It had always been so. She knew that.

'Well, you don't sound too heartbroken,' remarked McCloud drily. 'I'd guess there are a few ladies around

Saddleford who won't be sorry to find you're still unattached.'

Jared smiled, but he made no comment, and Robyn wondered what he was thinking. There was no doubt his return to Saddlebridge—however brief that return might be—would attract a certain amount of attention. And there were several young women, women younger than herself, who would be more than willing to welcome him back. Robyn felt suddenly very old.

And, as if noticing how strained she had become, Jared seemed to take pity on her. 'You know,' he said, and although she tensed at his words, he was settling back in his seat as he spoke, 'I think I will try and doze, after all. You don't mind, do you, Robyn? I'd like to be wide awake when I meet the old man.'

CHAPTER TWO

IT WAS just after half-past eight the next morning when Robyn turned the Ford estate car between the gates of Morley Textiles. Parking in the space reserved for the managing director, she uncoiled herself from behind the wheel, and made a determined effort to act naturally as she walked across the cobbled yard to the office block. There were bound to be faces looking out of windows, wondering how she was going to react now that Jared had come back, speculating about her, and Daniel's, position, now that the younger son was evidently to inherit his father's business, and she had no wish to feed their curiosity.

If only that was all she had to worry about, she thought drily, mounting the external wooden staircase to her office. Whether or not Jared chose to take up Ben's offer was immaterial to her. The insurance Stephen had left would ensure Daniel's future was secure, and that was all she cared about.

All the same, she was aware that convincing the staff of the fact was another matter altogether, and she was quite prepared for the divisions of loyalty any change of status would bring.

Meanwhile, she had a business to run, and it wasn't easy to concentrate on that while her thoughts continued to dwell on what might be happening at the house. She couldn't forget that Daniel had shown a disturbing fascination for his uncle's company the night before, and that although Mr McCloud would be taking him to school shortly, he had just been sitting down to his breakfast when she left. Of course, Jared was not up yet, and there was every likelihood that he wouldn't be

20

before Daniel left the house, but he could be; he *could* be.

Entering the office which Ben Morley had used until his stroke, Robyn firmly put all thoughts of Jared—and Daniel—aside, and shed her tweed jacket on to the old-fashioned coat-stand that stood just inside the door. She saw, with some gratitude, that Mr Matthews, the caretaker, had lit the fire for her arrival, and already its crackling warmth was banishing the grey light of a misty morning. Jared would find working in England again much different from working in Australia, she reflected unwillingly, warming her cold hands over the flames. Should he decide to stay, of course, she added impatiently, aware that she was allowing thoughts of Jared to intrude once again. For heaven's sake, it was by no means certain that he would stay. In his position, she doubted she would even consider it. He had made a good life for himself at the other side of the world, that was obvious from things he had said over dinner the night before. She knew that—and so must Ben.

A knock at the door which led to her secretary's office provided a welcome distraction. 'Come in, Joan,' she called, turning from the fire with some relief, only to find Maurice Woodhouse entering the room.

Joan Hedley's office opened into the corridor that led from one end of the old building to the other; consequently, unless they used the outer door, all Robyn's visitors came that way. All the same, she had not been expecting to see Maurice Woodhouse at this hour of the morning, and his coming to her office usually meant trouble.

He had disapproved of her promotion to acting managing director ever since Ben had put her there, and although he must know as well as anyone that it was really Ben he should blame, he had always directed his resentment towards Robyn and no one else. Perhaps he thought she had persuaded Ben to make her his deputy, Robyn thought wryly. If only he knew. Nothing could be further from the truth.

'Good morning,' he said now, levering his rotund body through the door and approaching Robyn's desk with an air of satisfaction. 'Well? Where is he, then? Didn't he drive down with you? I'd have thought he'd be wanting to get his hand in as soon as possible.'

Comprehension dawned. 'Oh—you mean Jared,' Robyn declared, turning from the fire to take up her position behind the desk with a certain sense of triumph. 'He's not here, Mr Woodhouse. As far as I know, he's not even out of bed.'

'But he *is* coming?'

Maurice Woodhouse regarded her dourly, and Robyn thought how pleasant it would be to hand over dealing with Morley's chief accountant to someone else. He had always tried to intimidate her and, if he hadn't succeeded, it was due in part to the fact that she could meet him on eye-level terms. For once, her height was not a disadvantage, and she straightened her spine now and faced him squarely.

'I don't know,' she replied, in answer to his question. 'Probably not today, anyway.'

Maurice Woodhouse frowned. 'What's that supposed to mean?'

Robyn controlled her temper. 'What is what supposed to mean, Mr Woodhouse?'

'You know.' He sighed. 'When is he coming, then? Didn't he tell you?'

Robyn looked down at the pile of mail Mrs Hedley had left on her desk to give herself time to compose her answer. Then, adopting a polite smile, she said, 'I don't even know if he intends to come to the office—today, or ever,' she responded smoothly. 'Now, if you've no further business, Mr Woodhouse——'

'You mean there's some doubt about it?' The man was not to be sidestepped and Robyn's nails dug into the desk, where the leather inlay gave way to weathered mahogany.

'I mean that you know as much as I do, Mr Woodhouse,' she replied steadily. 'If you want to know what Jared intends to do, I suggest you ask him. You know the number. Give him a ring.'

Woodhouse scowled. 'Well, it's a bloody rum show to me,' he muttered, pushing his hands into the pockets of his jacket. The suit had seen better days, and there were shiny patches to show this was a habit of his. But for once Robyn had him at a disadvantage, and it wasn't altogether unenjoyable.

'Yes—well, we'll both be enlightened in the fullness of time,' she declared briskly. 'Until then, I suggest we function as usual. Was there a problem, or did you just come to welcome Jared home?'

Woodhouse sniffed. 'You know that combing machine's on the blink again, don't you?'

'The engineer is coming to fix it today,' Robyn averred, flicking through the pile of letters. 'Anything else?'

'You haven't forgotten the representative from Weatherill's is coming this afternoon?'

'No. I haven't forgotten.' Robyn could afford to be patient. It was so good to feel in charge for once. 'Is that all?'

Woodhouse gave a reluctant nod. 'Doubtless Mr Morley will be putting me in the picture later today,' he declared. 'He'll know what's going on. I'll speak to him.'

And the best of luck! thought Robyn childishly, pulling a face at his back as he went out the way he had come in. Miserable old devil! She doubted women's emancipation got any further than his front door.

Joan Hedley came in as the chief accountant went out, just in time to catch the tail-end of Robyn's grimace. 'I hope that isn't for me,' she remarked good-humouredly, coming into the office and closing the door, and Robyn collapsed into her chair with a disarming giggle.

'That man is impossible,' she exclaimed, shaking her head at the older woman. 'I think he thought Jared would step immediately into Stephen's shoes. He actually expected him to be here this morning. He can't wait to get me out of this office.'

'Ignore him,' advised Joan Hedley shrewdly, taking up a position across the desk from her employer. 'So— is Jared enthusiastic about working at Morley's? Or hasn't Ben broached that yet? I can imagine he'd want to pick his moment.'

Joan Hedley had been at Morley's almost as long as Ben himself, and her plump, gregarious presence had been a source of comfort to Robyn in her first traumatic days as Stephen's successor. She had come to rely on her for more than just her knowledge of the business, and because she had no one else to talk to, Mrs Hedley had been the recipient of many confidences.

Now, accepting that Joan would understand the ignominy of her position, Robyn sighed. 'He didn't know about Ben,' she admitted ruefully. 'Stephen can't have written to him, or if he did, the letter never connected. In any event, he came home expecting to stay only a few days, and I had to tell him that Ben was disabled.'

'Dear me!' Joan was surprised. 'That must have been quite a shock for him. Had there been some mix-up over the mail?'

'I don't know.'

Robyn bent her head. In all honesty, she couldn't decide whether Ben had ordered Stephen not to inform his younger son, or whether Stephen himself had decided to keep the news from his brother. Obviously, if Stephen had done that, it would explain Ben's increasing bitterness towards Jared since his illness. Certainly, since Stephen's death, his attitude towards his younger son had changed, but that could have been caused by the circumstances of Stephen's death, and a desire for forgiveness before it was too late.

Whatever, at dinner the previous evening, Robyn had been unable to gauge what might have passed between the two men during the late afternoon hours they had spent closeted together in Ben's study. The truth was, she had been more concerned with ensuring that Daniel did not make too many demands on his uncle, although that excuse for keeping her son and her brother-in-law

apart was as transparent as her excuses for not wanting
to go to the airport had been.

Their arrival at the house had passed without incident. Saddlebridge had looked quite beautiful in the
dying rays of a watery sun, the tall pines that formed a
backdrop on the low hills behind giving its time-worn
walls an air of stability. Robyn had always loved the
house, even when she was a child and a visitor at
Saddlebridge only at Stephen's father's invitation. The
vicarage, where she had been brought up and where she
had lived until her parents' deaths when she was eighteen,
stood only a few hundred yards away, across the fields,
and from her bedroom window she used to look at
Saddlebridge and promise herself that she would have a
house like that one day.

Of course, in those days she had never considered that
marriage to Stephen would grant her wish. On the contrary, until Stephen was twenty-two and home from university, she had had more in common with Jared. But
Stephen's return had changed many things, and she had
been flattered to find herself the object of his attentions...

But that was all in the past and, observing Jared's
reactions to his old home, she had realised that, in spite
of his long absence, he still had some affection for the
place. Indeed, as he entered the square hall, with its
angled staircase and the gallery above, she had sensed
his emotion, and only Mrs McCloud's intervention had
prevented her from saying something she would probably
have regretted afterwards.

Ben's emotion when he saw his son again was genuine
enough. Whatever differences they had had in the past
had been diluted by time and distance, and Jared's
concern at finding his father in a wheelchair was too
sincere to be faked.

The two men had retired to Ben's study before Daniel
got home from school, and his disappointment at not
being able to greet the uncle he had boasted about to
his friends had made Robyn glad that Ben's study was
sacrosanct.

'You'll see him later,' she had told the little boy firmly, picking up the satchel he had dropped on the hall floor and leading him into the kitchen. 'Come on. Mrs McCloud's made some ginger biscuits for you. I promise I'll let you meet him before you go to bed.'

Robyn had thought she was being extremely reasonable, in the circumstances, but she had not accounted for her son's curiosity. In spite of the fact that it was Monday, and the day *Blue Peter* was on children's television, Daniel had been hanging about in the hall when Jared had emerged from his father's study, and consequently Robyn had missed the first words they had said to one another. By the time she'd discovered what was happening, they were in Daniel's bedroom, sprawled out on the carpet, assembling the complicated track of his motor-racing kit.

It had been difficult to decide what Jared had been thinking at that moment. When she had appeared in the doorway, her face flushed with vexation, mouthing silly phrases about Daniel making a nuisance of himself and her not knowing where he was, Jared had got immediately to his feet and apologised for monopolising the boy. 'I didn't realise you might be worried,' he'd said. 'Dan and I have just been getting to know one another.'

'Don't call him Dan!'

Her reaction to his abbreviation of the boy's name had revealed how uptight she was, and Jared had made some excuse about changing for dinner and left them. Left her with Daniel's indignation, too, she remembered. And provided her son with the perfect excuse to appeal to his grandfather to be allowed to stay up for dinner. In the normal way, Daniel was in bed before Robyn and Ben had their evening meal, but for once Ben had been sympathetic.

'Why not let him stay up, Robyn?' he'd suggested, even though he usually didn't like the boy seeing that he had to have his food cut up for him. 'It is a special occasion, after all.' And what could Robyn have said which would not have sounded ungracious at the least?

'So how did they get on?' Joan was asking now, and Robyn dragged her thoughts back to the present with a distinct effort.

'You mean—Jared and Ben?' she murmured softly, and Joan shrugged.

'Who else?' she asked, and Robyn forced a smile.

'Um—fairly well, I think,' she replied, making an effort not to think about her son and Jared. 'In any event, they're still talking to one another, which is something. When—when Jared was younger, their conversations were more like confrontations.'

'I know.' Joan laughed. 'They've had a few of those in this office over the years. I used to think it was because they were so different, but now I'm sure it was because they are so much alike.'

'Alike!' Robyn sounded sceptical. 'I wouldn't have said Jared was like his father. Stephen, perhaps.'

'Oh, Stephen looked like him, I grant you that,' said Joan consideringly. 'And in some ways Stephen was like his father, too. They neither of them—well, made very good husbands, did they?'

Robyn bent her head. 'You could say that.'

'Oh, I know what I'm saying, all right,' said Joan wryly. 'And, as far as Stephen was concerned—well, I think you know, I'm not trying to hurt you. But Ben—he had two bites of the cherry, so to speak, and both times he ended up in the divorce court. Not that he wasn't well rid of Stephen's mother. She was a right bitch at times, and I think they deserved each other. But Jared's mother, she was different, and I think Ben resented the boy because he reminded him of what happened.'

Robyn looked up. 'What did happen? I don't think I understand.'

Joan frowned. 'You mean, no one ever told you?'

'Told me what?'

'That the night Jared was born, Ben was in Leeds with another woman.'

'No!'

'Oh, yes.' Joan grimaced. 'It's old history now, but Eve—that was the second Mrs Morley's name, of course—well, she went into premature labour, and had to be rushed into Sheffield General. For a while, it was touch and go whether either she or the baby would survive. They were desperate to find Ben, to tell him, to get him to the hospital to be with her, but no one knew where he was. At least, that was what they said at first. Later on, one of his pals got worried and spilled the beans, and that was how they found him.'

Robyn's lips parted. 'I never knew.'

'Why should you? You were only a kid at the time. Anyway, that was the beginning of the end so far as Eve was concerned. She stuck it out for a few more months, and then she walked out on him, too.'

'Leaving her son behind,' said Robyn. 'Oh, I could never do something like that.'

'Well, Jared was Ben's son, too,' said Joan wryly. 'And she knew he could do more for him than she could. I don't think she ever realised that Ben would blame Jared. I think he did love her, you see. Even if he had a funny way of showing it. He was really cut up when she died.'

'I see.' Robyn shivered. At least she had been spared that particular humiliation. And Daniel need never know the kind of man his father had been.

'Anyway, we'll see what happens now,' remarked Joan lightly, as Robyn turned back to the letters. 'Jared always did have a conscience, which is probably just as well. He may have come home intending not to stay but, unless he's changed completely, I don't think he'll be going back.'

Robyn tilted her head. 'He's six years older, Joan. He's twenty-seven now. Not a boy any more.'

Joan regarded her shrewdly. 'So you do think he's changed.'

'I didn't say that.' Robyn was evasive.

'What are you saying, then?'

'Oh——' Robyn picked up a biro and chewed the end uneasily '—I just think we should—reserve judgement.

He seems to have a very satisfactory life out in Sydney. Why should he give all that up just to please his father?'

'His *sick* father,' inserted Joan irrepressibly, making for the door. 'I'm going to make some coffee. Do you want a cup?'

All day, Robyn waited for Jared to put in an appearance, but at five o'clock, when she went out to get into her car, he had still not turned up. Folding her long legs behind the wheel, Robyn slammed her door rather more forcefully than usual, aware as she did so that she was endeavouring to expunge some of the frustration that had built up over the day. Perhaps because of Maurice Woodhouse's certainty that Jared would come in, she had convinced herself he would, too, and the fact that he hadn't had become increasingly suspect.

Where was he? she wondered. And where was Daniel? The possibility that they might be together was always foremost in her mind, and it was this, as much as anything, which had caused her to leave the office a full half-hour earlier than usual. In fact, lately she had still been working long after the rest of the staff had gone home, and because of the day she had taken off to go to the airport to meet Jared, she could have done with the extra time. But Daniel—and her peace of mind—had proved more important than the latest batch of production figures, and she had brought the file of papers with her to work on at home.

She could see the lights of Saddlebridge long before she turned on to the private road that led to the house. It stood in a wooded valley, just outside of the village of Saddleford, and the road winding down into the valley over Saddleford Tor gave a bird's-eye view of its many chimneys. It was some twenty minutes drive from the mill at Ebbersley on a good day, and perhaps fifteen minutes longer if the roads were icy. Saddleford Tor had been known to claim its own share of victims in the bad weather, but Robyn had driven that way so many times she was sure she could have done it blindfold.

However, this evening, all she had to contend with was the slow-moving stream of vehicles held up by a heavily laden tractor, which shouldn't have been out on the road after dark, anyway. Patience, Robyn, she schooled herself, as the cavalcade descended towards the village at a frustrating fifteen miles an hour, but her fingers were gripping the wheel with unwarranted force by the time she reached the turn-off for home.

Light was spilling from several windows as she brought the estate car to a halt on the tarmacked forecourt before the house. The mellow illumination from half a dozen uncurtained windows acted like floodlights on the drive, and Robyn allowed the familiarity of the scene to soothe her ruffled nerves. She was behaving foolishly, she chided herself, collecting her bag and briefcase from the back of the car. Rushing home, because she was afraid of what Jared might say to her son. What could he say, after all? Daniel was only a child, a baby; too young to be involved in affairs which had occurred long before he was even born. Just because she had once, very briefly, done something she had lived to regret, was no reason to assume Jared might use that knowledge to turn her son against her. Jared wasn't like that. He was not vindictive. If he had intended to cause trouble, he could have done so years ago. But he hadn't. He had gone away. And his reasons for coming back now were nothing to do with her.

All the same, as she walked into the house, the presentiment that all was not as it should be swept over her again. Everything looked the same. There were flowers in the silver bowl that stood on a rectangular table below the curve of the stairs, spilling their reflected colour in a waterfall of autumn shades. The lights were on in the gallery above, and the soft illumination gave warmth to the family portraits that mounted along the stairs. There was the smell of home baking emanating from the area of the kitchen, and Mrs McCloud herself to greet her as she took off her jacket to hang it away.

But, although she endeavoured to dispel her unease, it persisted in invading her stomach. Where was Daniel? she wondered. Why hadn't he come running to meet her, as he usually did? And where was Jared? What had he been doing all day?

'You're early, Robyn,' said Mrs McCloud pleasantly, taking her jacket from her, and draping it over her arm. 'You're looking tired. Did you not have a good day?'

For tired read old, thought Robyn tensely, running a nervous hand down the seam of her skirt. 'Just average,' she replied, glancing about her with assumed non-chalance. 'Er—where's Daniel? He's usually the first to hear the car.'

'Och, he's not here,' said Janet McCloud comfort-ably, turning to hang Robyn's jacket in the closet, and thus missing the revealing look of dismay that crossed her mistress's face at her words. 'Jared's taken him down to the village. Your father-in-law decided he wanted lamb chops for dinner this evening, and I didn't have a spoonful of mint jelly in the house.'

'I see.'

Robyn had managed to control her features by the time Janet turned from the closet, but her response must have sounded clipped, because the housekeeper gave her a rueful smile. 'He didn't expect you'd be back so early,' she said. 'But they won't be long, and in the meantime, why don't I make you and Mr Morley a nice cup of tea.'

Tea! Robyn caught her breath. Yes, perhaps that would be a good idea. If she put several spoonfuls of sugar into it, maybe it would relieve the shock she had just suffered.

Nodding now, she summoned a tight smile. 'Why not?' she said. 'Where is Mr Morley? I expect he's waiting for a run-down on the mistakes I've made today.'

Janet laughed. 'He's in the library. He had me light the fire in there earlier today. You know, he really seems to have taken new heart since he learned Jared was coming home.'

There was nothing Robyn could say to that, and the two women parted company—Mrs McCloud to prepare a tray of afternoon tea, and Robyn to go in search of her father-in-law and regale him with the day's events. What Robyn would have really liked to do was seek the sanctuary of her room, in an effort to come to terms with the fact that Jared was Daniel's uncle, that it was natural that her son should find his father's brother an exciting person to talk to, and that, having so recently lost his father, he should want to be with him. But, of course, she couldn't—not least because she wanted to be there when they got home. She wanted to see for herself how Jared and Daniel reacted to one another, and to gauge from Daniel's expression if any damage had been done.

The library at Saddlebridge overlooked the gardens at the back of the house, although at this time on a winter's evening the long velvet curtains were drawn against the chilly landscape outside. A large, comfortable room, it served as both library and living-room, Robyn sharing Ben's assertion that it was less draughty than the sitting-room. Many of the ground-floor rooms at Saddlebridge were only used in summer now, when it wasn't necessary to heat them to a living temperature. Since Ben's illness, and its consequent curtailment of much entertaining, the family confined themselves to the library and the sitting-room, using the morning-room to eat in instead of the lofty dining-hall. Of course, there was Ben's study, too, and his private apartments, where he could go to get a little peace and quiet. Daniel could be quite demanding on occasion, but even he knew better than to invade his grandfather's private domain.

Now Robyn opened the library door, and put her head round it. 'Am I intruding?'

Ben Morley was seated in his wheelchair beside the wide fireplace, gazing into the flames cast by a handful of logs burning in the grate. He wasn't doing anything, just watching the flames, his hands folded together over the rug that warmed his knees. One side of his face was slightly distorted, the paralysis which had followed the stroke leaving the muscles on the left side of his body to droop and atrophy. But that side of his face was turned away from her, and his smile was warm as he greeted her and bade her to come in.

'Sit down,' he said, and although his speech was distorted, too, Robyn had no difficulty in understanding him. 'Jared and Daniel have gone down to the village. But I don't expect they'll be long.'

'No. Mrs McCloud told me,' said Robyn, taking the armchair opposite. 'Goodness, it's warm in here. Have you got the radiators on, as well?'

'Jared was cold,' said Ben defensively, and then, seeing the faintly sceptical gleam in her eyes, he grimaced. 'Well, *I* was cold, then. It's been a cold day. It could freeze tonight.'

'It could,' agreed Robyn drily, and said no more about the temperature in the room. Instead, she loosened the collar of her shirt and ran her cold fingers into the opening. 'So—how are you?'

'I'm all right.' Ben was always offhand about his health. 'How are you? Did Merrick come?'

Merrick was the representative from Weatherill's, the company Maurice Woodhouse had mentioned earlier in the day. 'Yes, he came,' she said, easing her shoulders back against the squashy leather upholstery. 'He said it's going to cost us rather more to replace the conveyor belt than we had expected.'

'Oh, well...' Ben was philosophical. 'It has to be done. It's been breaking down far too frequently lately. We're getting behind on orders. And now that Jared's here...'

Robyn bent her head. 'Have you talked to him?'

'Who? Jared?'

'Who else?'

'Of course I've talked to him.' Ben was impatient now. 'What do you think? That we just sit staring at one another?'

Robyn sighed and lifted her head. 'That's not what I meant, and you know it.'

The right side of Ben's mouth twisted. 'You mean—about him staying,' he said, and it wasn't a question.

'I mean about him staying,' agreed Robyn tensely, wondering what she would do if Jared agreed to do as his father wished. She had intended to stay at Saddlebridge, whatever happened, for Daniel's sake. But that was before she had seen Jared again, before she had realised the past was never dead.

'Well, of course he's going to stay,' Ben declared fiercely. 'He's my son, isn't he?'

Robyn held herself stiffly. 'You've actually asked him?'

Ben muttered something not very complimentary under his breath. 'I don't have to ask him,' he admitted, after a moment. 'Now, where the devil is he? I want some tea.'

'Janet's bringing some,' said Robyn, unconsciously relaxing again. To reinforce her words, there was a tap at the door at that moment, heralding the arrival of the housekeeper with a loaded trolley.

'Dear me, you cannot breathe in here,' she exclaimed, as she set the trolley by Robyn's chair. 'Would you not like me to put a guard around that fire, Mr Morley? We don't want you catching fire, now do we?'

Ben gave her a sarcastic look. 'There's no danger of that,' he assured her grimly. 'But pour me some tea, Robyn. I can always use it to damp myself down.'

Janet's good-humoured features took on a reproving expression. 'Just because Jared's come home, and you're feeling full of yourself, don't go overdoing it. We'll have to pick up the pieces after he's gone, just you remember that.'

'He won't *be* going,' said Ben irritably, his good hand kneading the arm of his chair, but, before either Janet or Robyn could make any reply, there was the sound of running footsteps across the hall and presently Daniel appeared in the open doorway, flushed and beaming and gasping for breath.

The sight of her son had always given Robyn a feeling of joy. Tall for his age, with silky dark hair and a faintly olive complexion, he was a good-looking boy, with none of the tubby stockiness of some of his schoolmates. He wore the grey trousers and green and grey striped blazer of the small preparatory school he attended with an easy indolence, reminiscent of his father, but for once Robyn could not rise to greet him with her usual surge of pride. Instead, she knew a sense of indignation that he should not have been here when she got home, and a bitter condemnation at his evident state of excitement.

'Mum?' he said, a little less confidently, reacting to her grim expression. 'You're home early.'

'And you're late,' said Robyn coldly, hearing the repression in her voice, but unable to do anything about it. 'And how many times have I told you not to run about the house? Your shoes scrape the floor, and Mrs McCloud has just spent half the day polishing it.'

'Hardly that,' said another voice, as the tall lean frame of her brother-in-law appeared behind her son. One hand came to rest on Daniel's thin shoulder, and because she refused to lift her eyes to his face, she saw the way his strong fingers squeezed the flesh reassuringly. 'Not unless she wants us to break a leg,' Jared appended drily. 'Isn't that right, Janet?'

'Och, I dare say you're right; about the polishing, anyway. But,' she glanced awkwardly at Robyn's taut features, 'the little one oughtn't to run about the house. It's not—proper.'

'It's not important,' Jared corrected her crisply, pushing the boy before him into the room. 'Dan, go and tell your grandfather where we've been,' he added in an undertone. 'I want to have a private word with your mother.'

'I wish you would call him Daniel,' hissed Robyn tensely, busying herself with pouring Ben's tea. She had no intention of having any private words with Jared. Not until she had had time to control the emotions she had felt on seeing them together.

'Now—or later. It's up to you,' said Jared, taking no notice of her muttered reproof, and it took all Robyn's self-control to remain seated when what she would really have liked to do was leave the room.

'Tea, Ben?' she said instead, aware of her son's troubled stare as he took up a position beside his grandfather's chair. 'Er—would you like a sandwich? Or would you rather settle for one of Janet's famous scones?'

'Just the tea,' said the older man frowning, evidently aware of the sudden atmosphere in the room. 'Um—two spoons of sugar. That's right. Thank you, that's all I need.'

'Can I have a biscuit, please?' asked Daniel, watching his mother doubtfully, and although she wanted to re-assure her son, too, Robyn heard herself caution him once again.

'It's *may* I have a biscuit, please,' she corrected him bleakly. 'And no, you may not. You'll be having your supper in less than an hour.'

Daniel's mouth quivered, but for once he didn't argue with her. Instead, he flung himself down on the floor in front of the fire and regarded her reproachfully with un-comprehending green eyes.

'Where have you been?' Ben asked, in the vacuum that followed this latest exchange, and Daniel struggled to regain his confidence.

'We went to Bakewell,' he told his grandfather rather timidly. And then, aware that he had his mother's at-tention as well, he scrambled into a cross-legged pos-ition and added with more confidence, 'They didn't have any mint jelly in Saddleford, you see, and Uncle Jared said we might as well try somewhere else. That's why we've been so long. We went over the moor road, and when we came back Uncle Jared let me steer the car all the way down into the village.'

'Did he?' Ben's response was only mildly reproving, but Robyn knew an almost uncontrollable desire to scream. What a crazy, reckless thing to do! To let a boy of *seven* steer a powerful car like the Rolls-Royce. It was ridiculous, madness! Just the sort of thing Jared would do, to show her how easily her son could be corrupted.

She couldn't take any more. Putting her half-empty cup of tea aside, she got abruptly to her feet. 'If you'll excuse me,' she said, realising as she did so how ridiculously formal she sounded. 'I—er—I want to go over some papers before dinner.' She licked her dry lips. 'Daniel, I'll see you upstairs in fifteen minutes. If you're thirsty, ask Mrs McCloud to give you a glass of milk, and then start getting undressed if I'm not there.'

Daniel nodded. 'All right.'

'Good.' Robyn walked to the door. 'I'll see you— later,' she added, addressing her remark to no one in particular, and let herself out of the room without a backward glance.

She heard the library door open again as she went up the stairs, but she didn't stop to see who had emerged. Daniel or Jared; she had no wish to speak to either of them at that moment, and she gained the sanctuary of her own room with a heartfelt sigh of gratitude.

But her relief was short-lived. She had scarcely time to switch on the lamps and acknowledge the pink and gold appointments of the room, before someone knocked at the door behind her. She knew who it must be. Daniel was unlikely to push his luck a third time, and there was no earthly reason why Janet should have followed her upstairs. It had to be Jared, and she clasped her hands impotently, wishing she could just pretend not to hear.

Shivering slightly, she moved away from the door, but before she could compose herself to make any response the handle turned, and the door opened. As she swung round then, marshalling her defences, Jared came into the room, and her eyes widened indignantly at this display of downright arrogance.

'What do you think you're doing?' she exclaimed, as he closed the door behind him, and Jared's lips twisted at her transparent outrage.

'What do you think?' he countered, leaning back against the panels for a moment before advancing across the soft gold carpet. 'I told you I wanted to talk to you. I do. About my son!'

CHAPTER THREE

'*Your* son?'

Robyn felt as if every muscle in her body had frozen into immobility. Which was probably just as well, she reflected later. Without that traumatic stiffness, her legs might well have refused to support her. As it was, she could at least face Jared with a simulation of impassivity, even if inside herself she was a petrified mass of jelly.

'Yes, *my* son,' said Jared flatly, pausing directly in front of her and surveying her without emotion. 'You're not going to try and deny it, are you? We both know it's true, and it's a little late now to make an issue of it.'

Robyn swallowed. 'I don't know what you're talking about!' she exclaimed, totally incapable of responding in any other way. 'Of course Daniel's not your son. He's Stephen's. Stephen was his father. And just because he's dead is no reason to try and cast doubts on the relationship.'

Jared expelled his breath heavily. 'So that's the way you're going to play it,' he said, folding his arms across his chest. He was wearing a dark suit today, she noticed, the kind of suit he would wear to go in to the office, and she wondered if he had considered doing that and then had second thoughts. In any event, the dark grey mohair was an attractive foil to the sun-bronzed darkness of his skin, the bleached lightness of his hair bright against the formal collar of his jacket.

But she shouldn't be thinking such thoughts, she reminded herself unsteadily. What he was wearing, how he looked, whether or not she had once found him attractive, were not points at issue here. He didn't know— he couldn't know—anything about Daniel. He was

39

simply baiting her, testing her, trying out a theory; anything to get her to say something to incriminate herself.

'I'm not sure what you mean by "playing",' she said, turning deliberately away to glance at her reflection in the leaved mirrors of the dressing-table. But what she saw did not please her. She looked a mess, she thought critically, seeing nothing to admire in her pale, strained features and angular body. Even her hair, which had once been rich and lustrous, seemed to have lost its shine, and she couldn't help the treacherous thought that he must see how she had aged.

'Will you look at me when you talk to me?' Jared snapped then, catching her arm and swinging her round to face him. His strong fingers ground the thin layer of flesh against the bone, and when she winced he released her abruptly. 'Get it into your head, Robyn,' he muttered, as she massaged the place where his fingers had been, 'I know. Do you understand me? I know Daniel's my son.' He swore softly as she continued to stare blankly at him. 'I've known for years, didn't you realise that? Ever since he was born, I guess. But there was nothing I could do about it then. Now there is.'

Robyn's frozen limbs were thawing, and she began to tremble. 'You don't know anything——'

'Don't I?' Jared's mouth was grim. 'How long were you married before Daniel was born? Eight months, wasn't it?'

Robyn's heart was pounding. 'He was an eight months' baby.'

'Was he?' Jared looked at her contemptuously. 'That's not what I heard.'

'What could you hear? You weren't even here when Daniel was born,' she protested swiftly. 'You were away at college. You didn't even come home for his christening.'

'No.' Jared inclined his head. 'And you know why.'

'I don't.' Robyn pressed the palms of her hands together. 'In any case, how do you know Stephen and I didn't—didn't——'

'Anticipate the happy day?' Jared suggested sardonically. 'You forget, Robyn, you weren't exactly—experienced, when I touched you.'

'Which makes it all the more despicable that you did!' she choked. 'How can you boast about a thing like that?'

'I'm not boasting.' Jared's jaw was grim. 'I'm just trying to get you to be honest, for once in your life.'

'And how honest were you? Seducing your brother's fiancée?' she demanded harshly. 'In any case, after that I had nothing to lose, did I?'

Jared's nostrils flared. 'I didn't seduce you.'

'You're saying it was my fault?' Robyn quivered uncontrollably. 'I suppose it might sound like that to an outsider. After all, I was older than you. I should have known better than to trust you——'

'For God's sake!' Jared cut in to this painful tirade. 'I'm not blaming anyone——'

'How could you?'

'—for Daniel's conception——'

'Daniel is *not* your son!'

'—I'm only trying to make you see it's no use pretending any more.'

'I'm not pretending.'

'You are,' Jared groaned. 'Robyn, for once in your life, be honest with me. Admit it. Admit that I'm Daniel's father. For pity's sake! Tell me the truth!'

'I am telling you the——'

Robyn broke off abruptly as the door opened behind him. Her fingers sprang to her lips, as if to stifle her words, and Jared turned slowly to confront the subject of their disagreement. Daniel, his expression mirroring his confusion at finding his uncle in his mother's bedroom, clung curiously to the handle, his eyes darting doubtfully from one to the other.

'Mum?' he said appealingly, and, realising this was her opportunity to escape any more questions, Robyn brushed past her inquisitor.

'I thought I told you to get undressed,' she exclaimed, detaching her son's fingers from the door and urging him outside, into the corridor beyond. Be thankful he didn't, she admonished herself silently. Without Daniel's intervention, goodness knew what Jared might have done.

'I heard voices,' said Daniel, looking at her anxiously, and Robyn's mouth suddenly felt unpleasantly dry.

'Voices?' she echoed faintly, and Daniel nodded.

'Were you and Uncle Jared arguing?' he asked innocently, revealing by his question that he had heard nothing incriminating. 'Don't you like Uncle Jared, Mum? Is that why you were cross because I was out when you got home?'

Robyn felt an unwelcome wave of colour invade her cheeks. 'Don't be silly, Daniel!' she exclaimed, hurrying him along the corridor towards his own room. 'I—of course I like Uncle Jared. It's just that—well, we were talking about something that happened a long time ago.'

'Before I was born?' asked Daniel persistently, and Robyn, aware that Jared had come out of the room behind them and was standing watching their hasty retreat along the corridor, nodded unwillingly.

'Um—long before you were born,' she agreed, propelling him into his own room. 'Now, come on. It's time for your bath. I'll go and turn on the taps, while you take off your clothes.'

It was comparatively easy to avoid Jared for the remainder of the day. Pleading a headache, she managed to excuse herself from the evening meal, consoling her conscience with the thought that Ben would probably appreciate the chance to have a private talk with his son. Instead, Robyn spent the evening going over the production figures she had brought from the office, finding some escape from her thoughts in the questions she still had to answer.

All was not well with Morley Textiles. She didn't like to worry Ben, but since Stephen's death she had discovered a number of discrepancies in the figures. She wasn't absolutely sure, but it looked suspiciously as if someone had been withdrawing capital from the company over a number of years. Since Ben's crippling illness, the amount of plant investment had dropped considerably and, in consequence, they badly needed an injection of funds. Morley's was a private company, with a limited number of shareholders, and any drain on capital assets was bound, sooner or later, to have an effect. She would gladly have discussed the figures with Maurice Woodhouse, if he had shown himself even half-way willing to accept her as Stephen's deputy. But he hadn't. Instead, she had been left with the unpleasant suspicion that perhaps he had something to hide for, failing that, the alternative was too unpalatable to consider. Despite his faults, she refused to believe that Stephen had been systematically defrauding the company in his father's absence. The idea was too ludicrous. Stephen wouldn't have done that. There had to be another solution.

Later, lying in bed, Robyn wondered why she was trying so hard to find an answer. It wasn't really her problem—not any more. Jared—or if not Jared, then someone else Ben appointed—was going to have to take charge of Morley Textiles. She had been simply a substitute, and an amateur one at best. She had more important problems to contend with. Particularly now.

She was too practical to believe that that one brief confrontation with Jared was all she was going to have to face. He hadn't finished with her yet. She had glimpsed the impotent fury in his face when Daniel had innocently interrupted them, and if he could have sent the boy away without arousing any suspicion, he would have done it. But he had known that alienating possibly his greatest ally would not be the most sensible thing to do, and in consequence she had got away with it. But that wouldn't always be the case, she knew that. She couldn't rely on Daniel to extricate her from every difficult situation. On the contrary, it was Daniel himself who was at risk here, and she mustn't give Jared the chance to use her son against her.

All the same, until tonight she had had no idea how precarious her position might be. To think she had been afraid that Jared might choose to resurrect a relationship that should never have been allowed to happen! She had actually flattered herself into believing he might still find her attractive, and she had steeled herself to repulse his advances. How naïve she still was. Jared had torn her foolish notions of romance down about her ears, and attacked the one area of her life she had thought inviolable. But Daniel was hers; he was her son; and no one, least of all the man who had violated her, should flaw that association.

And, if she stood firm, she had nothing to worry about, she told herself for the umpteenth time. There was nothing he could do, nothing he could prove. Daniel was Stephen's son; everybody believed that. Heavens, she had told herself so so many times, she almost believed it herself...

In spite of her troubled thoughts, Robyn fell asleep at last, and it wasn't until her alarm woke her that she stirred to reluctant consciousness. In the normal way, she had no difficulty in getting up in the morning, but the sense of something ominous hanging over her head made this morning slightly different. Robyn had a strong desire to bury her head in the pillow and hibernate until Christmas. Perhaps, by then, the problem of Jared would have resolved itself, she thought hopefully, although something told her that running away from her troubles was not likely to improve their character.

She was drying her hair in the bathroom when Janet McCloud appeared with a tray of morning tea. 'I wondered if you were up,' she said, when Robyn grabbed her robe and came to the bathroom door. 'It's nearly eight o'clock. Don't you want any breakfast?'

Robyn managed a smile. 'Not this morning, thanks. Um—is Daniel up?'

'Up and dressed, and having breakfast with his uncle,' said Janet, unaware that anything she had said should perturb her employer's daughter-in-law. 'Don't you fret. I checked that he washed behind both ears. You just take your time now. You're looking rather peaky.'

Peaky! Robyn had an hysterical desire to laugh. If only Janet knew, she thought unsteadily. How much more of this could her nerves take? What was Jared trying to do to her?

It was too much trouble to try and gather the newly washed tangle of her hair into a neat chignon. Instead, she threaded it into a single, chunky braid, securing it with a leather thong before snatching up the clothes she had worn the night before. The cream shirt and plain navy skirt would have to do for another day. Flat-heeled shoes completed her ensemble, and she was half-way down the stairs before she realised she had forgotten to put on any make-up.

'Damn!' she muttered frustratedly, halting at the first landing, and then shrank back against a portrait of an earlier Morley ancestor as the morning-room door below the angle of the stairs opened and Jared himself emerged. He wasn't alone. Daniel was at his heels. And, as Robyn steeled herself to go and interrupt them, the boy caught Jared's hand and looked up at him expectantly.

'Can we?' he exclaimed, and Robyn felt like an eavesdropper, listening in on a private conversation.

'We'll see,' Jared responded tolerantly, ruffling the boy's hair before opening the closet door and pulling out a leather jacket. It was an old jacket that Ben had sometimes worn, and Robyn had forgotten who it had belonged to until now. But seeing it fit over Jared's broad shoulders, with evident familiarity, adding another layer of warmth to the elegant dark suit he had worn the day before, she remembered.

'I've never been to York before,' Daniel was saying now, watching his uncle with interest. 'Grandpa was always too busy before he was ill, and Mum isn't really interested in stuffy museums.'

Jared thrust his hands into the pockets of his jacket. 'And what about your father?' he enquired, causing Robyn to catch her breath instinctively.

'Oh, Dad always said he didn't have the time,' confided Daniel frankly. 'We didn't see a lot of Dad, actually. Mum used to say he had a lot to do, looking after the business when Grandpa couldn't, but I don't think it was just that.'

'Don't you?' Jared seemed to hesitate a moment, and then he said, 'Why not?'

Robyn gasped then. Had the man no scruples? she wondered incredulously. Pushing herself away from the wall, she started down the stairs to break up this unholy alliance, but before she could interrupt them, Daniel added artlessly, 'Well, one of the chaps at school said my Dad was going out with his mother and——'

'*Daniel!*'

Robyn's outraged use of her son's name halted him in full spate, and she had the doubtful satisfaction of seeing his face suffuse with colour.

'Oh—hello, Mum,' he mumbled, casting a guilty glance at Jared from beneath his thick dark lashes. 'I didn't know you were there. I was just seeing Uncle Jared off to work.'

Robyn transferred her gaze to her brother-in-law, the actual words her son had used to excuse himself registering less at that moment than her anger at Jared's underhanded means of getting information.

'Have you no shame?' she demanded, staring at Jared with scornful eyes. 'My God! I didn't think you'd sink as low as to pump Daniel about his father! Stephen's dead, for heaven's sake! At least have some respect for his memory!'

Daniel looked near to tears, and Jared's mouth thinned to a cruel line. 'You know I could argue that Stephen should have had more—respect for his—family,' he commented coldly. 'And we all create—complications when we—play games in our own—backyard.'

The pauses in his narrative were eloquent with the real message he was trying to convey, and Robyn flinched from the raw hatred gleaming in eyes, as cold as a mountain lake. It was a warning, plain and simple, and she knew it. But who was he threatening to tell? Daniel? Or his father?

Jared's hand, patting Daniel's shoulder, reassured the boy. 'Cheer up,' he said, and the smile he gave the child transformed his grim features. 'It's not the end of the world,' he added, turning towards the door. 'Don't let a little difference of opinion upset you. Your mother and I have never seen eye to eye.'

It was not until the outer door slammed behind him that Robyn recalled what her son had said earlier. Looking down into his troubled face, she exclaimed fiercely, 'Where did you say he was going? As I came down the stairs, you said something about him going out.'

Daniel moistened his lips. 'Uncle Jared?'

'Who else?' Robyn was in no mood to be patient.

'Why, he—he's gone to the mill,' admitted Daniel unhappily. 'Oh, Mum, why are you looking like that again? I thought you and Grandpa wanted Uncle Jared to take over at Morley's.'

Sitting in the estate car some fifteen minutes later, on her way to Ebbersley, Robyn realised she should have taken the time to talk to her son before leaving the house. But her automatic reaction had been to get to the mill as quickly as possible, if only to reassure herself that Jared was not spreading his lies there, and creating problems she hadn't even considered.

She should have talked to Daniel first, she fretted now, realising she had been hopelessly naïve in imagining she could keep Stephen's behaviour from her son. But she had known nothing about this incident at his prep school, and the idea that Julia Forrester's son had actually bragged about his mother's affair with her husband was quite incredible. Did the woman have no shame? Of course, Julia was a widow, and perhaps she had considered she had nothing to lose in making their relationship public knowledge. But Stephen should have had more sense. Had he always been so indiscreet? Had she, Robyn, just been too trusting to notice what was going on?

Rubbing the tip of her nose with her knuckle, Robyn remembered clearly how shocked she had been the first time she found Stephen out in a lie. But, of course, she had been pregnant with Daniel at the time, and so full of her own guilt herself, she had foolishly done nothing about it.

And that had been the beginning of the end for their marriage, she admitted. Old habits die hard, and even clichés have a grounding in the truth. And, in all honesty, she had not been able to put all the blame on his shoulders. She had betrayed him before their marriage, nothing could alter that, and she had never found any pleasure in sex since. Oh, she had tried; God, how she had tried! She had even gone to see a marriage guidance counsellor, in the hope that someone else might be able to help her. But, in spite of her participation, nothing had worked. She had had to accept the unpalatable fact that it was as much her fault as his.

At least, that was what she had thought up until now. But when it came to Daniel, she was forced to draw the line, and the idea that her son believed his father was a womaniser caught at her emotions with a painful intensity.

And why had Daniel told Jared? she asked herself frustratedly. Why had he never confided in her? Why tell someone who was little more than a virtual stranger to him, when the person who loved him most in the world could have consoled his confused little heart?

She shook her head, forced to concentrate on the twisting curves of Saddleford Tor. The traffic this morning was thick and heavy, and the mist from the moors eddied across the road in wraithlike swirls. November, she thought wearily, why had Jared come home in November? Why couldn't it have been summer, with so many more opportunities for escape?

But Jared hadn't chosen his time, she reminded herself severely. He was here because Stephen was dead, and Ben had sent for him. She couldn't blame Jared for coming. She could only blame herself for handling it so badly.

She had expected to see Ben's Rolls-Royce occupying the space allotted to the managing director, but when she drove into the mill yard there was no sign of that elegant vehicle. The only car she didn't immediately recognise was a black Volkswagen Golf, with year-old number-plates, parked without ceremony beneath the office steps.

Now what? she wondered, deciding Jared had had second thoughts about coming to the mill after all. Could the car belong to the engineer from Weatherill's? Had the week's estimate they had given her been shortened overnight?

Locking the car, she slung her tweed jacket about her shoulders and headed for the steps. She would soon know. There were lights on in her office, which meant Joan Hedley was around. At least the secretary could be relied upon to handle any visitors in her absence. With her knowledge of Morley's, she could have run the place herself.

Perhaps she should talk to Joan about the accounts, Robyn reflected, as she climbed the steps. Sooner or later, someone was going to have to mention them, and perhaps it would be more sensible to get that particular problem out of the way before Jared became involved. It was silly to want to protect Stephen after the circumstances of his death, but she had to maintain the fiction, if only for Daniel's sake.

She had her arms full, with her handbag and her briefcase, and the additional effort of trying to keep her jacket about her shoulders, so she used her elbow to press down upon the handle of the door. She was concentrating so much on negotiating this obstacle that, when the door opened inward, she almost lost her balance, and it was left to the man inside to save her from a fall.

Strong hands prevented her from sprawling on the rug and, although her briefcase tumbled from her grasp, she was able to secure her footing. All the same, her jacket slipped off her shoulders so that the lean brown fingers encountered only silk-covered flesh, and her skin prickled alarmingly beneath each separate pressure.

He released her almost at once, but not before Robyn had experienced a most unwelcome reaction to his touch. During her embarrassing display of clumsiness, she had been made unavoidably aware of the warm male scent of his body, and when her breasts brushed the rougher texture of his jacket, she felt an unfamiliar tightening in her stomach. A sense of heat spread from there, down the quivering muscles of her thighs, and although she put it down to simple nervousness she couldn't deny the panic deep inside her. Once again, she wanted to turn and run, but she doubted if she had the energy.

'Are you all right, Robyn?'

As Jared bent to pick up her jacket and then close the door behind her, Robyn saw with some relief that they were not alone. Joan Hedley was standing by the desk with the mail; it was she who had spoken, and as Robyn took a cautious step forward, she quickly came towards her.

'I—er—I'm fine,' Robyn assured her hurriedly, casting a backward glance over her shoulder, and then switching her gaze back to Joan before Jared could meet her gaze.

'You nearly measured your length,' chided Joan, picking up her briefcase, and setting it on the desk. 'Come along. Sit down. You look as if you need something warm inside you.'

'Oh, no—really,' murmured Robyn anxiously, loath that Joan should leave them right at this minute. Once she'd got her breath back, once she'd controlled whatever impulse had aroused those feelings inside her, she would be OK. But, just at this moment, she needed Joan's support.

'Nonsense.' Joan was determined to be sympathetic. 'How about you, Jared? Would you like a nice cup of coffee? I know, let's all have a cup, shall we? Then you can tell us all about what you've been doing in Australia.'

'Why not?' Jared essayed evenly, and Robyn wondered if Joan had deliberately seated her at this side of the desk so that Jared could take his father's place. 'That sounds good,' he added, taking up the position that was vacant. 'Sugar, but no cream in mine, please, Joan. I guess you know how Mrs Morley likes hers.'

'Just about,' agreed Joan wryly, going out of the door, and as it closed behind her Jared sank into his father's chair.

There followed one of the most pregnant silences Robyn had ever had to endure. Seated in the visitor's chair, at right angles to the desk, she was intensely aware of Jared's gaze boring into her profile. What was he thinking? she wondered, pressing her damp palms down upon quivering knees. And why the devil didn't he say something—*anything*—instead of simply staring at her, subjecting her to this nerve-wracking appraisal?

'I—I suppose I should thank you,' she ventured at last, when the awful cessation of sound in the room was beginning to deafen her. If it was his intention to humiliate her, she had to thwart it, and allowing him to make the rules was not going to accomplish anything. She must not make the same mistakes with him that she had made with Stephen. Start as you mean to go on, she told herself fiercely, disliking having to resort to another cliché. But if once she let Jared get the upper hand, her position at Saddlebridge would become intolerable.

'Not if you don't want to,' he answered now, settling back in his chair and surveying her beneath lowered lids. 'Perhaps I should ask you if you really are all right. As Joan pointed out, you do look a bit—drained.'

Robyn turned her head. 'Don't you mean *old*?' she enquired stiffly, tilting her chin. 'You were never one to mince your words, Jared. What you mean is, I look my age. Don't worry. You won't offend me by speaking the truth.'

Jared pressed his hands down on the rim of the desk and came upright. 'That wasn't what I said—or what I meant.'

Robyn forced herself to meet his gaze. 'No?'

'No.' Jared's lips twisted. 'I didn't realise you wanted compliments from me, Robyn. My initial impression was that you still hated my guts.'

Robyn withdrew her gaze abruptly. It was difficult to make any response to that shocking pronouncement, and for several seconds she stared at her hands, clenching over her knees.

Then, realising she could not allow Joan to come back with the situation in its present state of impasse, she said huskily, 'I don't hate you, Jared. Why should I? I just—resent your treating me like a fool, and turning my son against me.'

Jared sucked in his breath. 'You're crazy! I'm not turning Dan against you. You're making a pretty good job of that for yourself.'

'*Me?*'

Robyn was forced to look at him then but, as if growing tired of the argument, Jared shook his head. 'Let's leave it for now, shall we?' he suggested flatly. 'I didn't come to the office to get embroiled in personal affairs. So long as you're OK, that's all that matters. I guess we've both changed in lots of different ways.'

Robyn expelled her breath unevenly. 'All right.'

'Good.' Jared seemed content with her answer. 'So—let's talk about something else, shall we? Bring me up to date with what's been happening. I'd like to know a little about our position before old man Woodhouse starts breathing down my neck.'

CHAPTER FOUR

IN SPITE of its inauspicious beginning, the rest of the day was not half as bad as Robyn had anticipated. To be honest, she had to admit that most of its success was due to Jared's willingness to deal with her on a purely impersonal level, and, aside from a few interruptions, they covered a great deal of ground.

There were times during the day when Robyn was tempted to ask Jared what he intended to do about the business, when she knew an almost overpowering impulse to find out exactly what his future intentions were. But asking questions of that nature was too partial in the present situation, and, although she argued that she, of all people, had a right to know where she stood, she decided it was up to Ben to put her in the picture.

Joan eased the situation, of course, bustling in and out of the office, asking questions about Jared's life in Australia, and teasing him about the girls he had known there. She seemed to notice nothing amiss in the fact that the younger woman did not join in their careless bantering, and Robyn found it easiest to close her ears at these times. It was natural, she told herself, that she should feel some sense of distaste at Jared's laughing revelations. After all, too many things had happened for her to ever feel at ease with him again. The best they could achieve was a working relationship, with the possibility of renewed hostilities breaking out at any time.

At lunch time, she joined Joan Hedley in the staff canteen as usual. She had intended to skip the meal—she was never very hungry at lunch time, anyway—if Jared had been disposed to join them. But, just before twelve, he announced he intended to have a drink at the pub with Frank Beasley, so for an hour, at least, Robyn was able to relax and be herself.

'He hasn't changed much, has he?' Joan remarked, digging into steak and kidney pie with enthusiasm, and looking askance at Robyn's wilting cheese salad. 'I remember Ben bringing both boys to the office when they were still at school. Jared looked ever so sweet in his school uniform. If I'd had any kids, I don't think I could have sent them away to school like that.'

Robyn's lips twitched in spite of herself. 'Sweet?' she echoed. 'Jared looked *sweet*?'

'Yes.' Joan made a defensive face. 'He always was the nicest of the two. Oh—sorry, Robyn!' She sighed. 'Me and my big mouth! It's just that—well, I suppose I always had a soft spot for Jared, him being the youngest and all.'

'It doesn't matter.' Robyn managed to dismiss her apology. 'It wouldn't do for all of us to feel the same, would it? I suppose—I suppose my being older, more Stephen's age, if you like, I saw them differently.'

'Hmm.' Joan nodded. 'Although, you know, when you were younger, I used to think you were fond of Jared, too.'

'Fond?' Robyn struggled to control her colour. 'I— well, I suppose I was—very close to both of them. And when my parents died——'

'Oh, yes.' Joan shook her head. 'That was a tragedy, wasn't it? Ben certainly came to the rescue then, didn't he? I suppose you felt you had a lot to thank him for.'

'Yes, I did.' Robyn's tongue circled her upper lip. 'I had no relatives, you see. My mother and father were both only children, and when they were killed...'

'Ben picked up the pieces,' finished Joan gently. 'Of course. But then, he was only looking to the future, wasn't he? I mean, he always wanted you to marry Stephen, you know. I heard him say that, long before you two made it official.'

'Did he?'

Robyn couldn't remember that. As far as she was aware, Ben's suggestion that she should come and live at Saddlebridge had been entirely arbitrary. It had been five years after her parents' deaths that she had actually married Stephen. She could hardly believe that her father-in-law had been thinking of that when he offered her a home.

'Well, anyway, you did it, didn't you?' Joan pursued now, watching her intently. 'Married Stephen, I mean,' she added. 'Did—er—did you ever regret it?'

Robyn felt a deepening of colour below her cheekbones. 'I suppose you think I should,' she conceded after a moment, and now Joan's plump features showed her discomfort.

'Not necessarily,' she murmured defensively. 'Oh, I'm just being an inquisitive old woman. Don't take any notice of me. I shouldn't have asked that question.'

'But you did.' Robyn toyed restlessly with the lettuce on her plate. 'I suppose that's what everybody's asking. Particularly now.'

Joan shrugged. 'Oh, I don't know——'

'Please.' Robyn was impatient. 'At least be honest with me, Joan. We both know how—and where—Stephen died. Carnthwaite bridge is on the way to Charnley. No one's been able to prove anything, but I doubt that he was alone when it happened.'

Joan stared at her. 'Do you think—*she*—left him there, without even calling the police?'

Robyn lifted her shoulders. 'Why else was he going in that direction?' She sighed. 'Oh, the police have been very tactful, due no doubt to Ben's influence, but I'm not a fool. The chances are that—that Stephen was dead and she was afraid of being implicated. It would have caused quite a scandal, wouldn't it? And all to no avail.'

'But he might still have been alive!' exclaimed Joan fiercely. 'If the ambulance had got there sooner——'

'No,' said Robyn flatly, interrupting her tirade, and Joan frowned.

'How do you——'

'His—his neck was broken,' said Robyn steadily. 'I imagine that's why the police didn't push the matter. There was no question of the time of death. Stephen died when the car plunged down the embankment.'

Joan shook her head. 'Oh, Robyn! I'm sorry.'

Robyn took a deep breath. 'Yes—well, it's all over now.'

'And you don't resent what happened?'

'Why should I?'

'Well...' Joan shifted uncomfortably. 'Now that Jared's come back... Oh, you know what I mean. Jared's probably going to take over the company. Don't you mind that Daniel's going to lose everything?'

'Ah...' Robyn acknowledged the proof of the gossip that was sweeping the mill. 'Well, that's no problem. Stephen may have had his faults, but he didn't neglect his financial responsibilities. Daniel and I are well provided for, and—and if Jared does decide to stay, we can easily make other arrangements.'

'Other arrangements?' Joan looked puzzled.

'Of course.' Although, until she voiced them, Robyn had hardly been aware that she had been thinking along these lines. 'Obviously, if Jared comes back to live at Saddlebridge, Daniel and I will leave. After all, he may decide to get married, and the new Mrs Morley wouldn't want us as unpaying tenants.'

Robyn left the mill before Jared, driving home through a veil of mist, thicker than the one that had coated the moors that morning. She had discovered that the black Golf was Jared's car, hired from the garage in Saddleford the night before. That was why he had had no need to use his father's Rolls. The powerful little hatchback was far easier to handle on the twisting moorland roads. It was strange; she would have expected him to hire a big Ford or a Rover. He could even have contacted one of the larger dealers in Sheffield and arranged for them to provide him with a Mercedes or a Volvo for the duration of his stay, but he hadn't. A psychiatrist would probably say he didn't need the support of phallic symbols, she reflected wryly. Unlike Stephen, who had driven a Jaguar for the past ten years.

Daniel was watching out for her when she got home. He looked over her shoulder expectantly as she came through the door, and she determinedly squashed her irritation at his obvious disappointment that Jared wasn't with her. Instead, she bent down and put her arms around him, giving him a warm hug; and, although he squirmed away from her, she could tell he was half relieved.

'Did you have a good day, darling?' she asked, straightening and unbuttoning her jacket. 'Have you been to see Grandpa? Is he feeling all right this evening?'

'Grandpa's fine,' said Daniel confidently, taking her jacket from her and hanging it away in the hall closet. He was proud of his recent ability to reach the hooks in the closet, and Robyn's nerves steadied at the familiar demands of home. 'And I came top in the arithmetic test we had this morning,' he added.

'Top!' Robyn was impressed. 'Did you tell Grandpa?'

'Yes.' Daniel closed the closet door and looked diffidently up at her. 'He said I must take after Uncle Jared. He said, at my age, Dad was no good at sums at all.'

Robyn felt as if a cold hand had invaded her stomach. 'Oh,' she said, her nerves responding to this new threat. 'Well, I shouldn't take too much notice of Grandpa. If your father hadn't been any good at sums, he could never have run Morley Textiles, could he?'

Daniel looked anxious. 'You're not still mad at me, are you, Mum?' he mumbled unhappily. 'I mean—because of what I told Uncle Jared.'

'Don't be silly!' The sharp words were out before she could prevent them, and Daniel stepped back a pace automatically. 'Oh——' Robyn sighed, and made a helpless gesture. 'Of course I'm not mad at you, Daniel. I just—don't think you should repeat schoolboy gossip to your Uncle Jared. He'll probably be returning to Australia in a few days, and I don't want you to get—hurt.'

'Grandpa says that Uncle Jared's going to stay here, and live with us,' argued Daniel swiftly, evidently as willing as she was to forget what he had heard about his father. 'He says that he only went to Australia because, so long as Daddy was alive, he had no interest in the company.'

Robyn could feel the muscles of her face tightening. 'Yes,' she said stiffly. 'Yes, well—your grandfather may be hoping——'

'No, he says Uncle Jared *is* going to stay,' Daniel interrupted her blandly, unaware that he was causing her distress. 'Isn't that great? He'll be able to use the room next to yours. There'll be four Morleys at Saddlebridge, just like there was before.'

'No!' Robyn almost choked on the word, and Daniel halted uncertainly.

'No?' He looked at her bewilderedly. 'But—why?'

'Why?' Robyn met her son's blank stare and chickened out. 'Um—well, your father hasn't even been dead two months!'

'Oh.' Daniel's face cleared. 'And you don't want Uncle Jared to sleep in Daddy's room. I never thought of that.'

'No. That's not what I——' Robyn broke off abruptly. 'Look,' she put a hand on his shoulder and propelled him towards the kitchen, 'you go and see what Mrs McCloud's got for your supper, hmm? I want to go and have a shower.'

'Aren't you going to see Grandpa first?' asked Daniel in surprise, and Robyn forced a thin smile.

'Not just at this moment,' she said, heading towards the stairs. 'You can tell Grandpa I'm home, and that I'll see you both in a little while.'

Closing the door of her room some few minutes later, Robyn leaned back weakly against the panels. At least she didn't have to worry this evening that Jared might come storming into her room and demand something from her she was not prepared to give. He was still at the mill, or at least he had been when she left; and if she knew Maurice Woodhouse, he would take the opportunity to confide his opinion of her efforts to the new managing director, if indeed Jared did intend to step into his brother's shoes.

The prospect made her feel unutterably weary and, stepping out of her shoes, she padded over to the bed. The temptation to take off all her clothes and crawl between the sheets was almost overwhelming and, perching on the edge of the mattress, she used both hands to resist the cowardly impulse.

She had to think, she told herself severely, lifting first one foot and then the other, surveying her toes, as if she might find the solution to her problems there. If what her son had said was true—and it was by no means certain that Jared was intending to return to Saddlebridge on a permanent basis—she and Daniel would have to find somewhere else to live.

The idea was daunting, to say the least. In spite of her desire to take herself and her son away from Jared's influence, she still had to consider where she was going to live. Did she intend to buy a house in Saddleford or Ebbersley, so that Daniel could continue at his present school and continue seeing his grandfather? Or was it her intention to move right away, and put this whole section of her past behind her?

She had no doubt how much easier it would be now if, when her parents had died, she had been left to fend for herself. If, at that time, she had had to find somewhere to live and a job of work to do, she might never have become involved with any of the Morleys. Their childhood friendship would have dwindled and been forgotten, and who knew, she might have married someone who could melt her frozen emotions.

But, instead, for the past fourteen years, she had been cushioned against the harsher realities of life. Ben had always treated her like the daughter he had never had, and only now was she realising how unreal her life had been.

She sighed and, getting up from the bed, she crossed the floor to her dressing-table. Sinking down on to the padded stool, she cupped her face with long, slender fingers, and studied her reflection. What had Jared *really* thought when he saw her? she wondered reluctantly. Probably that she neglected herself, she decided, smoothing a faint blemish in her cheek. When he had gone away, she had at least retained some confidence in her appearance, she acknowledged dully. But years of living with Stephen, of finding him out in a score of different ways, had taken their toll and, in spite of her insistence that she had been to blame, his continued pursuit of other women had become a burden.

It wasn't so much what he had been doing. She could live with that. Indeed, she was shamefully aware that she had welcomed the cessation in the demands Stephen had made upon her. When he had suggested moving his belongings into one of the spare rooms so that he wouldn't disturb her if he came home late, she had been only too happy to agree, and she had been grateful not to have to find excuses. But the constant gossip was what had hurt her most, invading her defences and undermining her confidence. She had even stopped going into the village, because of the unspoken sympathy she could sense behind each friendly word, and if people thought she was stand-offish, it was a façade she had adopted.

Even so, over the years, she had learned to hide her feelings. Maybe that was why the almost six years between her and Jared's ages seemed to have stretched to ten and beyond. She probably looked old enough to be *his* mother, she thought, with rather less perspicacity. At any rate, he probably thought so, she reflected, even if he hadn't said it.

As she pressed her lips together in a sudden surge of indignation, Robyn's hands sought the leather thong that bound the chunky braid, and tore it free. Then, threading her fingers through the heavy mass, she pulled it loose about her shoulders, grimacing as its inky darkness gave her the sudden appearance of a witch. A witch with grey eyes, she assessed herself bitterly. They should have been green, like Daniel's—like Jared's.

By the time she had showered and changed into a one-piece black lounging suit, and secured her hair again in a more mature style, Robyn felt less threatened. Once again, she was allowing events to control her, she told herself severely. It was up to her to make her own decisions. She had nothing to fear if she kept her head. If she let Jared see she was running scared, then she deserved to be defeated.

All the same, walking into the library some fifteen minutes later took no small amount of courage. She didn't deceive herself that Jared's attitude at the mill would percolate into their personal relationship. He had come to England for a purpose, and she was only now beginning to suspect what that purpose might be. Whatever Ben said, Jared's motives were not wholly altruistic. But she could not tell his father what his real intentions were.

In the event, Ben was alone when she invaded his sanctuary, and his lined face showed his pleasure at her appearance. 'That's new, isn't it?' he asked, after she had asked after his welfare and received his usual disparaging reply. Looking down at the tapering legs of the trousers, Robyn had to acknowledge that she had not worn the suit before. 'It looks good,' her father-in-law continued, as she seated herself in the chair opposite and crossed her long legs. 'It's a change to see you wearing something youthful. Since Stephen died, you seem to have lost all interest in—well, in fashion.'

Since long before that, amended Robyn silently, only Ben hadn't noticed in those days. Or, if he had, he had never said anything. She wondered if Stephen's father still believed that she had been ignorant of his son's imperfections. She could hardly believe it, and yet Ben had always treated her with affection and respect. Perhaps that was his way of making up for what Stephen had done. Or perhaps he really thought she was that naïve! Oh, Ben, she thought unhappily, were we all deceiving each other?

'So what happened?' the old man asked now, and Robyn had to force herself to attend to what he was saying.

'What happened?' she echoed a little blankly. 'I'm afraid I——'

'Jared went to the mill, didn't he?' Ben's undistorted eye stared at her unblinkingly, and she expelled her breath.

'Oh—oh, yes,' she nodded, moistening her lips. 'Yes, he was there.'

'And?'

'And?' Robyn caught her lower lip between her teeth. 'Well, I think I've put him in the picture—as far as I can, of course. I believe Maurice Woodhouse wanted to have a word with him after I left.'

'And did he say anything to you?'

'To me?' Robyn looked at him uncomprehendingly. 'What about? He said a lot, of course. I don't think he's too keen on that timework scheme Stephen introduced, but you weren't very keen on——'

'About *staying*!' Ben interrupted her impatiently. 'Did he say anything to you about staying? Come on. You know what I'm talking about. Did he or didn't he?'

Robyn blinked. 'But I thought you said—at least, Daniel said——'

'Never mind what I said or what Daniel said. I want to know what Jared has said to you. He must have said something. You and he used to be so close!'

Robyn felt warm colour invade her cheeks. 'We were never *close*!'

'Nonsense! Of course you were. You were always the one Jared used to confide in.' He sighed. 'It's not as if I'm asking you to break a confidence or anything. I just want to know what his feelings are. Do you think he's prepared to stay? Has he given you any notion at all of what his plans might be?'

Robyn swallowed. 'But you said——'

'Look, I've told you. Forget what I said. That's not in question here. I want to know what the situation's like in Australia. Is there some woman there I should know about? What has Jared said to you?'

What indeed? thought Robyn painfully. If only she could discuss the things Jared had said with her father-in-law. But she couldn't. That aspect of their relationship could never be spoken of, and everything else was coloured by that knowledge.

'I don't honestly know what he thinks, or what he plans to do,' she replied at last. 'He—he seemed interested in what was happening, but you know him better than I do. Don't you know how he feels?'

'If I did, I wouldn't be asking you, would I?' muttered Ben dourly. 'Oh, I don't know, Robyn. I was sure when I sent for him that he'd jump at the chance to step into Stephen's shoes. Now I'm not convinced.'

Robyn expelled her breath a little unevenly. 'Oh,' she murmured. 'Um—why?'

Ben moved his shoulders in the semblance of a shrug. 'I don't know exactly. He's changed. Don't you find that? I've talked to him. He knows how I feel. But I'm damned if I can get a straight answer from him.'

Robyn bent her head. 'I see.'

'It's so damned galling,' the old man added bitterly. 'Who would have thought I'd have to go begging to him? He knows I'm vulnerable. He knows I can't *make* him do what I want. Do you think he's only humouring me by going to the office? Do you think he has any intention of moving back to England?'

Robyn shook her head. She didn't know how to answer him. For her own part, the idea that Jared might choose to return to Australia was a tantalising prospect. If he *did* refuse his claim to the mill and returned to Sydney, he was unlikely to come back, and the one fear she had had all these years would be removed. She and Daniel could stay at Saddlebridge, and the prospect of moving need never arise.

It was a selfish hope and she knew it, but she had lived too long with her fears for them to be put aside to appease an old man's whim. Besides, until Stephen's death, Ben had given little thought to his younger son. Could he really expect Jared not to see the hypocrisy behind his belated summons to the family home?

'I think—I think you'll have to wait and see,' Robyn said now, getting up from her chair and moving across to the tray of drinks sitting on the cabinet in the corner. She was suddenly in need of sustenance. 'Do you want a soda? Or are you going to wait until Janet brings your tea? She's late, isn't she? It's almost—heavens! *Six!*'

'Exactly.' Ben was offhand now. 'I had my tea almost an hour ago. Don't tell me this business over Jared is getting to you, too. Going straight upstairs when you get home. Not even asking how an old man was.'

Robyn sighed. 'I needed a shower, Ben. It's been a long day.' She paused. 'Now—do you want anything?'

'Yes. A stiff brandy and soda,' said Ben harshly, and Robyn gazed at him impatiently.

'You know the doctor said——'

'Yes, yes. I know what the doctor said,' Ben mimicked her irritably. 'But one alcoholic drink isn't going to kill me, more's the pity. Go on. Pour me one. Or do you want me to come over there and spill brandy all over the carpet?'

Robyn was reluctant, but she was quite aware that Ben was likely to do exactly as he said. And, considering how much he used to like his pre-dinner drink in the evenings, he had been extremely patient with the restrictions Dr Harrington had put upon him. With a feeling of helplessness, she measured a small amount of brandy into a balloon-shaped glass, and then added a good half of a bottle of soda to dissipate its potency.

She was handing the glass to Ben when the library door opened. Expecting it to be Daniel, she turned, with a smile on her face, to greet the newcomer. But it was not her son, it was Jared; and the sight of his tall, loose-limbed indolence, after the conversation she and his father had just been having, brought the embarrassing glow of colour back into her cheeks.

Jared frowned when he saw the glass in his father's hand, and brows, which were several shades darker than his hair, arched disapprovingly. 'Ought you to be drinking that?' he asked, addressing his question to his father, yet leaving Robyn in no doubt as to who he considered deserved the blame. But, before she could defend herself, Ben intervened.

'What do you care?' he demanded, fixing his son with an aggressive stare. 'What else is there for me to do, stuck here like a condemned prisoner? Not even sure the company I've worked and slaved for is going to pass on to my own flesh and blood!'

'Ah!'

Jared's expellation of breath was the only audible sound in the room after his pronouncement. Robyn took refuge in the gin and tonic she had poured herself, hardly daring to look at either man as the pregnant silence stretched. Oh, why had Ben had to make that statement while she was in the room? she asked herself wearily. She had known he was getting desperate, but it was less than three days since Jared had set foot in England. Couldn't he have waited? Couldn't he have played Jared's game a little longer? Who could tell? From Jared's point of view, the longer he stayed without making a decision, the more likely he was to remain. Saddlebridge was like that. It tended to wrap its coils about you and, after a while, you didn't want to leave.

She swallowed another mouthful of the gin, feeling its warmth spreading into her stomach, alleviating the chill that had suddenly gripped her. What was she thinking of? she thought frustratedly. Why should she care if Ben blew his only chance to persuade Jared to come back? *She* didn't want Jared to stay. If he stayed, she and Daniel would have to go, and that was something she didn't care to contemplate.

The action of Ben swallowing his brandy and soda in one gulp seemed to bring the uneasy silence to an end. Crossing the room to take the empty glass from his father's hand, Jared gave a faintly ironic smile.

'OK,' he said, straightening with the glass in his hand, surveying its pale dregs with a considering eye. 'OK. I'll stay.'

Robyn caught her breath, but the sound was drowned by Ben's sudden choking laugh. 'Do you mean it?' he exclaimed, grasping his son's wrist with his good hand and gazing up at him disbelievingly. 'My God! Do you mean it? Hell, Jared, I don't know what to say! Just that—well, I'm very happy. Very happy indeed.'

Jared's smile thinned. 'There is a condition.'

'A condition?'

Ben looked confused, and Robyn felt the paralysing grip of apprehension invade her limbs. Why was she so sure the condition had to do with her? she asked herself anxiously. It could be anything. It could even involve her departure from Saddlebridge as part of the deal. After all, Jared *wouldn't* want her here if he brought another woman into the house. There couldn't be two mistresses at Saddlebridge, and she couldn't believe there was not some woman in his life at the present time.

'Yes, a condition,' Jared was saying now, forcing her to pay attention to his words. 'As a matter of fact——' he turned his head and looked at her '—it has to do with Robyn.'

'Robyn?' Ben frowned. 'What about Robyn? This is her home, Jared. I thought that would be understood——'

'Oh, please!' Robyn broke in to his words, her quickened breathing giving a nervous tremor to her speech. 'I—well, that is—we—Daniel and me, I mean—naturally we can't stay here indefinitely——'

'If you'll both stop trying to anticipate me, I'll explain,' said Jared flatly, setting his father's empty glass on the tray and surveying the other two people in the room with a cool green gaze. 'As I said, it does have to do with Robyn, but not in the way either of you think. I suppose mainly it has to do with—Dan,' he added, and Robyn's heart took a sickening leap.

'Dan?' said Ben doubtfully. 'What about Dan?'

'Well...' Jared was evidently enjoying Robyn's consternation and was in no hurry to relieve it. 'We all know that if—if Stephen hadn't died, Dan would have eventually inherited the company.'

'Yes, yes.' Ben was impatient. 'So?'

'So, I propose I make Dan *my* heir. It makes sense, doesn't it? It's only fair,' he added, his green gaze vanquishing the instinctive defence Robyn strove to gather. 'Morley's should be his. I think we're all agreed on that. And it means Robyn and her son can stay on here at Saddlebridge.'

'But we can't!' protested Robyn, in a strangled voice, almost forgetting that they had an audience, but Ben soon reminded her.

'Why not?' he demanded impatiently. 'Of course you'll stay here. It's your home. Where else would you go?'

Robyn made an effort to clear her throat. 'It—it's very kind of you—both,' she said, almost choking on the words, 'but I'm sorry. I—we—can't accept.'

'Don't be silly, Robyn!' A patronising note was creeping into her father-in-law's voice now. 'Your staying here has never been in question.'

'Not to you, maybe,' said Robyn doggedly, avoiding Jared's inimical stare. 'But—but ever since—since Stephen died——'

'Don't you mean, since I came home?' inserted Jared coldly. 'Ever since I came home, you've had to face the possibility of leaving.'

'No.' Robyn held up her head. 'No, that's not what I mean.'

'In any event, this conversation is unnecessary,' declared Ben, his gnarled fingers clasping and unclasping over the arm of his chair with increasing agitation. 'You're staying, and that's an end of it. This house is big enough, goodness knows. And, if Jared does get married, and his wife doesn't want to share the house with another woman, we'll face that problem when it comes.'

'No——'

'I'm afraid it has to be yes,' said Jared evenly. 'That's the condition I'm making. That you and Dan stay here. I like the boy, and I think he likes me. I want to know him better. It'll be good for him to have a younger man in his life. He needs a father. Surely you wouldn't deprive me of the chance to get to know my own— nephew?'

CHAPTER FIVE

'IS UNCLE JARED going to stay? Is he? Is he? Grandpa says he is, but you said he wasn't.'

Daniel looked innocently up at her from the soapy depths of his bath, and Robyn felt a desolate pang of desperation. Was there no escape from Jared? Was there no place in this house where she could be free of his pervading influence? Even her son seemed determined to force her into the ignominious position of defending her beliefs, and she had no doubt that, given the alternatives, Daniel would opt for staying here.

'I—don't know,' she said now, wiping a sudsy bubble from her sleeve. 'Daniel, stop splashing about like that! You're wetting the floor, and I don't want to have to get changed again.'

Daniel sniffed, rubbing his nose with a soapy finger. 'You don't want him to, do you?' he accused her unhappily. 'Ever since Uncle Jared came back you've been ever so crotchety.'

'I have *not* been crotchety——'

'Yes, you have.' Daniel hunched his shoulders. 'I just wish I knew why. Why don't you like him?'

'Liking or not liking him has nothing to do with it,' exclaimed Robyn, not altogether truthfully. 'I just think that—well, now that—Uncle Jared has come home, we don't belong here any more.'

Daniel's jaw sagged. 'Did he say that?'

'No. Oh, no.' Robyn couldn't bring herself to actually lie to her son. 'But—well, surely you can see, this is Uncle Jared's home now, and if he gets married and has a family of his own...'

'...he won't want us here any more,' finished Daniel miserably. 'Oh, cripes! I never thought of that.'

69

'No, well—you wouldn't, would you?' Robyn sighed, wishing they had never started this conversation. 'Now—have you washed behind your ears?'

'Hmm.' Daniel was thoughtful and, propping one elbow on his knee, he cupped his chin in a soapy hand. 'But—couldn't we stay here until Uncle Jared gets married?' he asked hopefully. 'I mean, it could be ages and ages, couldn't it? We don't have to leave straight away, do we?'

'You don't have to leave at all,' declared a voice from the doorway that Robyn was rapidly growing to hate. Turning her head, she found Jared propped against the frame and, absorbed as she had been in the effort of preventing Daniel from soaking her suit, she had no way of knowing how long he had been standing there. She had thought when she had escaped upstairs, ostensibly to supervise her son's bath, that any further discussion of that particular subject this evening might be avoided. But evidently Jared had come upstairs to get changed, and he was not above eavesdropping if he thought it might prove beneficial.

Ignoring her son's delighted face, Robyn got quickly to her feet. 'That's not true,' she said, realising she could not allow this to go on a moment longer. 'I'm sorry, Daniel.' She cast a regretful glance over her shoulder at the boy, before confronting Jared's enigmatic gaze. 'We'll stay at Saddlebridge until Christmas. After that, Daniel and I will be moving into our own home.'

Jared's lips thinned. 'Will you?'

The menace was evident behind the casually spoken words, and it took a great effort for Robyn not to be intimidated by it. 'I think so, yes,' she managed stiffly. 'I'm—I'm grateful for the offer, but I really can't accept.'

'But why not, Mum?'

Daniel's cry of disappointment was a faint echo of the cold determination in Jared's voice. 'Yes, why not?' he asked implacably. 'It's what I want; it's what Dan wants; it's what my father wants. Are you seriously thinking of taking a sick man's only grandson away from him?'

'You—*devil!*'

Robyn had her back to Daniel, so the mouthed words were not visible to him, but Jared could read them, and his lips twisted malevolently.

'Such language!' he mocked in an undertone, and then, raising the level of his words, he added, 'I'm so glad you're giving the matter some thought. It does seem foolish to move away from Saddlebridge when there's absolutely no need.'

'Oh—*great!*'

Daniel's excitement caused great scoops of water to spill on to the bathroom floor and, on the pretext of asking Janet for a towel to soak the overflow up, Robyn strode towards the door. She was tempted to try and force her way past Jared, but the idea of challenging his superior strength deterred her. Instead, she stopped in front of him, her desired intentions evident, and with an infuriatingly mocking smile he stepped aside.

She halted half-way through the door, however, and, endeavouring to control her anger, she advised Daniel to get out of the bath and start drying himself. 'I shall expect you to be in bed in fifteen minutes,' she added, aware of the resentful note in her voice, but unable to do anything about it. 'You hear?'

'Yes, Mum,' said Daniel glumly, his enthusiasm doused. Telling herself that her anger was justified, Robyn walked quickly towards the stairs.

However, after informing Janet of the spillage, Robyn did not return to the bathroom. Instead, she went to her own suite of rooms, wishing she could close the door on her troubles as easily as she could close the door of her room. No matter which way she turned, Jared seemed able to thwart her, and when it came to her son, she dared not run the risk of Jared using an old indiscretion against her.

An old indiscretion? She shook her head, as she moved away from the door. Was that all it had been? Certainly, it had been a mistake, a terrible mistake, and one she had suffered from for the whole of her married life.

And yet, before it had happened, her relationship with Jared had been so different. From the very beginning, when she had first come to live at Saddlebridge, they had been good friends. Of course, Jared had only been thirteen years old when she came to live here, and she supposed his liking for her had been not dissimilar to Daniel's liking for Jared. Perhaps he had even had a crush on her, she admitted, feeling a constriction in her throat. In any event, he had made her feel this was her home in a way Stephen, away at college at that time, had never done. In fact, in those early days, she had resented the times when Stephen was at home and Jared had deserted her for more boyish pursuits. That was in the days before Stephen really noticed her and, remembering now, she had to admit that what Joan Hedley had said was true. She had been fond of Jared then— but only as an older sister was fond of a brother, she amended swiftly. She had not been attracted to him, not at all; it would have been ludicrous.

Nevertheless, as Jared grew older, she had been aware that his attitude towards her was changing. His sixteenth birthday had been a case in point, and she remembered very clearly the kiss they had exchanged in the morning-room at Saddlebridge. At twenty-one, she had considered herself very mature and, after giving Jared the gift she had bought for him, it had seemed the most natural thing in the world to lean forward and kiss his cheek. But Jared had turned his head—deliberately, she now knew—and instead of brushing the newly roughening skin of his cheek, her lips had encountered the parted sensuality of his mouth. She flinched even now at the memory of that blatant caress. For some ridiculous reason, she hadn't drawn back as soon as she discovered her mistake. Instead, she had let him step nearer to her, and the warm invasion of his tongue against her teeth had turned her limbs to water.

Of course, she had been able to rationalise it later. It was around the time when she was first becoming attracted to Stephen, and it had been a simple matter to persuade herself that the brothers were sufficiently alike for her to have mistaken one for the other. In any case, anything else would have been totally humiliating, and she had made sure never to make the same mistake again.

And, in spite of her misgivings, her relationship with Jared was not permanently impaired. On the contrary, she missed him terribly a couple of years later when he went away to university, and even Stephen's increasing interest couldn't quite compensate for Jared's absence.

Well, not immediately, she acknowledged quickly. Not having Jared for her partner at tennis, or missing his companionship when she went riding, was soon forgotten when Stephen asked her to marry him. He had been home from college for some time then, and lost no time in staking his claim to her affections, so their engagement was announced at Christmas, and the wedding planned for the middle of May the following year.

She knew Stephen's father had been delighted at the prospect of making her a real member of the family at last, but she had never suspected that he might have had some part in Stephen's decision. It was not until afterwards that her doubts were conceived, and by then it was too late to do anything about it. Besides, she had initially blamed herself for Stephen's indiscretions. She was firmly convinced that she had been the cause.

Pressing her palms together, Robyn allowed the recollection of the events that had precipitated that guilt to sweep over her. She had been such a fool, she remembered bitterly. She should have known better than to trust Jared after what had gone before. But the truth was, she had felt a little sorry for him and, because Stephen was away, she had fallen into his trap.

The sequence of events which had changed her life had begun at Christmas, she acknowledged. It was Jared's first holiday at home since he had gone away to Oxford, and his attitude towards her then should have warned her he was no longer the boy who had gone away. She went to meet his train in Sheffield, and she was astonished at the change in him. He was thinner and taller and, with a day's growth of beard on his chin, he was also extremely attractive.

Even so, after a moment's initial embarrassment over the kiss they exchanged—the abrasive brush of his chin against her cheek had been absurdly intimate—Robyn soon found herself talking to him quite easily, dropping back into the casual camaraderie of Jared's pre-college days without too much difficulty. They talked about the university, and his father; they even laughed about her efforts to organise a Christmas pageant at the church; and it wasn't until she started bringing Stephen's name into the conversation that she noticed a certain sense of withdrawal in Jared's attitude. She didn't mention the proposed engagement, which was to take place on Christmas Eve. Although she knew it was foolish, she was curiously loath to admit that to him. Instead, she talked of other things, and despised her lack of courage.

For Stephen's part, he treated his brother with the same air of condescension he had always adopted. He had always used the six years there were between them to sustain his authority, as if he knew that allowing Jared to get beneath his guard would defeat his seniority. In consequence, he saw nothing amiss in Jared's behaviour, probably assuming Jared's new aloofness was an acknowledgement of his own superiority.

But Jared wasn't stupid, and Robyn knew that he had immediately guessed that things had changed. She saw him watching her and Stephen together, and she knew he suspected what had happened. But even so, he said nothing, and because she was a coward, Robyn said nothing, too.

A few days before Christmas, she held the final rehearsal for the pageant. Most of the participants were boys and girls from the village school, and Robyn had devised a colourful display incorporating the traditional scenes of the nativity into a medieval tableau. The children's parents had spent weeks designing the costumes and, set against the turreted backcloth Robyn had painted, the effect was quite enchanting.

It was Ben who suggested she should take Jared along to the rehearsal. 'Didn't you say you were having some problem with the spotlights?' he'd asked, at dinner the night before. 'Let Jared have a look at them. It will give him something to do. And,' he paused, 'it might persuade him to shave.'

Jared's unwillingness to use his razor at least once a day was causing a growing rift to develop between him and his father, and Robyn wished Ben wouldn't use her to get back at his son.

Nevertheless, Jared had shaved when he appeared at lunch the following day. 'What time are we leaving?' he asked, seating himself opposite her at the table in the morning-room; and, not for the first time, Robyn wished that Stephen and his father did not take their midday meal at the mill.

'You don't have to come, you know,' she murmured, serving herself from the bowl of beef broth Janet had set between them. 'As a matter of fact, the spotlights are fixed. Simon Heslop mended the fuse on Tuesday. If that's the reason you're coming, there's really no need. I'm sure you've got better things to do than watch a lot of children falling over themselves.'

'Like what?' Jared asked quietly, his green gaze steadily on hers.

'Well——' Robin lifted her shoulders helplessly '—don't you have people—*friends* you want to see? I can think of a dozen girls who'd jump at the chance to spend the afternoon with you,' she added somewhat patronisingly, and then wished she hadn't when his gaze never wavered.

'But not you,' he remarked, looking at her over the rim of the soup spoon he was raising to his mouth.

'I didn't say that.' She was flustered, and it showed, and she wondered when he had acquired this capacity to disconcert her like this. He hadn't used to be so un-

predictable. But then, she had never really had anything
to hide.

'So—I'll come with you, if you'll have me,' he appended drily, and she managed a thin smile.

'Oh—of course,' she agreed, dragging her eyes away
from his and concentrating on the soup in her plate. At
least they would not be alone, she reminded herself
grimly. One of the advantages—or disadvantages, de-
pending on your point of view—of working with
children, was their ability to be everywhere at once. There
was no facility for privacy at the church hall, and Simon
Heslop, the vicar's curate, was unlikely to permit Jared
to threaten his authority.

What Robyn had not taken into account was the drive
to and from the village hall. It would have been stupid
to take two cars, so they used the Range Rover Ben kept
for the bad weather. It was natural, therefore, that Jared
should drive, and Robyn sat beside him, wondering why
she felt so on edge.

The rehearsal was a complete fiasco. The children
playing Mary and Joseph could do nothing but giggle
all the way through, and it was obvious that Simon, who
played the Lord of Misrule, had forgotten his lines.
Robyn found her temper increasingly difficult to control
and, although she knew it was just an amateur presen-
tation and that the audience would be hopelessly par-
tisan, she couldn't help feeling impatient and letting her
feelings show.

By the time they left the church hall, she was ridiculously near to tears, and it didn't help when Jared chided
her for her behaviour. 'They're only kids, you know,'
he remarked, as they left the lights of the village behind
and turned on to the private road that marked the
boundary of Saddlebridge. 'They want to have fun, not
produce a performance to rival Olivier's! It's only a
village pageant, Robyn—not *Twelfth Night*!'

'Of course, you *would* say that!' she countered,
needing a whipping boy, and he was there. 'Naturally,
I can't hope to compete with anything you're likely to

see at Oxford, but I take this seriously, and I resent being made to look a fool!'

'You didn't look a fool,' said Jared flatly. 'In fact, as an amateur production, it's pretty good——'

'Talk about being damned with faint praise!' Robyn interrupted bitterly and, with an oath and a squeal of brakes, Jared brought the four-wheeled vehicle to a standstill.

They were still about half a mile from the house, on the narrow country road that circled Saddlebridge, and Robyn looked about her anxiously as the engine died, wishing she had had the sense to keep her arguments to herself until they were safely home.

'Now,' said Jared, switching on the interior light, and half turning in his seat to face her. 'Why don't we discuss what this is really about? Steve's asked you to marry him, hasn't he? Why don't you come right out and admit it?'

Robyn's lips parted. 'I—well, what if he has? What has it got to do with you?'

'Oh, come on.' Jared was impatient now. 'I guess you've been waiting for me to get home to give lover-boy your decision.' His fingers, resting on the back of her seat, suddenly stroked her neck and she flinched in sudden alarm. 'You know you can't marry him, don't you, Robyn?' he added, his voice incredibly sensual. 'That would be a crazy thing to do, wouldn't it? You're not in love with him.'

Robyn was absolutely stunned. She had known Jared might not be enthusiastic about her engagement to Stephen, but she had never dreamt he might mount an all-out attack. Good heavens, she thought incredulously, any minute now he's going to tell me I love him instead!

The idea was so ludicrous, she knew she had to stop him before he said something he would later regret. Obviously, he considered one term at Oxford had given him the ability to interpret her feelings in a totally subjective way, but, unless she prevented him from going any further, the situation between them would become intolerable.

'As—as a matter of fact, you're wrong,' she got out quickly. 'I—I do love Stephen. And—he knows it. It's a secret really, but I know he won't mind if I tell you. We—er—we're getting engaged on Christmas Eve.'

The remainder of the Christmas break was something of an anticlimax after that. In spite of the excitement of her engagement, Robyn couldn't forget Jared's expression when she had told him she was going to marry his brother. He had looked—*stricken*; that was the only word she could think of to describe his face. Although she told herself she had had no choice but to break the news to him, she still felt absurdly responsible for ruining his holiday.

Even so, it had had to be done, and when, two days into the New Year, Jared suddenly announced he was going to spend the rest of the holiday with some friends in Switzerland, Robyn mentally breathed a sigh of relief. Jared would soon find someone else with whom to console himself, she told herself firmly, and dismissed the fleeting trace of irritation she felt at this prospect as simple possessiveness.

It wasn't so easy to make excuses for herself when Jared failed to come home at all at Easter. She didn't want to be the cause of banishing him from his home but, short of confiding her fears to Stephen, there was nothing she could do about it.

And then, about a month before the wedding, Jared did come home. Stephen was away at the time in South America, visiting their suppliers in Brazil and Argentina, and when word was sent by his tutor that Jared had contracted bronchitis his father sent a reluctant Robyn to Oxford to bring him home for rest and recuperation.

'God knows what he's been doing,' Ben had told her tersely, his expression a mixture of irritability and concern. 'According to this chap, Fellowes, he's only narrowly avoided getting pneumonia. Go and fetch him, Robyn. He's more likely to come if you ask him. Tell him I expect him to spend at least two weeks at home, and I won't listen to any excuses.'

Robyn tried to protest that he should make the request personally, but Ben always had an excuse. 'I can't leave the mill to run itself,' he argued firmly, 'what with Stephen being away and all. Don't let me down on this, Robyn. I thought you had a soft spot for him yourself.'

And so Robyn drove down to Oxford with David McCloud, and persuaded a curiously apathetic Jared that he would recover that much quicker at home, with his family to look after him. He seemed indifferent, and the journey back to Saddlebridge was decidedly awkward. Ever since that exchange in the Range Rover, there had been a definite barrier between them, and, although she kept telling herself that once she and Stephen were married things would be different, she didn't quite believe it.

Once they arrived at Saddlebridge, Janet took one look at Jared's thin pale face and insisted he went straight to bed, and for the next few days Robyn saw nothing of him. She knew how he was progressing because Ben spent a lot of time with his son, but personally she was quite happy to keep out of his way.

Then, one morning towards the end of the week, Jared came into the library where Robyn was writing some letters. It was an unusually bright morning, after a week of almost continuous rain, and a clump of late daffodils were daring to raise their heads outside. The lawns, too, had benefited from their thorough soaking, and were greener than before. There were lambs in the fields beyond the paddock, and the sun was glinting brilliantly off the rocks of Saddleford Tor.

'Oh...' Robyn looked up in some confusion at her brother-in-law-to-be's appearance. Only last night, Ben had confided in her that he was worried about his son's apparent indifference to his recovery, and to see Jared standing there before her, pale maybe, but unquestionably fitter than he had been, was quite unnerving. 'Are you feeling better?'

'Some,' agreed Jared evenly, crossing the room to the window, to stand with his hands in the pockets of his black suede trousers, staring out on to the burgeoning life of the garden. He was wearing a black sweater, too, that accentuated the extreme lightness of his hair; seated at the desk, Robyn found her eyes were irresistibly drawn to the arrowing of silvery-blonde hair that brushed the neckline of the woollen garment. She remembered feeling an almost tangible desire to touch that vulnerable part of his anatomy, and she had to drag her eyes away and concentrate on the letter she was writing.

'What are you doing?' he asked at last, turning to face her, and once again she was obliged to keep a strict hold on her emotions.

'Nothing much,' she remarked dismissively. 'Writing to a schoolfriend, that's all.' She omitted to mention that the schoolfriend in question was to be one of her bridesmaids when she married Stephen.

'Want to go for a ride?' he enquired unexpectedly, and she caught her breath.

'To go for a ride?' she echoed disbelievingly. 'But—you can't! You've been in bed for the best part of a week!'

'I haven't.' Jared came to stand in front of the desk, and she was dismayed to find the hot colour was flooding into her cheeks under his cool appraisal. 'I've just been keeping out of the way, that's all.'

Robyn swallowed. 'What do you mean?'

'I thought that was what you wanted.'

'What *I* wanted?'

'Well, you haven't exactly fallen over yourself to find out if I was OK, have you?'

Robyn wet her lips with a nervous tongue. 'Your father——' she began, and with a twisted smile Jared inclined his head.

'Oh, yes. My father's kept you informed.'

'Well, he has.'

'I'm not arguing, am I?' Jared sighed. 'So—OK. Will you go for a ride with me?'

'On—on horseback?'

'Well, I don't mean in the Range Rover,' remarked Jared drily, and she felt her breathing quicken alarmingly.

'I—don't think your father would—approve,' she said at last, and Jared uttered an imprecation.

'I'm not a child, Robyn, even if you'd prefer me to act that way. I'm all right, I tell you. I'm a bit weak, but who wouldn't be after swallowing gallons of Janet's chicken broth and little else? What I need is some exercise, and some fresh air. Now—are you going to come with me, or do I have to go on my own?'

'You can't go on your own.'

Robyn's response was instinctive, and Jared arched his brows quizzically. 'Well?'

'All right.' Much against her better judgement, Robyn agreed to accompany him, and fifteen minutes later they were clattering out of the stable yard and on to the open moorland behind the house.

In fact, she enjoyed herself enormously. It was months since she had done more than exercise the bay mare Ben had bought her for her twenty-first birthday—not since Jared had gone away to college, she realised ruefully—and it was marvellous to get right away from the house, and give the spirited animal its head. On top of this, the air was pure and clear, like wine—and, like wine, it was intoxicating.

By the time they cantered back to the stables, she realised that for the past hour she had forgotten the reasons why she and Jared had spent so little time together at Christmas. The morning had passed without any tension or cross words between them and, seeing the healthy colour glowing in Jared's lean features, she felt an answering glow of achievement that she had had some part in his recovery.

That evening, she and Jared had dinner together. Ben was spending the evening at his club in Leeds and, over smoked salmon pâté and a creamy fricassee of chicken, they renewed their old friendship. Of course, Stephen's name didn't figure too strongly in their conversation, although Robyn did express regret that her fiancé would not get to see his brother on this occasion. Jared made some remark about the demands of running a business and the subject was abandoned. If Robyn recognised a certain reticence in his manner, she was happy enough to have avoided another unpleasant scene.

And, during the days that followed, she began to wonder if she had imagined the things he had said to her on that never-to-be-forgotten ride home from the church hall. Jared was so nice to her, so much *fun!* And she was guiltily aware that she wasn't missing Stephen at all.

The weather remained dry and mild, and most mornings they took the horses out for their daily exercise. Jared's father initially expressed the hope that his son was not running the risk of further pulmonary complications by overdoing things, but the evident improvement in Jared's condition was all the proof he needed that this was not so.

It was arranged that Jared should return to Oxford at the end of the following week; he had spoken to his tutor on the phone and assured him that all was well. As his time at home drew to a close, Robyn knew a quite unwarranted feeling of depression. She told herself it was because Stephen was still away, and that as soon as her fiancé returned home she would feel altogether different, but for the time being, nothing could alter the fact that she was dreading Jared's departure.

They spent the Friday before he left in Sheffield, doing last-minute shopping for things Jared was needing. The doctor had suggested that wearing a T-shirt under a sweater might prevent his catching another similar chill, which had almost turned to pneumonia, and although Robyn suspected he'd never wear them she insisted on his buying half a dozen to take back to college. The doctor had also recommended that he should wear a pyjama jacket, as well as trousers, to sleep in, and although Jared protested that he had plenty of pyjamas

at home, Robyn bought him two new pairs in Marks and
Spencer's. She was perfectly aware that the expensive
silk pyjamas he had at home had never seen the light of
day—or night—in Oxford, but perhaps something more
practical might convince him of their value.

It was quite late when they got back to Saddlebridge.
They had called for a drink on the way home, and it
was after six when they reached the house. However,
there was no sign of Ben's Rolls-Royce, and Janet met
them with the news that Mr Morley was dining with his
accountant.

'He's given David the night off,' she added. 'He says
if he decides to come home, he'll get a taxi. If not, he
might spend the night at his club.'

'Oh.' Robyn acknowledged this news with an unforgivable sense of anticipation. At least she would not have
to spend the evening steering Ben's conversation away
from his elder son. And she and Jared would be able to
talk, without the confining influence of his father.

'No sweat,' said Jared now, evidently misinterpreting
Robyn's sudden silence. 'Hey, why don't you take the
evening off, too, Janet? Rob and I can fend for
ourselves. We might even go out. Isn't that right,
Robyn?'

'What?' Robyn endeavoured to concentrate on what
he had said. 'Oh—yes.' She gave Janet a warm smile.
'Why don't you? Take the evening off, I mean. You and
your husband could go out somewhere, if you wanted.
You know Ben won't mind if you borrow the car.'

Janet's lips tilted. 'You know, we might just do that.'
She hesitated. 'If you're sure you and Jared——'

'We're not completely helpless,' said Jared drily. 'Go
on. Enjoy yourselves. Believe me, at college I usually
make do with a burger.'

'But you're not at college now,' murmured Janet
doubtfully. 'And your father——'

'My father's not here,' declared Jared flatly. 'There's
just Rob and me. And we're giving you the evening off.
Are you going to turn us down?'

Of course, after that, Janet could hardly refuse. Besides, it was obvious she wanted to take them at their word and, by the time Robyn excused herself to take her own purchases upstairs, Janet was on her way to their apartments at the back of the house to tell her husband the good news.

Putting the tights and make-up she had bought away in her drawers, Robyn couldn't prevent the little frisson of excitement that ran up her spine at the thought that she and Jared were going to be alone in the house. It was ridiculous, and she was certainly old enough to know better, but he was an attractive man—*boy*, she corrected herself severely—and it was flattering to know that he enjoyed her company rather than that of someone of his own age. Of course, it was possible that there was someone back at college he would rather be with, but that was not something on which she allowed her mind to linger. Instead, she turned her efforts to reminding herself that she was to be married in a little over three weeks, and that fantasising about Jared was both dangerous and juvenile.

She heard the Rolls-Royce purr away down the drive as she was trying out the new dusky pink eye-shadow she had discovered in Rackham's. The tyres crunching over the gravel brought her surreptitiously to her window, and she peered round the curtains with a definite feeling of stimulation.

Curbing her anticipation, Robyn left the window and returned to her experimentation. For heaven's sake, she scolded herself severely, she had spent the weeks between Christmas and Jared's unexpected homecoming despising him for trying to come between her and Stephen. And now, here she was, acting like a schoolgirl because they were to spend the evening alone in the house.

Putting the suddenly offensive eye-shadow aside, she stared at her reflection. What she saw, delectable as it was, did not please her. Her eyes were brilliant, there was becoming colour in her cheeks, and the glossy curtain of her hair gleamed with good health. She did not look like a girl who was pining for the fiancé who had been away for the better part of three weeks. She looked like someone's mistress, waiting for her lover, and that was a situation she could not allow to proceed. The last thing she wanted was for Jared to think she was attracted to him. The safest course would be for them to go out for the evening, too. That way, they would have other people around them, and no opportunity to tread on dangerous territory.

It was so silly, really, she thought, as she went downstairs. It wasn't as if she was highly sexed or anything. She had had no difficulty whatsoever in sustaining her innocence throughout her relationship with Stephen, although she acknowledged that his reticence stemmed more from a desire not to annoy his father than from any particular consideration for her feelings. Even so, he had respected her desire not to anticipate their marriage, and she innocently believed that since their engagement there had been no one else.

She paced about the library for a good half-hour, waiting for Jared to put in an appearance and, by the time she lost patience and went looking for him, she had forgotten her earlier apprehension over the dangers of their relationship.

Instead, after making a tour of Ben's study and the morning-room, and even looking into the kitchen to see if he was there, she made her way back up the stairs again, taking the corridor to his room without even turning a hair.

She knocked at his door with rather more hesitation, but, on receiving no answer, she speedily knocked again. 'Jared,' she called, wondering, somewhat belatedly, if anything could be wrong. 'Jared! Are you in there? Come on. Can't you answer the door?'

'Coming!'

The lazy response reassured her that at least he was not suffering any after-effects of their trip. But her nails curled into the palms of her hands with impatience as he kept her waiting several more seconds before opening the door.

When he did she felt an instantaneous surge of some emotion she didn't care to identify. Instead of the jeans and sweater he had worn to go shopping in Sheffield, he had on one of the thin shirts they had bought there, and beneath his dark blue underwear his long legs were bare.

'Oh—sorry about this,' he said carelessly, and she knew, infuriatingly, that he was aware of her disconcertment. 'I've just had a shower, and when you knocked I wasn't dressed. D'you want to come in? I shan't be a second.'

Robyn shook her head. 'No—I—that is, I just thought perhaps we should go out tonight.' She moistened her lips. 'What do you think?'

'Should?'

Jared was too astute, and Robyn coloured. 'All right— might, then,' she amended tersely. 'I thought we might go out tonight. As—as Janet's gone out.'

'We're alone, I know,' said Jared drily, turning back into the room. 'Look—do you mind closing that door? I know this house is centrally heated, but I have just had a shower, and there's quite a draught from the hall.'

Robyn hesitated. 'But, well—what do you think?'

Jared turned his head. 'I think you're scared of being alone with me,' he retorted flatly. 'But—OK. If that's the way you want it.'

Robyn took a deep breath and stepped into the room, closing the door behind her. 'I am not scared of being alone with you,' she declared, although her hand still lingered on the handle. 'And—and if you believe going around half naked is likely to embarrass me, you couldn't be more wrong. You forget—I've known you since you were a toddler! And you used to wear a lot less than that to swim in the pool!'

'Ah,' Jared's lips twisted. 'But you have to admit, I am bigger now,' he remarked mockingly. 'I remember you, too, Robyn. And you were always afraid to take a chance.'

'That's not true!'

'It is true,' he said, turning back to her, and she had to force her eyes not to move from the open V of olive skin visible above the neckline of his shirt. 'You always took the safest way out of any situation. That's why you've let Steve and my father browbeat you into this engagement. You knew it was what my father wanted, and because you felt so grateful to him for taking you in when your parents were killed, you never even hesitated when Steve popped the question.'

'That is not true!' Robyn swallowed convulsively. 'I love Stephen.'

'Do you?' Jared took the steps necessary to leave only a foot of space between them. 'Is that why you're trembling like a leaf because you're afraid I'm going to touch you?'

Robyn quivered. 'You flatter yourself!'

'No, I don't.' Jared made no move to touch her, but continued to regard her with lazily sensual eyes. 'I just know a little more about this feeling there is between us. I know what it means, and I'm tempted to show you what it means, too.'

Robyn's breathing quickened. 'You have no shame, do you? You know I'm your brother's fiancée, and yet you stand there——'

'—half naked——' he inserted sardonically.

'—and tell me there's something between us.'

'There is.'

'There isn't!'

'Do you want me to prove it?'

'No. I mean——' Robyn was pressing herself back against the door so hard, her shoulderblades ached '—there's nothing to prove. Except your disloyalty to your brother. And—and to me.'

'Don't talk such utter crud!' exclaimed Jared harshly, moving to rest one hand on either side of her as she pressed herself against the door. 'Where's the point in being loyal, when the woman I love is doing her level best to ruin both our lives?'

He was so close now, she could feel the warmth of his body, smell the aroma of the soap he used. She sensed the heated urgency of his emotions and acknowledged the need to fight against a temptation quite as old as time.

'You—you don't love me, Jared,' she got out unsteadily.

'Don't I?' His eyes dipped to rest on the rapid rise and fall of her breasts, apparent beneath the finely knit wool of her sweater.

'No, I—Jared, stop doing that! I'm trying to discuss this sensibly, and you're deliberately trying to disconcert me.'

'How am I trying to do that?' enquired Jared softly, and she despised the way his husky voice scraped across her senses. 'I haven't even touched you.'

'Just—stop looking at me like that,' exclaimed Robyn tremulously. 'And—and put some clothes on. If—if anyone was to come in here now——'

'Yes?' Jared arched one enquiring brow.

'Well—what would they think?'

Jared half smiled. 'The same old argument, hmm, Robyn? I'm behaving naturally, and you can't stand it.'

'You are *not* behaving naturally!' she told him unsteadily. 'You're taking advantage of—of a situation. If your father knew——'

'Oh, yes, I wondered when that was coming.' Jared's mouth curled. 'If my father knew, he'd thrash me, is that what you think? Well, sorry, Robyn, but I don't think my father could do that any more. Whether you believe it or not, I am not a boy any longer.'

Robyn swallowed. 'Then stop behaving like one.'

'OK, I will.' He straightened abruptly, releasing her from the prison his arms had created. 'Go on. Get out of here. I don't need the aggravation.'

Robyn shifted away from the door with some relief but, now that she was free to go, she was curiously loath to do so. She didn't want them to part on this note; she didn't want Jared to return to Oxford with the remembrance of this scene as his companion. Things had been so good between them these past days, and she wanted them to remain that way. How she wished she had never started this; but she had, and she had to finish it.

'Jared . . .' she began awkwardly, as he snatched up a pair of dark grey trousers and started putting them on. 'Jared, please! I want us to be friends.'

'Friends?' He didn't even look at her. 'I can't be your friend, Robyn. You and I have nothing more to say to one another.'

'That's not true.'

He turned to look at her then, pushing the hem of his shirt into his trousers as he did so. 'Will you stop saying that?' he snarled, and she had to force her eyes not to follow the movements of his hands. 'I know what I'm saying, believe me. And if you want me to remember that you are Steve's fiancée, and I'm only your brother-in-law-to-be, you'd better leave, right now!'

Robyn sighed, taking an involuntary step towards him. 'Jared,' she began again, 'Jared, it needn't be this way . . .'

'Needn't it?' Jared's face was a guarded mask, but Robyn was too intent on what he was saying to pay a lot of attention to visible danger signals.

'No,' she persisted, her confidence growing when he didn't immediately rebuff her. 'Look—we've had a good time this week, haven't we? We've had some fun. We always have fun. We like doing the same things. Jared, how can we not be friends when we enjoy being together?'

Almost without being aware of it, she had narrowed the space between them as she spoke. Now, there was scarcely an arm's length between them and, although that knowledge was a little intimidating, Robyn couldn't move back again without losing her advantage.

There was silence for a long moment, but instead of easing the tension it seemed to heighten it. The air between them seemed to vibrate with it, and Robyn, who had been convinced she could convince him, was suddenly equally as convinced she couldn't. She didn't trust his silence; she didn't trust the abnormal stillness that surrounded him; and when he expelled his breath on a long sigh, she started at the sound like a frightened gazelle.

But even then she didn't act on her awareness. With Jared's direct green gaze holding hers, she felt a curious paralysis in her limbs, a kind of hypnosis that kept her where she was, even when he put out his hand and rubbed his knuckles down her cheek. The hard brush of his fingers against her flesh was not sufficient to release the awful magnetism that held her, and the years she knew there were between them seemed suddenly reversed. She was the junior, held in thrall by his superior perception; she was the innocent, made helpless by his superior knowledge.

'I did warn you,' he said at last, in a thick voice she hardly recognised. 'I did warn you, Robyn!' And before she could react, he pulled her into his arms, and found her mouth with his with unerring deliberation.

CHAPTER SIX

AFTERWARDS, Robyn had managed to convince herself that Jared had given her no chance to resist. The recollection of what had happened had become confused in her mind, and she had succeeded in persuading herself that Jared had forced himself upon her. What other reason could there have been for what had occurred between them? What other excuse could there be for the way she had behaved? She could not accept that she had willingly betrayed Stephen. That way had led to disaster, and the ruin of their future together.

Today, however, allowing every detail of that evening to ressurrect itself, Robyn could not be so sanctimonious. It had been hypocritical of her to put all the blame on Jared's shoulders. God forgive her, she had not exactly put up much of a fight. From the minute he had touched her, she had been aware it was a losing battle.

But why had she known that? she asked herself now, pacing restlessly about her bedroom. What was there about Jared that had caused her to behave so uncharacteristically? Had she been flattered by his attentions? Had she been so desperate for affection that she had unwittingly encouraged his advances? Goodness knew, she had been aware of his attraction, but objectively, she had thought; like a sister might be aware of a brother.

Perhaps the fact that Jared had evidently had some experience had had something to do with it. At that time, she had assumed he was more experienced than Stephen, and she had despised him for using her as he had so many others. It was only after her marriage that she had discovered her mistake. And then she had dismissed them both as being tarred with the same brush.

But, whatever her subsequent thoughts had been, at the time she had seemingly made only a token effort to resist him. When his lips had touched hers, she had lost the will to fight him, and her awareness of his superior strength had been a convenient vindication.

All the same, he had not kissed her like Stephen kissed her. Her fiancé's soft, wet-lipped caresses were nothing like the firm possession of Jared's mouth. When Stephen kissed her, he breathed into her mouth; Jared, quite simply, took her breath away.

They were both breathing heavily when his lips left hers and sought the sensitive hollow where her neck curved into her shoulder. Pushing the soft collar of her sweater aside, Jared allowed his tongue to search out the quivering softness of her skin, and Robyn's limbs suffused with heat at that unfamiliar invasion. She wasn't used to such intimacies, or to such a sensual approach, and her unsuspecting body was contributing to her betrayal.

She remembered saying, 'No, Jared!' or 'We can't do this,' or some such thing, but her protests were as unconvincing as her response was positive. In any case, Jared wasn't listening to her. He was intent on arousing emotions she had not even known she possessed at that time, and his hands left her shoulders to seek the narrow contours of her hips.

He drew her hard against him, against the rigid bones of his pelvis, and the unmistakable thrust of his manhood rising between. The pulsating throb against her stomach seemed to ridicule her claims that he was still a boy, and the potent pressure of his body seemed to turn her bones to water. He was so lean and strong and masculine; so *young*, she acknowledged now, with a bitter grimace. But old in the ways of making love, she added grimly. While she had been just a novice in comparison.

Even so, when his mouth had returned to hers, she had been ready and eager to accommodate him. However much she might despise herself now, she had not repulsed his escalating passion. On the contrary, she had been more than willing to part her lips and allow the intimate invasion of his tongue. And once she felt that intrusion, moist and sensuous, stroking the sensitive places of her mouth, she had realised how treacherous her own senses could be.

She didn't remember how they got to the bed, she only remembered the feeling of softness against her bare skin. The buttons of her sweater had posed no obstacle to Jared's searching hands, and the heat of his body against her flesh was a natural escalation. He had cupped her breasts in his hands, she recalled shudderingly, taking each of them to his lips in turn, caressing their tips with his tongue and turning her bones to water. She hadn't been frigid then; she had been hot and eager and shameless, meeting his forbidden passion with an urgency she could hardly understand now, letting him have his way and encouraging him to do so.

Maybe her eyes had been closed, she thought now; maybe she had succeeded in convincing herself that it was Stephen who was making love to her. But, whatever her excuse at the time, afterwards she had never experienced such a lack of inhibition again. Afterwards, she had lost the ability to feel such emotions surging inside her, and there was no one to blame but Jared for her arrested sensibilities.

She shook her head bitterly. If only she had known what she was inviting, she thought. If only she had perceived what those heated moments of passion would cost her! But at the time, she had been too bemused to think of anything, too much at the mercy of her senses to consider anything so nebulous as the future.

Had her eyes been closed when she had helped Jared shed his clothes? she asked herself scornfully. Had she not seen his hands slide the close-fitting jeans from her own body, and follow their passage with his lips? Had her legs not parted to the sensuous brush of his tongue against her inner thigh? And had she not grasped his hair and brought his lips to hers again in a fever of blind infatuation?

Of course she had done all those things. She had
arched her back and rubbed herself against his lean hard
strength. She had even found the urge to touch him quite
irresistible, and she could still recall the feel of his pulsating maleness in her hands.

Jared had said, 'Oh, God!' and 'Robyn!' in a choked
voice, and she had known a never-repeated surge of satisfaction at his evident pleasure in what she was doing.
So much so that she had wound her legs about him, and
after that there had been no possibility of preventing the
inevitable.

Shaking her head now, she tried to put those thoughts
away from her, but the memories were unravelling like
a long-tangled skein of wool inside her head. No matter
how unwelcome the truth might be, she had to accept
her share of blame for Jared's irresponsibility, and the
knowledge of her guilt was like a worm inside her brain.

The fact that it had never happened again was no vindication. It had happened once, and that was enough.
No matter that, for a brief space of time, she had experienced emotions she had never known before or since.
What they had done had been unforgivable, and she, as
the elder, should have had more sense.

However, at the time, sense had been one thing she
was lacking. It had taken the painful experience of
Jared's invasion of her body to alert her to the horror
of what she was doing, and by then it had been much
too late. No matter that his face had expressed his astonishment that she was still a virgin. The damage had
been done, and Robyn's remorse had been shattering.

But, although she would have left him then, Jared
would not let her. 'Do you think I can let you go now?'
he demanded, stilling her struggles with urgent hands.
'Do you think that's all there is to it? Pain?' His lips
twisted. 'Oh, Robyn, I have to show you that it's not.'

And, in spite of her initial efforts to thwart him, he
did. Although she wanted to break free of him, the
hungry brush of his mouth and the caressive touch of
his fingers was shamefully pleasurable, and when he

started to move, she found herself moving with him. The accelerating thrust of his body was unbearably persuasive, and although she tried to think of Stephen and pretend that it was he who was doing this to her, it became totally impossible. It was Jared whose heated body aroused an answering heat in hers, so that their sweat mingled between them; it was Jared who smoothed the moist hair back from her forehead, and looked down at her with a savage possession, Jared who drove her to the edge of ecstasy, and Jared who held her as the throbbing climax of their mutual release tipped them over into a mindless languor...

Withdrawing now from that unwelcome remembrance, Robyn pressed hot palms to her suddenly burning cheeks. Oh, God, she thought sickly, she hadn't wanted to remember how he had made her feel! Or, afterwards, the overpowering sense of shame she had experienced. She recalled how she had scrambled off the bed while he was still drowsing, evading his lazily extended hand and gathering her scattered clothes together. She hadn't stopped to dress. She had scurried back to her own room like a frightened rabbit, and when Jared eventually came knocking on her door it had been securely locked. She supposed he could have forced his way in, if he had been so determined, but maybe shame at his own actions had restricted his efforts to verbal persuasion. Then, when she had refused to answer him, he had gone away, and it wasn't until the next morning that she had had to face him.

Her lips twisted now. He had actually expected her to break her engagement to Stephen, she remembered tensely. He had even suggested she should wait until he had finished his degree and marry him, and she had taken the greatest pleasure in telling him she wouldn't marry him if he was the last man on earth. She hated him, she despised him, and she told him that, so far as she was concerned, Stephen was worth a *dozen* like him.

If Ben had wondered why his younger son should suddenly pack up and return to college a couple of days earlier than expected, he had made no demur. Besides, he had had word that Stephen would be home at the beginning of the following week, and he expected Robyn, like him, to have more interest in that event.

And she had tried to. Indeed, when Stephen had come home, she had gone out of her way to show him how much she had missed him, and for a few memorable weeks she had been able to persuade herself that nothing monumental had happened. Most girls had had some experience of sex before marriage, and she had decided that Stephen would expect her to be no exception.

Except, that wasn't the end of it. She expelled her breath on a sigh. That was the only beginning. Within two weeks of their wedding, she became convinced that she was pregnant, and the precipitation was such that she knew it couldn't possibly be Stephen's child.

They were on honeymoon at the time that she diagnosed her condition, and the sunlit beauty of the Bahamas became a cruel backdrop to the reality of what had happened. She had thought she was safe. Stephen had been too careless, and too *drunk*, on their wedding night, to notice that she was no longer a virgin, and after satisfying his own needs he had slumped beside her, dead to the world. And, in the days that followed, she had discovered her husband didn't much care whether she participated in his lovemaking or not. So long as she made herself available to him, he was content.

Consequently, the revelation that she was expecting Jared's baby had shocked her to the core, and any hopes she might have had of Stephen's arousing some dormant response inside her was stifled by the stiffness that this horrifying development created. She even considered abortion in those terrifying early days, but eventually she came to realise that the child might be her salvation.

Once they were back in England, it hadn't taken her long to realise how naïve she had been about Stephen's character. She'd soon learned that there were other women in her husband's life, and her own lack of interest in sex was excuse enough, if any was needed, for Stephen to resume his old ways. When she'd eventually plucked up the courage to tell him she was pregnant, it had had no significant effect on his behaviour. Except that he had moved his belongings into the adjoining room, on the pretext of not disturbing her when he came home late at night, and, apart from an occasional visit, he never slept with her again.

There were times in those early days when she determined to tell him the truth, but she never did. He never suspected that Daniel was not his own child. But Jared did, particularly when the baby was born a scant eight months after the wedding. She saw the cold suspicion in his eyes, and for weeks afterwards she lived with the constant fear that he might choose to expose her. But he never did, and when Jared left for Australia she knew an overwhelming sense of relief.

Yet, although she had told herself that Jared's departure would make a difference to her relationship with Stephen, it never did. She soon came to the conclusion that Stephen had wanted her as a wife, but not as a mistress. He liked her; he treated her with affection; but whatever it was he wanted from a woman, it was not the familiarity to be found in his own bed. In consequence, Daniel became the whole focus of her existence, and she learned to dissimulate so well that she almost convinced herself that he *was* Stephen's son.

Of course, eventually, Stephen's affairs became an embarrassment. Initially, she heard of them by the gossip that circulated about him, but inevitably her own friends felt compelled to put her in the picture. After all, they argued, divorce was an acceptable alternative, and these days no woman was expected to put up with that sort of thing. That she had refused even to consider the possibility of a divorce had caused some people to decide that she was either completely stupid, or completely mercenary, but gradually the subject had been dropped. And then, Ben's stroke had created an entirely different situation, and no one expected her to walk out on her commitments any longer, when she was so obviously necessary to the old man's peace of mind.

But it was her own peace of mind that troubled her now. Jared's return, and the ultimatum he had announced only an hour ago in the library, had brought the whole thing back into perspective. Although, on the face of it, his offer sounded genuine enough, she knew it for the compromise it was. Jared was insinuating himself into her life again. He was making himself indispensable to his father, and in the process making himself an integral part of Daniel's future. And how long would he be content to call Daniel his nephew? Wasn't it only a matter of time before he chose to disclose his identity as the boy's father?

Robyn trembled. She felt so helpless. It was all very well insisting that Jared couldn't prove that Daniel was his son, but how would the boy react if he was faced with the possibility? In all honesty, he had had little in common with Stephen, whereas it was obvious that he admired Jared very much. Given that admiration, and the indisputable proof that his characteristics were more those of his father's younger brother, might not Daniel himself turn against her, and how would she bear it if the one person she cared most for in the world blamed her for keeping the truth from him?

She closed her eyes for a moment, unable to face the agony of such a prospect. She could not let it happen; she *must* not let it happen. But how was she going to control a situation that was already getting out of hand?

CHAPTER SEVEN

A WEEK later, Robyn was sleeping a little more easily, and her fears for herself, and Daniel, had been put on an indefinite hold. Jared had returned to Australia two days before, ostensibly to cancel the lease of his apartment in Sydney and tie up his affairs there. He was also to make arrangements to ship his personal belongings to England. As it was only three weeks to Christmas, Robyn was living in hopes that he would decide to spend the festive season in Australia. He had friends and business colleagues in the city, he had told his father so, and it was reasonable to assume that they would want to give him a suitable send-off. Besides, he was bound to have a more exciting time in Sydney than he would at Saddlebridge, and Robyn welcomed the opportunity it would give her to consider her own alternatives.

She received an unexpected invitation a few days after Jared's departure. Mark Kingsley, the new curate at St Peter's, called on Saturday morning to ask if she would be interested in sharing the production of a Christmas pageant with him. 'Mr Tomlinson says that you once helped my predecessor with a similar project,' he confided smilingly. 'I'd be unfailingly grateful if you could give me some advice.'

Mark Kingsley was some years older than his predecessor and, since his arrival in the parish, he had caused quite a stir among the female members of the Reverend Tomlinson's congregation. The fact that he was of a reasonable height and build, with similarly attractive features, and unmarried, made him a regular choice at dinner parties in the neighbourhood, but so far Robyn's association with him had been limited to a perfunctory introduction by the vicar one morning after service.

Now, meeting his appealing gaze, Robyn was absurdly flattered that he should have taken the trouble to ask her. It was years since any man had regarded her in any other capacity than that of Stephen's wife and, although she guessed he would never have approached her without some encouragement from the Reverend Tomlinson, she was tempted. It would be such a relief to be involved with something so *im*personal, and at least it would give her something else to think about.

'I realise you may not want to participate in any celebrations this year, Mrs Morley,' the curate added diffidently. 'I mean—I know it's only a little over two months since Mr Morley died, and—well, if you do feel you would rather not...'

'Oh, no!' Robyn linked her fingers together, holding her arms close against her midriff. 'That is—I'd be delighted to help you, Mr Kingsley.'

'Mark, please,' he amended quickly. 'And I'm delighted, too. When Arnold—that is, Mr Tomlinson, intimated you might be able to offer me some suggestions, I couldn't believe my luck. I've been in the parish over six months and, apart from seeing you in church once or twice, we've never had the opportunity to meet socially.'

'No.' Robyn made a concerted effort to control the wave of unexpected colour that invaded her cheeks. 'I'm afraid, since my father-in-law's illness, we don't entertain much any more.'

'Or accept invitations,' he inserted shrewdly. 'I did meet the late Mr Morley on occasion, but you weren't with him.'

'No.' Robyn's nails dug into her knuckles. 'Well—when do want to start?'

'How about this evening?' said Mark Kingsley at once, and Robyn's eyes widened in surprise. 'At dinner,' he appended. 'I believe the restaurant at The Stag in Ebbersley does quite a good steak.'

Robyn shook her head. 'Oh, but—I couldn't possibly——'

'Why not?' Mark frowned. 'Oh, I see. It's too soon after your husband——'

'No, it's not that.' Robyn's tongue circled her lower lip. 'I just mean—you don't have to take me out to dinner.'

'But I want to,' he replied lightly. 'I've wanted to ask you for weeks. Too many weeks for my own peace of mind, actually.' He grimaced. 'Please. Say you'll accept.'

Robyn was stunned. She had never dreamt that his enquiry might be anything more than an effort on the Reverend Tomlinson's part to get her involved in outside activities once again. So long as Stephen had been alive, she had avoided village gatherings, not least because she knew people were talking about her. Stephen's activities had been common knowledge for so long, and she had never known who was the more embarrassed by her presence, herself or other people.

But now, to receive this unexpected compliment...She didn't know what to say. 'I—it's very kind of you.'

'It's not kind at all,' declared Mark Kingsley firmly. 'You'd make me very happy if you'd accept. What do you say?'

Daniel's appearance at that moment gave her a welcome pause. Her son came bounding down the stairs into the hall with his usual lack of inhibition, and Robyn took the opportunity to reprove him to give herself time to think.

'Um—this is my son, Daniel, Mr Kingsley—*Mark*!' she amended ruefully. And then, with sudden inspiration, she added, 'I wonder, would it be possible for him to be involved in the pageant? I know he doesn't go to the village school or attend Sunday school at the church, but I'm sure he'd be enthusiastic, wouldn't you, darling?'

'Enthusiastic?' Daniel frowned. 'To do what?'

'Mr Kingsley wants me to help him organise a Christmas pageant at the church,' Robyn explained patiently. 'What do you think?'

'Would I get to dress up?' asked Daniel at once, and Mark Kingsley laughed.

'I should think it's a distinct possibility,' he agreed. 'And I can't see any objections to you bringing him along, Mrs Morley. On the contrary, the more the merrier. Which gives me an idea. How does the prospect of Christmas in Sherwood Forest sound to you, Mrs Morley?'

'Oh—please call me Robyn,' she murmured self-consciously, aware that Daniel was watching their exchange with some interest. 'I—er—yes. Yes, that sounds—interesting.'

'Good. We'll discuss it this evening at dinner,' said Mark happily. 'What time shall I pick you up? Would half-past seven suit you?'

'Um——' Conscious that Daniel's ears had pricked up at this unusual occurrence, Robyn quickly decided to give in. 'Er—yes. Half-past seven sounds—fine. I'll look forward to it.'

'So shall I,' endorsed Mark with some satisfaction. 'OK, I'll see you later then, Robyn. Cheerio, Danny. It's been nice meeting you.'

Curiously, however, when the door had closed behind the curate, Daniel was rather less enthusiastic. 'Why didn't you tell him my name's not Danny, it's Daniel?' he demanded, leading the way into the library. 'You always tell Uncle Jared.'

'Oh, well...' Robyn made an indifferent movement of her shoulders. 'That's not important right now. What is, is that it's going to be fun helping to organise the pageant. I organised one years ago. Long before you were born, actually.'

Daniel frowned. 'I still don't see why you didn't tell him——'

'Because it would have been rude, that's why,' declared Robyn impatiently. 'For heaven's sake, Daniel, can't we get off this subject of what Mr Kingsley called you? Don't you think it will be fun getting dressed up? I shall have to look through the old clothes that are in the attic and see if there's something there we can make into an outfit for you.'

Daniel sniffed. 'Why don't we just buy something?' he asked sulkily. 'Besides, I don't know if I want to be in it. Is that Mr Kingsley going to help you? And why did you say he could call you Robyn?'

Robyn sighed. 'It's I who'll be helping him,' she amended firmly. 'And why shouldn't he call me by my Christian name? I'm not that old, Daniel—no matter what you think.'

'I didn't say you were.'

'No, perhaps not.' Robyn shook her head. 'Anyway, as for buying you something to wear, I don't think that's a very good idea. People don't do that sort of thing. All the children's mummies and daddies join in and improvise costumes—that is, they make them up from odds and ends. You don't want to be the odd one out, do you? And I am capable of producing something fairly decent.'

Daniel flung himself into an armchair and propped his chin on one hand. 'Well, I wish Uncle Jared was here, then I could ask him to join in, too,' he declared gloomily. 'Why couldn't he have just asked someone to send his things here, instead of going all the way to Australia just to pack them himself?'

Robyn went to put another log on the fire. 'It wasn't quite that simple,' she said a little tautly, over her shoulder. 'Uncle Jared has an apartment in Sydney, and—lots of friends to say goodbye to. I expect he'll stay there over Christmas, so there's no question of him being involved in the pageant.'

Daniel sniffed again. 'Knickers!'

'*Daniel!*'

'Well . . .' He was unrepentant. 'I was hoping that during the Christmas holidays he might come sledging with me. Mr McCloud says that he's heard we're going to have a white Christmas. It would have been fun to have someone to play with. Dad never had the time to do anything like that.'

Robyn sucked in her breath. 'Well, you know I'll come sledging with you,' she exclaimed, and Daniel grimaced.

'I know, Mum,' he muttered. 'But it's not the same. All the chaps go with their dads. You know what I mean. Girls aren't the same!'

Robyn forced a faint smile. 'I suppose I should take that as a compliment,' she remarked drily. 'At least you still think of me as a *girl*, not an old lady!'

'Oh, Mum!' Daniel pulled a wry face. 'You're not old. Not really, anyway,' he appended grudgingly. 'But I wish you hadn't said you'd help Mr Kingsley with the pageant. I don't think I like him, and I don't think Uncle Jared will, either.'

'Well, fortunately, what your Uncle Jared thinks or doesn't think is of no concern to me,' declared Robyn, somewhat aggressively. 'And now, I think you ought to go and help Janet organise some lunch. Your grandfather wants me to go over the production figures with him before Monday and, as you and I are going shopping in Sheffield this afternoon, now would seem as good a time as any.'

However, during the next week, Robyn couldn't help the illogical pleasure she got from the suspicion that Jared would not approve of her friendship with Mark Kingsley. Even Ben raised his eyebrows at the news that she was having dinner with Mark for the second time in four days, and although he didn't say anything his attitude spoke volumes.

For her part, Robyn was enjoying herself. Aside from the niggling awareness of Daniel's disapproval, she looked forward to her outings with the curate, and Mark's admiration did wonders for her self-esteem. For years, she had regarded herself as a woman approaching middle age, with nothing to look forward to but Daniel's future. To suddenly find herself the object of an attractive man's attentions restored a small measure of confidence to her, and she found herself looking in shop windows when she and Daniel went into town, studying current fashions in a way she hadn't done for ages.

There was no word from Jared, but Ben was not perturbed. 'He'll be back soon,' was his interpretation of his son's silence. 'Now that things are settled, there's not a lot to write about, is there? It couldn't have worked out better, could it? Imagine him making Daniel his heir! I never would have thought he had it in him.'

Robyn could have said that she had never actually endorsed the new arrangements, but she knew it wouldn't do her any good to make waves. Her compliance had been taken for granted and, until her own plans were finalised, it was easier to keep her own counsel. Besides, when it came to it, it was not going to be easy to thwart the old man. But in six months, Daniel would be old enough to go away to school, and when that happened, it would be a whole different situation.

In the meantime, she could quite see that her friendship with Mark could ease her position considerably. Not that she had any serious interest in him. She didn't. But she did enjoy being made to feel young and attractive again, and, in spite of Daniel's opposition, the plans for the pageant were gradually taking shape.

In the event, Daniel chose not to participate, and Robyn was not entirely convinced that Ben was not responsible. Her father-in-law seemed to take a delight in finding excuses why she shouldn't spend several evenings of the week at the church hall, and in consequence Daniel was often given permission to stay up for supper, just to keep his grandfather happy. It was a form of blackmail, and Robyn knew it, but with Christmas approaching she was inclined to be lenient. After all, if Daniel had been taking part in the pageant, he would have been up anyway, and it would be his birthday soon, and eight seemed considerably older than seven.

A week before the celebration, David McCloud's prediction of a white Christmas seemed to be coming true. It snowed hard all day Tuesday, and when Robyn went out to get into her car to drive home from the mill, she almost lost her balance on the slippery surface of the yard.

'Don't worry,' she assured Joan Hedley, who had followed her down the steps, 'the main roads will be well salted. I just wish we had an indoor car park. It's going to take me fifteen minutes to clear the build-up from the windscreen.'

The road over Saddleford Tor was the most treacherous stretch of the journey, but the conditions had persuaded everyone to drive carefully, and she made it down into the valley without incident. Indeed, she felt quite pleased with herself for having braved the icy roads alone, and she was in no mood to listen to Ben when he argued that she should not go to the church hall that evening.

'If I can drive home from Ebbersley, I can drive the couple of miles into the village,' she exclaimed impatiently. 'Mark's only got a few more days before the performance. I can't let him down when there's absolutely no reason why I shouldn't go.'

Ben sniffed. 'And is that all there is to it?' he asked, voicing his opinion for the first time, and Robyn frowned.

'All there is to what?' she enquired, deliberately misunderstanding him, and Ben regarded her dourly, his blue eyes remote.

'You're not telling me all this enthusiasm you're exhibiting is solely confined to amateur theatricals, are you?' her father-in-law demanded tersely. 'It seems to me, that young curate has more interest in you than he does in the pageant. Do I have to remind you that Stephen's not been dead six months yet? Do you want people to talk?'

Robyn caught her breath, stung by the unfairness of his remarks. 'Talk?' she echoed, controlling the sudden break in her voice. 'Do *I* want people to talk? I think that's a comment you might have offered to Stephen himself, or is there one law for women and another for men?'

Ben had the grace to colour, but he was not repentant. 'I know Stephen had his faults,' he declared. 'None better. But the lad's dead now. Can't we at least try and preserve his memory?'

Robyn's hands clenched. It was the first time in her life she could remember she and Ben having a conversation of this sort, and she realised with a pang that it was the first time she had really gone against his wishes.

'My—friendship, and that's all it is, whatever you think, with Mark Kingsley, in no way despoils my husband's memory,' she replied carefully. 'I cared for Stephen, and I'm sorry he's dead, but no one can pretend we had a normal marriage.'

'That's as may be.' Ben lifted one shoulder dismissingly. 'But don't imagine I'd countenance a *curate*——' and the way he said it was a scathing example of his frustration '—as a fit and proper person to bring up my grandson, because I wouldn't!'

Robyn was tempted to ask what he thought he could do about it, but old habits died hard, and she was loath to continue what was proving to be a most unpleasant conversation. Instead, she excused herself from the supper table and went up to her room to repair her make-up before going out, chafing at the realisation that Ben still thought he could control her life.

It was her own fault, she thought irritably, wiping away the smudge of mascara her shaking hand had left on her cheek. For so long, she had allowed herself to be controlled. In one respect, Jared had been right all those years ago. She had felt obliged to his father, and maybe that was why she had seen Stephen in a different light, instead of seeing for herself the kind of man he was.

Daniel was already in bed, and after saying goodnight to him she let herself out of the house without saying goodbye to her father-in-law. It was his own fault, she told herself grimly, wiping the latest layer of snow from her windscreen before opening the door of the estate car. He had to learn that Stephen's death had set her free in several different ways. Not least, it had given her the right to control her own, and Daniel's, lives, without the spectre of a custody battle should she and Stephen ever have split up.

Driving to the village was hazardous, particularly on the private road that bordered Saddlebridge itself. David McCloud had been out with the snow plough, clearing the roads around the estate, but further falls of snow and an ever-decreasing temperature had left the surfaces icy, and Robyn began to wonder if she hadn't been rather rash, after all.

Still, she refused to go back after what she had said, and Mark's welcome when she got to the church hall more than made up for any doubts she might be nurturing.

'What you need is a hot cup of coffee,' he said, pouring her one himself from the jug set on a Calor gas burner. 'There, that should warm you up. I wondered if you'd get here. It's been such a dreadful day.'

'Yes.' Looking round the sparsely populated hall, Robyn could quite see why he might have had his doubts. At least half the children hadn't turned up, and the chances of producing a realistic rehearsal tonight seemed very remote indeed.

'Well, we can always run through the script again,' declared Mark optimistically. 'Let's hope the snow is going to last. I've got high hopes for the pageant, and I know Mr Tomlinson is expecting a generous contribution from the proceeds for his charity for needy children.'

The rehearsal broke up soon after nine, with most people expressing the opinion that it would be wisest to get home before the roads froze over. Bidding the last group of parents goodbye, Mark gave Robyn a rueful smile, and when they were alone at last he pulled a wry face.

'So much for the dress rehearsal,' he said. 'I'll have to try and get everybody here on Thursday afternoon after school. We can't present the pageant without a proper rehearsal. Do you think you could possibly make it, about four o'clock?'

'I'll try,' promised Robyn, with a smile. 'Don't look so worried, Mark. It's not your fault the weather's turned so wintry. Besides, I can't remember the last white Christmas we had. It's quite romantic.'

'Romantic?' Mark regarded her whimsically. 'Yes, I suppose it is romantic. It's still snowing, you know. How would you feel if we got snowed in?'

Robyn decided it would be wiser not to get involved in a discussion of that sort, and without answering him she reached for her tweed coat. She had bought the coat on her last trip into Sheffield, and she knew its longer length and tightly belted waist complimented her tall, slender figure. Since her involvement in the pageant, she had taken more interest in her appearance, and, although she knew she had Mark to thank for that, she had no wish for him to misinterpret their relationship any more than Ben.

'I think it's time I was leaving, too,' she said, after looping the strap of her bag over her shoulder. 'Ben will worry if I'm late, and after what happened to Stephen...'

'Of course.' Mark was always understanding. 'You will drive carefully, won't you? The roads out there are treacherous.'

'I'll be careful,' Robyn agreed gently. 'See you on Thursday, then. About four o'clock.'

'Until then,' nodded Mark, pulling open the door to allow her to step outside; but the sudden gust of snow that swept into the vestibule of the hall caused Robyn to take an unwary backward step. It brought her up against the solid barrier of Mark's cassock-clad body, and his arms circled her immediately, to save both Robyn and himself.

'I'm sorry,' she gasped, as he kicked the door shut again, and she was able to struggle free. 'It completely knocked me off balance. I hope I didn't hurt you. I'm not usually so clumsy.'

'You didn't hurt me at all,' Mark assured her, reaching out a hand to brush some flakes of snow from her shoulder. 'In fact,' his eyes searched her face, 'I quite enjoyed it. It's been something I've been wanting to do, but I haven't had the nerve until now.'

Robyn caught her breath. 'Oh, Mark——'

'I know. It's too soon after your husband's death. I realise that. But I just want you to know that when you're ready—well, I'll be here for you.'

Robyn shook her head. 'Mark——'

'Please.' He lifted a hand to silence her. 'Don't say anything more right now. Really, I do know about these things. It takes time. I know that. Just—remember I'm here when you feel able to—reciprocate.'

Robyn sighed. She wanted to tell him that, so far as she was concerned, Stephen's recent death had little to do with it, but she was afraid she might shock him. Besides, much as she liked him, she knew she was unlikely to fall in love with him. She was unlikely to fall in love with anybody, she acknowledged ruefully. That particular emotion seemed to have passed her by.

'Thanks,' she murmured at last, realising that until after the pageant it would be easier to leave things as they were. It was a shame, really. She had enjoyed his friendship. But, if Mark was looking for a more serious relationship, she would eventually have to tell him how she felt.

She opened the door herself this time, using the handle to brace herself against the blast of cold air that swept into the hallway. Then, bidding Mark goodnight, she marched determinedly through the snow to where the estate car awaited her. She would be glad to get home she thought. It was getting worse instead of better.

She swept the snow from the windscreen with her hand, shaking the wet flakes from her glove before unlocking the door and getting inside. The engine fired immediately, and she breathed a deep-felt sigh of relief.

Lifting one hand to wave at Mark, who was still standing in the church hall doorway, she put the vehicle into gear, and then offered a silent prayer as she released the clutch.

Instant traction sent the estate car crunching across the cobbled forecourt, and she applauded David McCloud's caution in renewing the tyres at the start of winter. So long as she could keep the car moving, she ought to make it easily, and the roads were so deserted that she was unlikely to encounter any obstacles.

She was turning into the estate when the accident happened. One minute, she had complete control of the vehicle, and the next, the wheels were sliding away from her towards the ditch that ran beneath the hedgerow. She had been in second gear, anyway, and she swiftly changed down in an effort to brake the car, but it was no good. Like a slow-motion replay, the heavy estate car slid sideways towards the hedge, tipping down into the ditch and lurching sickeningly to a halt.

Robyn wasn't hurt, just shocked; but the awareness of the damage to the estate car meant less at that moment than her own unhappy predicament. She was at least a mile and a half from the house—less over the paddock, but she couldn't risk that tonight—with no earthly way of contacting the McClouds, short of walking back to the village to find a phone. And, although the village might be perceptibly nearer, it didn't seem sensible to go back on her tracks, when her chances of reaching Saddlebridge were probably no more hazardous.

In the meantime it was continuing to snow and, realising that every minute she delayed was making her journey that much more difficult, Robyn switched off the ignition, and pushed to open her door.

A few seconds later, she abandoned that attempt, and scrambled across the passenger seat to open the other door. Her door was jammed tight against the side of the ditch, and she knew a little frisson of panic before the passenger door gave in to her feverish pressing.

It wasn't easy clambering out of the car, particularly as the door was heavy and she had to support its weight as she levered herself on to the side. But eventually she succeeded, albeit soaking her thighs and laddering her tights in the process. Allowing the door to slam again, she shuffled down on to the snowy bank.

It was a white world that confronted her, artificially illuminated by the snow. Familiar landmarks were obscured by the all-concealing blanket, and she felt a renewed sense of panic at the daunting walk ahead of her.

Keep calm, she told herself fiercely. She was reasonably equipped for the weather. Her tweed coat was very warm and, although her boots were more fashionable than practical, at least her feet were dry, which was something in her favour.

They weren't dry for long, however. Once she had assured herself that there was no way she could get the estate car out of the ditch again, and had started up the track towards the house, the snow soon seeped through the boots' thin soles. In a matter of minutes she was squelching in water, and her toes felt colder than she could have believed was possible.

Was it possible to get frostbite in the space of a few minutes? she wondered, thrusting her hands deep into the pockets of her coat, and wishing she could do the same with her feet. What if they went numb? Would she still be able to walk? What if she slipped and fell? Would anybody find her? And, if they did, would it be in time to save her?

She was panicking again, and although she kept telling herself that she had nothing to panic about she couldn't quite convince herself that it was true. She thought of Mark at the church hall, only a five-minute walk from the rectory, where he had warm rooms, cared for by Mrs Tomlinson, the vicar's wife. She thought of Ben, probably dozing by the library fire, still resentful of her determination to go against his wishes. And she reluctantly thought of Jared, no doubt sunning himself on some Australian beach, far away from the shivering chill of a typical British winter. Bondi Beach was near Sydney, wasn't it? That was probably where he was. Stretched out on golden sands, with some bikini-clad girl beside him, totally indifferent to her predicament, or her chances for survival.

Survival! Robyn expelled an impatient breath. Her position was not *that* desperate. She was cold and wet, and a little frightened, yes; but not facing a life-or-death situation. She would just be home considerably later than she had anticipated. With a bit of luck, no one would even notice she was missing. It was her own fault, after all, and the last thing she wanted was for Ben to start worrying.

Or was it? Wasn't she secretly hoping someone would start worrying about her? Oh, what she'd give for the sight of the Range Rover, ploughing its way towards her. Or David McCloud himself—another human being!

The sound of the car's engine, when it came to her ears, was partially obscured by the wind, whipping up the snow around her. Indeed, because it came from the opposite direction from which she had anticipated it, she was half inclined to believe it was some hallucinatory distortion of the wind itself. It wasn't until headlights swept the snow ahead of her that she turned to see the vehicle bearing down on her, and then she turned to wave her arms, weak with sudden relief.

Her relief was somewhat modified by the fact that the car was unfamiliar. No one she knew drove a dark-coloured sports saloon, and it wasn't until the car stopped beside her and the door was thrust open from inside that she realised who was driving.

'I—*Jared!*' she exclaimed, grasping the top of the door for support and gazing at him disbelievingly. 'But you—you didn't let us know you were coming back——'

'Get in, Robyn,' he commanded harshly, cutting in on her stammered consternation, and gesturing impatiently with his hand. 'If I stop here much longer, I shan't be able to move either. Do you want that, or do you want a ride home?'

Robyn hesitated only a moment before stumbling across the snow and climbing into the seat beside him.

Time enough to consider what Jared's unexpected return might mean to her when she was warm again. Right now, all she could think of was getting her feet out of their freezing foot bath. Apologising automatically for covering the passenger seat with snow, and the carpet with wet prints, she slumped beside him, letting him take the strain of getting them back to the house.

Yet, in spite of her immediate needs, she couldn't help a sidelong glance in his direction. Jared was back, she acknowledged tensely, and this time it was for good. Her futile hopes of having a normal Christmas at Saddlebridge were melting as fast as the snowflakes clinging to her sleeve. If only she felt more ready to face him, she thought weakly, but once again he had taken the initiative.

'Where have you been?' he asked, as he set the car in motion again, and Robyn felt the warmth of his breath against her cold cheeks.

'To—to the village,' she answered, equally as noncommittally, and she was conscious of him turning to look at her again.

'To the village?' he echoed bleakly. 'What the hell for?'

His anger was steadying, and she clung to it. 'You don't have to swear,' she responded annoyingly. 'Is that how you speak to women in Australia?'

'Don't bait me, Robyn,' he growled harshly. 'Just tell me, who in their right minds would take a car out on such a night?'

Robyn looked at him then, a deliberately insulting stare. Even in the muted glow from the dash, she saw the way his knuckles tightened over the wheel.

'It wasn't snowing like this in London,' he inserted stiffly. 'And I should point out, it's not my car that's wedged into the ditch at the gate.'

Robyn looked away from him then, watching the white flakes driving into the windscreen. 'It wasn't snowing like this when I went out, either,' she declared at last. 'And—and Mark was counting on me.'

'Mark?' She heard the sudden suspicion in his voice, and enjoyed her momentary advantage.

'Yes, Mark Kingsley,' she replied triumphantly, forgetting her physical discomforts for a brief spell. 'He's the new curate at St Peter's. He and I are—friends.'

She had been going to tell him about the pageant, but something, some malicious imp inside her, restrained her from making a full explanation. Let him think what he liked, she thought recklessly. The sooner he learned she had a life apart from the demands of the Morleys, the better.

What she was not prepared for was that her deliberately provoking words would cause him to put an unwary foot on the brake. With terrifying ease, the car went into a sideways skid and, although Jared fought with the wheel, the powerful saloon plunged helplessly into the mound of snow David McCloud had pushed to the side of the road. Its increasing momentum took it solidly into the frozen mountain and, although Jared spent several frustrating minutes trying to get traction on the rear wheels, they were too firmly embedded to move.

It was the last straw to Robyn, who had only just been feeling some return of sensation to her frozen fingers. 'You—you idiot!' she exclaimed, turning to him furiously and beating futilely at the arm nearest to her, still resting on the wheel. 'Don't you know you never brake on ice? Or have you spent so long in a hot climate, it's addled your brain?'

'It's not *my* brain that's addled!' he snarled angrily, lifting his arm so that her fists encountered the hard bone of his wrist. 'Cut that out, for Christ's sake! You're not exactly in a position to trade insults! If you hadn't gone out on some hare-brained date with a creep who ought to know better, I wouldn't have had to pick you up.'

'What do you mean by that? "A creep who ought to know better"?' stormed Robyn in return. 'Are you implying he would have to be a creep to want to go out with me?'

'I didn't say that,' muttered Jared impatiently. 'But, for Pete's sake, Steve's only been dead a little over two months, hasn't he? This Mark's a curate, you say. Doesn't that mean he's supposed to have some respect for the institution of marriage?'

'You—you hypocrite!' exclaimed Robyn incredulously. 'How dare you sit there and criticise Mark, when you have so much respect for the institution of marriage, you didn't think twice about making me your mistress!'

'My mistress!' Jared stared at her in the gloom, his green eyes glittering with sarcasm. 'My God, Robyn, all we did was spend an hour in bed together before you *were* married! That hardly constitutes a major affair!'

'It ruined my life!' retorted Robyn recklessly, and Jared's eyes narrowed.

'So Dan *is* my son,' he declared triumphantly.

'I didn't say that.'

'You didn't have to.' Jared shook his head. 'Well, well, well! Perhaps I'm not so sorry I rescued you after all.'

'This is a *rescue*?' Robyn demanded tremulously, unable to continue the argument in her present state of brittleness. 'How do you propose to get us out of here? Do you have a fork-lift truck hidden in the boot?'

Jared turned and stared out of the windscreen at the obvious disablement of the bonnet, hidden in the mound of snow. 'We'll have to walk,' he said flatly, turning back to her. 'I'm sorry, but there it is. There isn't any alternative.'

'So what's new? enquired Robyn, turning and thrusting open the door at her side of the car. Immediately, a gust of wind and snow swirled into the car, and she shivered. She had hoped to be home and safe, and in a hot bath by this time. As it was, she had at least another half-mile to cover in company with this objectionable man.

As she put her booted feet to the freezing surface of the snow again, Jared swung himself across the seat to join her. Then, hauling a leather jacket from the back of the car, he pulled it on over the sweater and suede jacket he was already wearing.

She set off without waiting for him, leaving him to lock up the car. It was all his fault; everything was his fault, she told herself uncharitably. If it hadn't been for him, she would probably not have got involved in Mark's attempts to organise the pageant; if she hadn't got involved in that, she would not have been driving in these conditions and at this hour of the evening. He was to blame. Jared was to blame. She couldn't wait to get away from him, and everything he stood for.

Even so, after traversing a hundred yards without hearing him catching up with her, she felt compelled to turn and look back. After all, he had rescued her, albeit temporarily, and her conscience wouldn't allow her to completely ignore his presence.

However, when she looked back, he wasn't there. He had disappeared. The expanse of snow she had crossed stretched emptily into the distance, and for an awful, heart-shuddering moment, she thought she had imagined the whole incident. She had heard of people doing things like that, particularly when they were in similar situations. Imagining they were safe and warm, when in reality they were freezing to death.

Her breath caught in her throat. Panic, which had been briefly conquered, rose like bile in the back of her throat. Dear God, she hadn't imagined Jared's return, had she? Surely, at a time like this, he was the last man she should be fantasising about.

Then she gulped. In her panic, she had taken a few steps back the way she had come, and now she could see again the dark mound of the car buried in the snow drift. So, she trembled with relief, no hallucination then, but where was he? Surely she hadn't missed her way, while he had gone and left her?

His sudden reappearance from around the other side of the car brought angry tears to her eyes. Had he been hiding? The sadistic bastard! Had he deliberately concealed himself to give her a mild heart attack? He had almost succeeded, too, she acknowledged unsteadily. She was so cold, she was easily confused, and she guessed he knew her weakness and was deliberately playing on it.

Swinging about again, she ignored his sudden shout, and started back towards the house. Damn him! she cursed bitterly, plunging on through the thickening storm with eyes almost blinded by snow and self-pity. One day she would get even with him; one day she would have the last word. He would never know for sure if Daniel was really his son. That was her secret. That would be her vindication.

She was so intent on planning her revenge that she was totally deaf to Jared's warning shouts behind her. Besides, even if she had heard him, she doubted if she would have paid any attention to him. So far as she was concerned, at that moment Jared was all the monsters in hell, and the devil incarnate, and any warning he might be offering was bound to be a lie.

Consequently, her first intimation of the danger was when Jared grabbed her from behind, jerking her backwards and tumbling her, and himself, into a pile of wet snow. With the breath almost knocked out of her and Jared's weight on top of her, Robyn could hardly mouth the words of complaint that rose furiously inside her. 'How—how dare——' she got out thinly, gulping for air, and Jared levered himself up on his elbows, to look down into her pale, indignant face.

'The mere,' he said, breathless himself, and Robyn felt the resistance seep out of her at his horrifying explanation.

'No!' she said, even so, hardly daring to credit so awful a solution.

He nodded. 'Yes,' he contradicted her tautly, his breathing equally as shallow as hers. He slumped on to her again, as the after-effects of what had so nearly happened swept over him. 'My God,' he muttered, his face pressed into the hollow of her neck, 'I thought I wasn't going to be able to catch you. If you'd walked into the water, I doubt if either of us would have survived to tell the tale!'

'Oh, Jared,' she breathed, weakness overwhelming all else at that moment. Her hand came up and gripped the silky swathe of hair at the back of his neck. 'Jared, I'm sorry. I must have lost my bearings. With the snow covering everywhere, I completely forgot about the mere. Heavens, and it's swollen with all the snow we've been having! If I'd fallen in, you'd never have got me out.'

'I'd have had a bloody good try, or died in the attempt,' retorted Jared, lifting his face again. His green eyes raked her face in a penetrating appraisal. 'You crazy little bitch!' he added, with a return of impatience. 'I have no desire for Dan to inherit for a few more years yet.'

At the mention of her son's name, Robyn's fleeting sense of well-being dispersed. Whereas, moments before, she had scarcely been aware of the snow at her back, or the seeping wetness invading even her underwear, now its coldness penetrated even her skin. She was chilled, both inside and out, and common sense reminded her that just because Jared had saved her from drowning was no reason to believe he was any less determined to destroy her life.

'Let me get up,' she said, withdrawing her hand from his hair, and trying to push him away from her. But Jared seemed unwilling to be shifted.

'Not yet,' he said huskily, continuing to subject her to an unnerving scrutiny. With a growing sense of horror, she felt his cold hand against her cheek.

'Jared——'

'In a minute,' he insisted, allowing his hard knuckles to trail across the dry parchment of her lips. Then, when his thumb followed them, he pressed downward gently, parting her lips and pushing the pad of his thumb inside. He stroked it along the curve of her teeth until they felt as sensitised as the rest of her, and then slid his thumb between, to touch the involuntary participation of her tongue.

'So cold outside, and so warm within,' he murmured, and for a moment she was unable to answer him. 'You know, hearing my father talk about you, I half believed my memory had deceived me. But it hasn't, has it? Whatever the old man says about you being as dried up as an old maid isn't true. That's just his excuse for Steve making out with every available female in the district.'

Robyn gasped, shocked and hurt that her father-in-law should have spoken of her in that way. 'Ben—said that?' she choked, gazing up at Jared with disbelieving eyes, and then caught her breath instinctively as he suddenly bent his head.

His cold mouth touched hers gently at first, but then, feeling her involuntary withdrawal, he deepened the kiss. Pressing her back against the snow, he took possession of her mouth in a way that brooked no opposition, and the persuasive invasion of his tongue sent a heated warmth surging through her veins.

She had forgotten what it was like to be kissed by Jared. She had forgotten how helpless he made her feel, and how impossible it was to fight against him. It was crazy, she knew, and some sane corner of her mind stood back and mocked her foolish weakness, but she couldn't disguise her response to his touch. The coldness she had felt when Stephen had touched her, the downright revulsion she had experienced when Stephen had thrust himself upon her, and which she had come to believe was the legacy of what Jared had done to her, simply melted away beneath the searching hunger of Jared's mouth. The disturbing aggression of his tongue was no violation of her senses. It was a sensual reminder of the physical satisfaction they had once shared, and even through the thickness of their clothes she could feel his swelling arousal.

She was sinking into an imaginary haze of warmth and well-being, where all that mattered was that he should go on, drugging her with his mouth and crushing her beneath the hard pressure of his body, when Jared suddenly drew back from her. Immediately, the real awareness of how chilled she was swept over her, and without his broad protection she was once more exposed to the relentless fury of the storm.

'Come on. Get up,' he said, grasping her arm and hauling her to her feet with little regard for her finer sensitivities. 'If we're not careful, we're both going to die of exposure. Making love in a snowdrift may sound very romantic, but it's bloody cold in practice!'

Robyn pulled herself free of him, brushing snow from her sleeves and skirt with hands that were not quite steady. Would she have let him make love to her then, if he had wanted to? she asked herself incredulously. The answer was too emotive to even consider at the moment. The fact remained, she had let him kiss her, and responded. What price independence now, if he could undermine her will so easily?

'It's this way,' Jared directed, as she continued to avoid his gaze. 'Are you OK? Do you think you can make it? You wouldn't rather stay with the car, while I go for help?'

'No,' she mumbled at last, forcing her numb feet to move. The idea of staying in the comparatively warm car was appealing, but going with him seemed like a sort of penance for betraying herself and her son.

Refusing his offer of assistance, she trudged beside him up the track, following the line of heaped snow David McCloud had cleared earlier. Only dogged determination kept her going, forcing her to put one foot in front of the other over and over again, until the line of copper beeches that marked the beginning of the drive loomed familiarly before them.

'Not far now,' said Jared encouragingly. Chancing a look at him, Robyn saw his hair was white with snow. She probably looked worse than he did, she reflected dourly. Not exactly the image she had hoped to create for his return from Australia!

The sound of an approaching engine heralded David McCloud's arrival with the Range Rover. Seeing the two bedraggled hikers in his headlights, David swiftly brought the heavy vehicle to halt, leaning out to greet them with mild consternation.

'What's happened?' he exclaimed, and Jared gave him a wry look.

'Well, we didn't crash into each other, if that's what you're thinking,' he remarked, ignoring Robyn's instinctive withdrawal and propelling her grimly into the back of the Range Rover. 'But you might say we made similar mistakes,' he added, hauling himself into the seat beside the driver. 'For God's sake, turn this vehicle around and get us home. I'll tell you all the details when my extremities thaw out.'

CHAPTER EIGHT

HALF an hour later, Robyn was sitting in a deep, scented bath, sipping the hot toddy of whisky and water Janet had provided. She felt deliciously warm all over, the unpleasant side-effects of putting frozen limbs into heated water now having completely disappeared. She had washed her hair, too, and it was bound up now inside a heated towel, while the soapy suds of the water coated her emerging shoulders and arms in a concealing mantle of bubbles. She felt content—or almost. The memory of what had happened in the snow was still a painful reminder.

How had it happened? she asked herself impatiently, unable now to conceive how she had succumbed so easily to Jared's unprovoked assault. It wasn't as if the conditions had been conducive to a romantic interlude. She had been cold, and wet, and uncomfortable; and shocked, too, at the realisation of how close she had come to disaster. And yet, as soon as Jared had touched her, as soon as he had bent his head and stroked her helpless lips with his mouth, she had been vulnerable and, no matter how much she might despise herself, she had lost all awareness of her surroundings.

Perhaps the answer was that she had been in a state of ferment already. Perhaps the fact that she had had not one but three shocks in fairly swift succession accounted for her willingness to give in to his lovemaking. After all, she had to have been in something of a daze when she set off into the snow, or she would never have walked towards the mere. The little lake—it was scarcely more than a pond in dry weather—had been providing a haven for ducks and wild birds as long as she could remember, and she must have been confused to lose her bearings so completely.

Nevertheless, whatever the reasons behind her collapse, it *had* happened. For several significant minutes, she had allowed Jared to get beneath her guard and, although she might not care to admit it, if he had chosen to prolong the interlude she might not have been able to prevent it.

And he must know that, she thought uneasily. Just as he also knew that Daniel was his son. He had virtually forced her to admit it, and it would take all her ingenuity to regain the ground she'd lost. She knew better than to take his lovemaking on its face value. It was just another way to gain his own ends. He didn't care about her. He only cared about Daniel.

She shivered a little, in spite of the warmth of the bath, and when the door opened behind her she knew an overwhelming sense of relief to escape from her thoughts.

'Could you make me another one of these, Janet?' she asked, finishing the whisky and holding out her empty glass.

The glass was taken from her hand, but it was not Janet's comforting voice that broke into her reverie. 'I'll get you one myself in a few minutes,' said Jared smoothly, walking casually into her line of vision and looking down at her with a calculating green gaze. 'So—how do you feel now?'

'Will you get out of here?' exclaimed Robyn indignantly, sliding down into the bath so that the swelling curve of her breasts was concealed beneath the soapy water. 'Janet will be back at any moment, and what do you think she'll think if she finds you here?'

'I don't particularly care what Janet thinks——'

'Well, I do!' Robyn was incensed by his arrogance. 'What do you want, anyway? As you can see, I'm quite all right, thank you. If you'd asked Janet, she would have told you.'

'I prefer to see for myself,' declared Jared easily, making no attempt to leave. 'You know,' he tilted his head to one side, 'this is the first time I've seen you in the bath.'

'I should think so.' Robyn was astounded by this conversation. 'Jared——'

'We have to talk,' he said abruptly, setting down the glass and resting his hands alarmingly on the sides of the bath. 'Tonight.'

'I don't think——'

'I don't care what you think,' he said, his tone hardening. 'You've mucked me around long enough, and after what happened tonight——'

Robyn groaned inwardly. 'Yes. Yes—well, I wanted to talk to you about that,' she allowed after a pause. 'I mean——' She raised her eyes to his dark-skinned face and then swiftly lowered them again. 'I—I hope you didn't get the—the wrong impression.'

'Could I do that?' he countered softly, though there was no tenderness in his voice. 'As I recall it, you weren't exactly averse to what occurred.'

Robyn caught her breath. 'I was—startled. I didn't know what I was doing——'

'Like hell!'

'I didn't.' Robyn was compelled to look at him again, and her breathing quickened at the raw frustration burning in his eyes. All trace of compassion had disappeared, and they were facing one another as aggressively as they had done the night he had told his father his conditions for staying at Saddlebridge. 'I didn't!'

'Well, let's see, shall we?' he grated, and, before she realised his intentions, he had grasped her shoulders and hauled her up out of the water. Then, careless of what her wet, soapy body would do to the grey silk shirt and darker grey cord trousers he was wearing, he lifted her bodily into his arms and carried her into the adjoining bedroom.

'Let me go!' she exclaimed, struggling frantically to free herself, but the life Jared had led had more than prepared him to deal with a hysterical woman's protests, and all she succeeded in doing was drawing his attention to the exposed fullness of her breasts. Creamy-soft and pink-tipped from the bath, they brushed persistently against the front of his shirt, and he would not have been human if he had not been aware of it.

'Calm down,' he advised her thickly, his arm hard beneath the curve of her thighs. 'Or I'll think you want me to do something about it,' he added, and she immediately went limp.

'But this is ridiculous!' she whispered helplessly, as he deposited her with less care than a sack of potatoes in the middle of her bed. 'Jared, what do you think you're doing?'

'I should have thought that was obvious,' he retorted, crawling on to the bed beside her. He knelt over her, supporting himself with a hand at either side of her head. 'This is where we left off, isn't it?'

'No——'

'I think it is,' he insisted softly, but there was no warmth in his voice. On the contrary, she had the distinct impression that, in spite of his contention, he had only contempt for what he was doing.

Yet, when he bent his head to rub his cheek along the curve of her breast she couldn't deny the involuntary quiver that assailed her. Far from wanting to push him away, she had the almost irresistible urge to arch herself towards that tantalising caress, and when the slight roughness of his jaw grazed her nipple, she knew a shuddering ache of longing curl in the pit of her stomach.

Consequently, she didn't move when he drew one exploring finger down the dusky hollow between her breasts, and then continued on to her navel. With a tight hold on her emotions, she watched his cool gaze follow his enquiring finger, noticing his eyes linger longest on her breasts and on the inky black triangle of silky curls that marked the gateway to her womanhood.

'You know, if I were to judge from the clothes you wear and the way you behave, I could be forgiven for believing what Dad said,' he muttered with sudden impatience. 'But he doesn't know you as I know you, does he, Robyn? You're just as beautiful as I remember. And God knows, I've thought about you like this, ever since I went away.'

His words were briefly sobering, and she struggled to find the right way to appeal to him. 'Your father doesn't know anything!' she cried. 'Not from me, at least. I've kept your secret all these years. Why, in heaven's name, are you tormenting me now?'

But she had been wrong to talk of secrets. 'Yes,' he said, loosening the buttons of his wet shirt and tugging it out of his trousers. 'You're pretty good at keeping secrets, aren't you? But you betrayed yourself this evening, Robyn. For once I got you to tell the truth.'

'What—what truth?' she stammered, playing for time, while the sight of his lean brown body, gleaming in the lamplight, aroused all sorts of crazy thoughts inside her. His chest was muscled and smooth and only lightly traced with hair, the nipples standing so taught and erect that she longed to reach out and touch them.

'About Dan,' he reminded her tautly, tossing his shirt aside and lowering his chest to rub himself sensuously against her breasts. 'About my son,' he added, his voice muffled in the hollow of her neck. 'Go on, Robyn, tell me whose son he is now.'

'Jared...' With his tongue stroking the sensitive skin behind her ear, Robyn was finding it incredibly difficult to say anything and, giving in to a totally uncontrollable surge of feeling, her hands grasped the hair that curled at his nape, to drag his head up so that she could look into his face. His eyes were not calculating now, nor objective; they were glazed with emotion, and her own gaze fell before the fervent urgency of his.

'Do it,' he said, as if reading her thoughts. 'Kiss me, Robyn. You know you want to, and God help me! I want it, too.'

But still she hung back, and it was left to Jared, with a groan of impatience, to capture her face between his two hands and bring her quivering lips to his.

She clung to him then, her hands fastened round his wrists, as he delivered a series of open-mouthed caresses, that aroused but did not satisfy her. Each time his mouth left hers, she moaned in protest, and eventually she was compelled to release his wrists, and wind her arms around his neck.

Then it was Jared who took control. With sure, impatient fingers, he unwound the towel from her hair, so that its silken dampness tumbled about her shoulders in wanton abandon. Shifting back on his knees, he unbuttoned the waistband of his trousers and tore down the zip, turning on to his side to press the corduroy material down below his knees.

'Help me,' he commanded, dragging her trembling hands to his body. Hardly aware of what she was doing, acting purely on instinct, Robyn turned him on to his back beside her and buried her face in the flat hollow of his stomach.

'Christ, Robyn,' he muttered, kicking himself free of his trousers and reversing their positions. 'Don't you know better than that? How much do you think I can take?'

'I—thought you wanted me,' she breathed unsteadily, and with a groan of anguish Jared closed his eyes.

'I do want you, damn you!' he swore savagely, and parting her legs, he thrust himself into her. 'Too bloody much!' he muttered seconds later, and she felt his shuddering climax and the warmth of his seed inside her.

The sudden cessation of movement, without any conceivable advantage to her, was depressingly familiar. It might be years since Stephen had touched her, but the memory of her own inability to respond was as sharp as ever. She was incapable of feeling anything, she thought bleakly, and the fleeting belief she had had that it might be different this time was just so much wishful thinking.

A tear squeezed its way out of her tightly closed lids and trickled miserably down her cheek. The heated emotion of moments before had all dissipated, and all she felt now was shame and humiliation. It was all so horribly sordid, and she despised herself for allowing it to happen.

Her tear rolled inexorably towards Jared's shoulder, for he was slumped across her, and she was too late to prevent it from touching him. Instead, he felt its moist progress and, as it alerted him to her presence, he groaned.

'I'm sorry,' he grunted, levering himself up on his elbows, and Robyn turned her hot face aside from his belated pity.

'You had been warned,' she said bitterly, and with a muffled expletive Jared captured her chin in one hand and turned her face back to his.

'What do you mean?'

'What do you think I mean?' she countered, keeping her lids lowered. 'I'm sure your father told you. Stephen wouldn't keep that to himself.'

'What?' Jared was impatient. 'For Christ's sake, what are you talking about?'

'Don't pretend you don't know.' Robyn dragged her chin out of his hand. 'You've just proved it. I don't enjoy sex. I never have. Need I say more?'

Jared caught his breath. 'You're joking!'

'I wish I were.'

Jared shook his head. 'I don't believe it. Minutes ago, you were as hot as I was.'

'Minutes ago, yes.'

'Yes. And I blew it,' agreed Jared, staring angrily down at her. Then, comprehension causing a deep line to appear between his eyes, he gasped, 'Hey, you really don't know what you did, do you?'

'What *I* did?' Robyn looked at him then, and the dawning amusement in his eyes filled her with hot embarrassment. 'Why, you——'

But the hand she would have raised to rake his chest, he captured in his and brought to his lips, his tongue finding the sensitive centre of her palm. 'Oh, Robyn,' he said huskily, 'don't you know it was my fault that you didn't make it? I was to blame. I lost control. When you—well, when you touched me, I just lost my head. I'm sorry.'

Robin quivered. 'You don't understand. Stephen and I—that is, I never—I never have——'

'Never?' Jared's eyes narrowed. 'Except once, hmm?'

Robyn looked away from him again, her face burning. 'I don't remember.'

'Then perhaps I'd better remind you,' said Jared thickly, and when she would have twisted away from him he imprisoned her between his thighs and sought her trembling mouth once again.

This time, he invited her to touch him and, although at first Robyn was unwilling to do so, his hungry, demanding kisses soon brought her to the brink of the unknown territory she had so briefly glimpsed before. His stroking fingers took possession of her body, and with his hands finding every nerve, palpitating beneath her skin, and the warm male smell of him in her nostrils, it seemed the most natural thing in the world for her to reach for him, too. Her hands skittered from the sweat-moistened expanse of his chest to the thickening arc of hair that arrowed down below his narrow waist, finding the hard, muscled contours of his thighs overwhelmingly appealing.

'Gently,' he groaned, moving out of her grasp so that he could find the tantalising dip of her navel with his tongue. 'This is for you, not for me.'

'Is it?' she breathed, her hands tangling in his hair, pressing his face against her stomach. Jared uttered a muffled laugh.

'Well, maybe not entirely,' he breathed, his laughter disappearing as he sought her mouth once again. Then, with a trembling sense of apprehension, she felt him sliding inside her once again.

But, this time, it was different. This time, there was no swift cessation of movement. This time, Jared measured his length inside her in steady, even strokes, so that in no time at all Robyn was moving with him, matching her movements to his, and hearing the panting sound of her own breathing echoing hollowly in her ears.

'Good?' he asked unsteadily, as her nails dug into the skin of his shoulders, and she could only nod incoherently. 'Just let it come,' he added, taking one of her taut, swollen nipples in his mouth, and with a shuddering sensation that swept from her thighs through every nerve and extremity of her body, she felt the miracle happening. The incredible, unbelievable swells of pleasure were sweeping over her in ever-increasing peaks, lifting her, lifting her, higher and higher, until a sensation of total fulfilment enveloped her. She was hardly aware of Jared's simultaneous release, or of the bone-crushing weight of his satiated body on hers. She was in a blissful lagoon of sensuous languor, with the barely acknowledged awareness that he was responsible . . .

It was the sound of someone next door, in the bathroom, letting the water out of the tub, that disturbed them. And even then, Robyn was in too bemused a state to fully appreciate what the sounds meant. But Jared must have realised it was Janet, and with a swift, jack-knifing movement he hauled himself off the bed and pulled on his cord trousers. Robyn stirred protestingly as he swept the quilt from under her and covered her with it, but, by the time she had comprehended exactly what was going on, Jared had picked up his shirt and was letting himself out of the door.

It wasn't a moment too soon. As Robyn reluctantly pushed herself up on her elbows, Janet came to the half-open bedroom door, putting her head round the panels to regard her mistress quizzically.

'Are you all right?'

Robyn felt the warm colour stain her cheeks. 'I—yes. Shouldn't I be?'

'It's just that it's not like you to get into bed without drying your hair first,' remarked Janet drily. 'I wondered if you'd felt ill, or something.'

'Oh! No.' Robyn shook her head, aware as she did so of the wild tangle of her hair, loose about her shoulders. She put up a nervous hand and touched it experimentally. 'I did—dry it with the towel,' she murmured, unhappily, sure Janet would see through any excuses she might make. 'I was just—tired, I suppose.'

'Mmm.' Janet's expression was hard to read. 'Oh, well, so long as you're all right.' She grimaced. 'You know, you should wear your hair loose more often. With you living in this house with only an old man and a child for company, I sometimes forget you're still a young woman. But looking at you now—well, I'd say you looked younger than Jared.'

Robyn's face burned, but she was sure now that Janet's remarks were not as innocent as they appeared. Had the housekeeper seen her with Jared? Had she put her head round the door a few minutes earlier and seen them together? Robyn's pulses raced, and a sheen of sweat glazed her upper lip at the images that her mind created. Yet what would have been more natural but that Janet should check that she had finished in the bathroom, before letting the water out of the tub? And just now her sharp ears must have picked up the sound of Jared's departure, and that had enabled her to make her entrance with every appearance of confidence.

Robyn flopped back against her pillows and regarded the housekeeper doubtfully. 'You know, don't you?' she said unhappily, the excitement she had felt when Jared had made love to her rapidly disappearing. She felt empty suddenly, and not a little appalled at her own shameless behaviour. Maybe if Jared had still been there, she would not have felt so bad. But he had gone. He had done what he had come to do, and left her to face the consequences. What had been such a source of delight was rapidly turning into something sordid.

Janet was looking a little flustered now, and Robyn knew a moment's malicious satisfaction at someone else's embarrassment. Then decency reasserted itself and, tucking the quilt securely beneath her arms, she made a dismissing gesture.

'Don't answer that,' she murmured quickly. 'I—it's nothing to do with you, I know. Um—thank you for tidying up the bathroom. That—er—that whisky and water you brought me, it really was very welcome.'

Janet nodded, looking somewhat relieved. But then, as if Robyn's words had given her an opportunity to say something else, she hesitated. 'We—that is, David and I—we always had a soft spot for Jared, you know.'

Robyn expelled a weary breath. 'I know.'

'What I mean is—that's not to say we would condone anything he did.'

Robyn tried to smile. 'No?'

'No.' Janet caught her lower lip between her teeth. 'Look, Robyn, this may be none of my business——'

'I agree.'

'—but, well—if you and Jared were thinking of getting together, I couldn't be more pleased, and I know David——'

'We're not,' said Robyn baldly.

Janet blinked. 'You're not?'

'No.' There was an almost masochistic delight in shocking the other woman.

'I see.'

'I'm sorry.' Robyn's lips felt stiff and unnatural as she said the words. 'Naturally, I'm grateful that he was around tonight——' *and let her make what she liked of that!* '—but, as you inadvertently pointed out, Jared is a little young for me.'

'I didn't say that,' protested Janet forcefully, but Robyn had heard enough.

'I'm sorry,' she said again, turning on to her side and curling her arm beneath her head on the pillow. 'And I am—very tired. Do you mind?'

For a moment, she thought Janet was going to stand her ground and say something more, but presently she heard a muffled 'Goodnight' and the door between the bedroom and the bathroom closed with a distinct click.

'Goodnight,' Robyn echoed miserably, burying her face in the pillow, and the tears she had shed earlier were nothing compared to the storm of weeping that swept over her then.

CHAPTER NINE

ROBYN had a surprisingly good night, considering her state of mind. But the exhaustion of her walk in the storm—and the lingering lethargy of Jared's love-making—had combined to overwhelm her mental distraction. In consequence, she slept like a baby, and awoke with a feeling of well-being totally out of context in the prospect of the day facing her.

Nevertheless, she got up with a sense of purpose, determining not to allow Jared any advantage because of the previous night's events. She would show him she could take what had happened in her stride, and that, whatever his intentions had been, she was as resolute as ever that he should get no confirmation of Daniel's parentage from her. She had not forgotten his attitude towards her when he first came home from Australia, and she was no longer naïve enough as to imagine that, just because he had made love to her, he had any real liking for her. He was using her, that was all. He was determined to get concrete proof that he was Daniel's father, and until he did he was unscrupulous enough to use any means at his disposal to achieve his ends.

All the same, it was galling to remember how weak she had been. Their lovemaking might have been the spontaneous result of a series of events, but from Jared's point of view it could not have been more conveniently timed. He had caught her unprepared and unsuspecting, and because he had such a devastating effect on her senses, she had been unable to resist him.

Still, looking at what had happened more positively, it had proved she was not the sexual freak she had always thought herself. She did have feelings, normal feelings; she *could* respond. Maybe she was not entirely to blame

135

because Stephen had failed to arouse her. Maybe he had not been the right man for her. With someone else, someone like—well, Mark, for example, she might feel completely different.

She was cleaning her teeth when she heard someone in her bedroom, and her heart skipped a beat for a moment before she heard Daniel's tentative, 'Mum? Mum, are you in there?'

Immediately, she rinsed her teeth and grabbed for a towel, blotting her mouth as she opened the bathroom door. 'Hi,' she said, stepping into the bedroom and giving her son a warm smile. 'How are you this morning?'

'I shan't be able to go to school again,' announced Daniel, by way of an answer, and Robyn automatically moved to the window and swept the curtains aside. She had been so engrossed in her personal problems, she hadn't given a thought to the weather, but now she looked out on a snow-covered world, brilliantly white beneath a blue sky.

'Mr McCloud says it will take at least until lunch time to get the roads cleared,' Daniel added, joining her at the window. 'Can I go out and build a snowman, Mum? The forecast says the cold weather isn't going to last, and I'd really like to make one before the snow melts.'

Robyn ruffled his hair. 'I suppose so,' she said, noticing he had already dressed in jeans and a wool sweater. 'You look as if you had already anticipated my answer. No school uniform, hmm?'

'Well...' Daniel had the grace to look slightly shame-faced. 'Uncle Jared said he was sure you wouldn't mind.'

The muscles in Robyn's face stiffened. 'Uncle Jared?' she echoed bleakly, and Daniel groaned.

'You're not going to be mad at Uncle Jared again, are you, Mum?' he pleaded. 'According to Janet, he——'

'Mrs McCloud,' corrected Robyn automatically, and her son sighed.

'OK. According to Mrs McCloud, then,' he said exaggeratedly, 'Uncle Jared practically saved your life last night.' His eyes gleamed. 'Is that right, Mum? Did he really pull you out of a snow drift? Jan—I mean, Mrs McCloud said you crashed the estate car, and you had to walk nearly all the way from the village.'

'Mrs McCloud exaggerates, too,' retorted Robyn irritably, leaving the window to rummage through her drawers for some clean underwear. 'I didn't crash the car; it just skidded into a ditch. And I was only about a mile from home when it happened.'

'But Uncle Jared did rescue you, didn't he?' Daniel persisted, and Robyn lifted her head impatiently to look at him.

'He picked me up in his car, yes,' she agreed levelly. 'And then he ran his car off the road, too. I'd say it was arguable who saved who. You can tell your Uncle Jared that, next time he starts bragging about his heroics!'

'But it wasn't Uncle Jared who told me,' protested Daniel, staring at her frustratedly. 'I've told you. It was Janet—oh, Mrs McCloud!'

'And who told her?' enquired Robyn tautly. 'Your Uncle Jared, of course.'

'No, it wasn't.' Daniel was determined to defend his hero at all costs. 'It was Mr McCloud, actually. He said you must have almost walked into the mere. He's been out already, with the snow plough, you see, and he said you were lucky to be alive. He found your scarf—you know, the one you were wearing when you went out last night—sticking out of a pile of snow near the lake. He said you must have fallen into it, and that Uncle Jared must have pulled you out.'

Robyn's lips tightened. It was too near the truth for her to want to argue, but that didn't stop her from feeling irritated that Jared should once again have glorified himself in her son's eyes.

'And what did Uncle Jared say to that?' she asked, curious in spite of herself, but Daniel only shook his head.

'He wasn't there,' he declared carelessly. 'He didn't come down until later.' And then, as if he had only just noticed her appearance, he let out a whooping yell. 'Hey, Mum! What did you do to your hair last night? Did the snow get at it or something? You look like you went in for one of those Afro cuts, honestly!' He grinned. 'I like it. It's really neat.'

Robyn, who had scarcely glanced at her reflection this morning, for fear of what she might see, now took a good look at herself in the mirror. Daniel's idea of what was or was not 'neat' was not hers, and she gazed, appalled, at the sight that confronted her. Generally, she either secured her hair in a hairnet or plaited it in a braid to go to bed, but last night it had been barely dry when she lay down to sleep, and this morning the result of that was, unfortunately, plainly evident. She looked, as the old saying went, as if she had been dragged through a hedge backwards, and in spite of the colour in her cheeks, she thought she looked more like a witch than ever.

'My God!' she exclaimed, putting up a hand to touch the tangle of black hair that rioted round her head. 'I look like nothing on earth, Daniel! How can you even suggest that it looks *neat*?'

'Well—it looks all right,' protested Daniel defensively. 'It makes you look—nicer, *younger*.'

'Really?' Robyn wondered if a conspiracy had been formed to annoy her. 'Well, as soon as I can get a brush through it, I intend to wear it the way I always do. I am not a teenager, Daniel, I'm your mother! I have no intention of going around looking like some university drop-out!'

'What's a university drop-out?' enquired Daniel, frowning, but Robyn was in no mood now to satisfy him.

'Let's hope you never find out, hmm?' she suggested, urging him towards the door. 'Go along now, make your snowman, if you must. I want to get dressed.'

'But you're not going to work today, are you?' Daniel persisted, as he reached the doorway. 'Grandpa says that Saddleford Tor will be really dangerous. Perhaps you could come and make a snowman, too.'

'Perhaps,' said Robyn, non-committally, thinking that if Jared was involved, she'd rather not be. And yet, wouldn't staying out of his way convince him that she was afraid to face him again? And, while that might be true, she couldn't allow him to know it.

'Oh, great!' Daniel exclaimed delightedly, charging off along the corridor with his usual disregard for property, and Robyn closed her door. Oh, to be as young and irresponsible as that again, she thought wistfully, leaning back against the panels. Had she ever been that young? she pondered. These days, it was difficult to believe so.

By the time she had brushed her hair and restored it to order, and dressed in one of her business outfits of hound's-tooth check skirt and beige wool sweater, she felt more equipped to face the day. Her smooth complexion revealed none of the anxious thoughts that still plagued her mind, and as she descended the stairs she was almost convinced that nothing Jared said, or did, could upset her.

The table in the morning-room was still laid for breakfast, with a half-full jug of orange juice sharing the honours with a pot of coffee, keeping warm over a low flame. But although Robyn could see her son through the window, making his snowman in the garden, there was no sign of her adversary, either at the breakfast table or outside. After helping herself to a cup of coffee, Robyn carried it through to the library.

As she had expected, her father-in-law was already in his position by the fire. Although, immediately after his stroke, Ben had had a full-time nurse to take care of him, these days he managed to look after himself with the help of the McClouds, grumbling about the regular health visitor, who insisted on keeping an eye on his progress.

Robyn half expected Jared to be with his father, and her frown mirrored her confusion that he was not. 'Um—good morning,' she murmured, allowing her tense nerves to relax once again. 'I—er—isn't Jared here? I—well, I thought he would be.'

'Telling me what a fool you made of yourself last night?' suggested Ben drily, looking up from the news-paper he was reading. 'I warned you about going out, but you wouldn't listen to me.'

Robyn sighed. 'It could have happened to any-one——'

'It *needn't* have happened to you,' retorted Ben, folding the paper and putting it aside. 'Do you realise, if Jared hadn't had the foresight to ring McCloud from London, no one might have noticed you were missing until it was too late? You didn't even come and say you were leaving.'

'Do you blame me?' Robyn walked to the window, and stared out at the snow. 'Anyway, you obviously know all about it. I'm sorry if I upset you. But you can't run my life for me, Ben. I have to make my own mistakes.'

'So you admit that it was a mistake, then? Going out with Kingsley, I mean?'

'No.' Robyn turned, coffee-cup raised to her lips. 'And I didn't go out with Mark, as you know. I just went to the rehearsal at the church hall, that's all.'

Ben grunted. 'You're not thinking of getting involved with him, then?'

Robyn gasped. 'That's my affair!'

'It's mine, too. And Jared's.'

'Jared's?' Robyn swallowed, stiffening. 'Do you mind explaining that?'

'Well, naturally it's of some concern to him if you're thinking of giving Daniel a stepfather. After all, if he's to make the boy his heir, he doesn't want some prissy curate filling Daniel's head with his ideas of how the mill should be run.'

'Oh! Oh, I see.' Robyn struggled to sustain her anger, but it wasn't easy when relief that Jared had not ap-parently betrayed her to his father was overwhelming all other emotions. 'Well, if—and I say *if*—that time ever comes, I'll be sure and let you both know well in advance,' she declared huskily. 'So,' she lifted her shoulders with the appearance of confidence, 'where is he?'

'Who? Jared?' She knew he knew exactly who she meant, and she remained silent. 'Well,' Ben was enjoying his moment of power, 'where else would he be on his first morning back? He's gone to the mill, of course. Where you'd be, I dare say, if you'd still been nominally in charge.'

The 'nominally' hurt, but Robyn ignored it. 'Do I take it my services there are no longer required?' she asked steadily, and Ben looked a little ashamed.

'No,' he said irritably. 'No, I should think Jared would be glad of your participation until the New Year, at least. But—well, you might as well know, Woodhouse has found some discrepancy in the figures. It looks as if—someone's been systematically defrauding the company, and Jared knows he's going to have to sort it all out.'

Robyn caught her breath. 'When did you find out?'

'As soon as Jared took charge. Old Maurice couldn't wait to tell him. Apparently, he'd mentioned the matter to you, but you'd just put him off.'

Robyn's jaw sagged. 'He didn't——'

'Well, anyway, Jared will get things straight.' Ben sighed. 'Don't look like that, Robyn. No one's accusing you. And you couldn't be expected to notice anything was wrong. You're not an accountant, are you?'

Robyn stared at him. 'What—what exactly did Maurice Woodhouse say?' she demanded.

'I don't know.' Ben was clearly unwilling to get into a discussion about it. 'For heaven's sake, Robyn, it's probably something and nothing! You know what old Maurice is like. He always did exaggerate.'

Robyn's lips trembled. But it wasn't with trepidation, it was with anger. *She* should have warned Jared of what she had found. She should have spoken to him before Maurice Woodhouse had the chance to enhance his reputation. Instead of imagining she had been the only person capable of detecting the discrepancies, she should have brought the matter up with Woodhouse himself.

Maybe he would have had more respect for her if he had known she had noticed the errors. As it was, he probably thought she was too stupid to read figures, and he had told Jared he had spoken to her to cover his own lack of confidence in her.

'Anyway,' continued Ben placatingly, 'I suppose you could hardly be expected to go in to the office today. McCloud says the front suspension of your car may be damaged. He's going to tow it into the garage as soon as the roads are cleared. It's best to have it examined; just in case there's anything wrong.'

Robyn pressed her now-empty cup between her palms. 'So how am I supposed to get about in the meantime?' she enquired in a tight voice.

'Well, you could always get a lift with Jared,' suggested Ben tentatively. 'It will only be for a few days, I should imagine. Unless you think he can manage without you.'

Robyn's nostrils flared. 'Is that what you think?'

Her father-in-law sighed. 'I think you're getting emotional, Robyn,' he declared, his agitated massage of the arm of his chair exhibiting his own tension. 'Would you ask Janet to get me some more coffee? I think this conversation has gone far enough.'

Robyn was tempted to ask him how she could be getting emotional when, according to what he had told Jared, she was just a dried-up old stick; but she thought better of it. Ben was a sick old man, after all, whatever his faults might be. And it wasn't anything to do with him that she felt so damnably helpless.

A slow thaw set in during the afternoon, and Janet informed Robyn that David had managed to pull her car out of the ditch and tow it into the garage in the village. With a bit of luck, there would be nothing seriously wrong with it, she thought, contenting herself with doing the household accounts, and writing some letters she had been putting off. The last thing she wanted was to have to ride to work with Jared, but until this matter of the company accounts was settled she knew that, whatever Ben said, she couldn't abandon her responsibilities.

Daniel had a fine day playing in the snow and, when he could eventually be persuaded to come indoors, he had a glowing, healthy colour. 'You should have come out, too, Mum,' he said, tucking into the plate of sandwiches Janet had provided for afternoon tea. 'Honestly, Grandpa, it was really great! And Mr McCloud says there could be some more snow tomorrow.'

'That's not what I heard,' said Robyn tolerantly, watching her son to avoid looking at her father-in-law. Although they had patched up their relationship at lunch time, she couldn't forget what had been said that morning. It was as she had feared, from the minute she learned that Jared was coming home. Nothing was ever going to be the same again. And, in spite of her resentment towards Jared for instigating those doubts, she couldn't help wondering if her position in this house had simply been a figment of her imagination.

The sound of the doorbell was a vaguely welcome distraction. Perhaps it was the garage, delivering her car, Robyn thought hopefully, looking towards the door. But, when Janet came to announce the visitor, it was not Sam Pearson who was waiting in the hall. 'It's Mr Kingsley, Robyn,' she said, glancing awkwardly over her shoulder. 'Shall I show him into the morning-room? I've not had the radiators on in the sitting-room.'

Before Robyn could speak, however, Ben intervened. 'No, show Mr Kingsley in here, Janet,' he exclaimed, twisting round in his chair. 'And fetch another cup. I expect the fellow won't say no to a cup of tea.'

Robyn got to her feet. 'Really, Ben, I——'

'What's the matter, Robyn? You're not ashamed of me, are you?' chided Ben ironically. Before she could denounce that thought, Mark came diffidently into the room.

'I say,' he said apologetically, 'if I've come at a difficult time——'

'Not a bit of it,' said Ben, gesturing with his good hand for Mark to take a seat. 'Daniel, offer Mr Kingsley a sandwich, there's a good chap. So, young man, how are you? Robyn tells me you're doing your best to put on a Christmas show.'

'A pageant, yes,' said Mark enthusiastically, evidently finding no difficulty in understanding what Ben had said. He took the seat he had been offered, but refused the sandwich a sulky Daniel unwillingly offered. 'With your daughter-in-law's help, of course,' he added gallantly. 'I don't think I could have managed without her valuable assistance.'

Robyn bent her head, refusing to acknowledge Mark's friendly salutation. She was still stunned by Ben's uncharacteristic show of cordiality. Usually, he avoided visitors like the plague, particularly well meaning ones, who were likely to sympathise with his condition.

'I'm sure Robyn's been a great help,' Ben was saying now, and Robyn could feel his eyes upon her. 'Of course, she hasn't been out much since Stephen's funeral. My son's death came as a terrible shock to all of us.'

'Of course.' Mark was suitably chastened, but the return of Janet with another cup and saucer and a fresh pot of tea rather spoiled the effect Ben was hoping to have, Robyn thought uncharitably.

'And how are you, sir?' Mark continued, when the housekeeper had departed, bringing a brief scowl of displeasure to the old man's features. Discussing his own health was not so amusing as using Mark to bait his daughter-in-law, and Robyn waited expectantly for the gruff dismissal she was sure was to come.

But to her surprise, Ben didn't respond in the way she had expected. 'Oh, I manage,' he said, adopting an air of pathos Robyn had never seen before. 'But, naturally, I rely on Robyn for companionship, and I have to say that, since she's become involved in this little production of yours, I've missed her. I really have.'

So that was it! Robyn stared at him resentfully. The old devil! He had invited Mark in, deliberately, to appeal to his sympathies. He was evidently not above doing that, if it meant he got his own way.

'But I understood your younger son was home,' Mark inserted now, and Robyn delightedly applauded his perception. She had expected Ben would have it all his own way, and it was reassuring to hear someone else defend her right to freedom.

However, Ben was not defeated so easily. 'Oh, Jared, you mean,' he said ruefully. 'Yes, he is home, as you say. But, unfortunately, since my elder son died, the mill has been left in rather inexperienced hands, and I think it's going to take Jared some time to put everything to rights.'

As Robyn seethed at this unwarranted criticism, Mark seemed to accept defeat. 'Oh, well, if Mrs Morley's absence is causing any trouble——'

'It's not,' put in Robyn flatly. Ignoring Ben's, and Daniel's, disapproving stares, she managed a smile. 'My father-in-law's only teasing you, Mark,' she added, flashing Ben a dare-to-contradict-me glance. 'If you only knew how independent he really is, you'd be amazed! And, as for needing my company—well, usually it's me who seeks him out.'

'Is that so?' Mark's relief was palpable, but Ben's hand had begun its familiar kneading of his chair arm. Maybe she was being mean in neglecting him, Robyn found herself worrying automatically. But then she remembered how Ben had disparaged her efforts at the mill, and hardened her heart. If she was ever going to make a life for herself, she had to start now. If she let the situation slide again, she might never find the strength to break away.

'Anyway, I really called to assure myself that you'd not suffered any ill effects from last night's little accident,' Mark added, surprising her once again. 'I met Mr Morley's chauffeur in Saddleford this morning,' he continued, explaining how he had come by that information. 'He said that you had had to walk some distance through the snow. I was appalled.'

'If you'd had anything about you, you wouldn't have allowed her to drive home alone,' retorted Ben, abandoning any further efforts to win sympathy, and Robyn sighed.

'Mark could hardly drive home with me,' she protested, and then broke off abruptly at the sound of voices in the hall outside.

'It's Uncle Jared! It's Uncle Jared!' exclaimed Daniel, his sullen expression leaving him as he ran towards the door. 'We're in here, Uncle Jared,' he yelled, jerking the door open, and Robyn met her father-in-law's amused gaze with unconcealed frustration.

Jared walked into the library without any self-consciousness, while Robyn had the utmost difficulty in even remaining where she was. She would have much preferred their first meeting since what had happened the night before to have been in private, but once again her wishes had to be subjugated to her brother-in-law's. It didn't help that in his dark three-piece suit and pale grey shirt he looked more attractive than ever; and the crisp bite of the wind had added colour to his dark face, extending his impact of healthy arrogance.

His eyes immediately sought Robyn's but, although she was aware of their appraisal, she refused to acknowledge them. In all honesty, she couldn't trust herself not to betray the painful embarrassment she was feeling, and instead she concentrated on Mark, trying to gauge his reaction to the other man.

'This is Mr Kingsley, from St Peter's,' said Ben at last, when it became obvious that Robyn was not about to make the introduction, and Jared's faintly quizzical expression lifted.

'Ah, yes, the new curate,' he remarked, and the way he said it made Robyn's blood boil. The trace of mild derision in his voice was not lost on her, even if Mark seemed to notice nothing amiss.

'That's right,' he said, getting politely to his feet to offer his hand. 'And you must be Robyn's brother-in-law, am I right?'

Robyn, chancing a glance in his direction, saw Jared's lips tighten. 'Jared Morley,' he agreed, taking the other man's hand with only a momentary hesitation. 'I understand you're the reason she drove into Saddleford yesterday evening. Wasn't that a rather foolhardy invitation, considering the conditions?'

Mark was taken aback, and Robyn had to bite her tongue to prevent the angry outburst that sprang to her lips at Jared's attack. How dared he? she asked herself incredulously. After what he did...

'As a matter of fact, I was surprised to see her myself,' Mark was saying now. 'So many people didn't turn up. It's a measure of her enthusiasm for the project that she was willing to take that chance...'

Jared frowned. 'The project?' he echoed. 'What project?'

'Oh, Mr Kingsley is trying to produce a Christmas pageant,' explained his father dismissively. 'You know, like Robyn produced herself some years ago. She's been helping him.'

'Has she?'

Jared's response was infuriatingly smug and, inadvertently meeting his gaze, Robyn had no doubts about what was going through his mind. He hadn't forgotten, any more than she had, that it was on the night of that other dress rehearsal that their relationship had changed so completely.

'Oh, yes,' Mark was going on now. 'It's been much easier with Robyn's assistance.'

'I bet it has.'

Jared acknowledged this with a mocking inclination of his head and, unable to prevent herself, Robyn intervened, 'As a matter of fact, we've helped each other,' she declared, standing up and aligning herself with Mark. 'Being with someone else—someone who didn't know Stephen—well, it's helped a lot. It's made me realise that life goes on.' She touched Mark's sleeve. 'I am grateful.'

'Oh—really——'

While Mark struggled to assure her that he had done nothing, nothing at all, Robyn enjoyed the unusual spectacle of Jared and Ben exchanging frustrated glances. And let them make what they liked of that, she thought maliciously. She was not an object, to be manipulated at will—even if past experience had led them to believe she was. She had a mind of her own, and it was high time she learned to use it.

However, when Daniel took the opportunity to claim Jared's attention for himself, Robyn's victory lost its bite. Moving away from Mark, she started gathering the dirty teacups on to the tray, and she wasn't surprised when Mark said he must be leaving.

'I'll see you out,' said Robyn at once, grateful for an excuse to get out of the room. And just for good measure, she added, 'Come along Daniel, you can get Mr Kingsley's coat.'

'Oh, Mum!'

Daniel's groan of protest was quickly stifled as his uncle pushed him gently but firmly in his mother's direction, with the promise that he would come and see his snowman later. Robyn quelled her own resentment at her brother-in-law's casual ability to restore her son's good humour, and took Daniel's hand firmly in hers. But it was frightening to see the power Jared had over the boy, and to anticipate what Daniel might do if he ever learned Jared was his natural father.

'I think you'd better abandon any thoughts of attending any more rehearsals until the weather improves, Robyn,' Mark observed, as he pulled on the warm overcoat Daniel had silently rescued from the closet. 'Besides, most of the work is done now, and with a bit of luck we may reach our target.'

'I'll come when I can,' replied Robyn firmly, despite Daniel's gloomy expression. 'I think we said tomorrow—at four o'clock, is that right?' She smiled at him enchantingly. 'I'll probably see you then.'

Mark took a step towards her, and then, remembering Daniel's presence, checked himself. 'Until tomorrow,' he agreed, his lips lifting with satisfaction. 'I shall look forward to it. And perhaps, afterwards, we might have dinner, hmm?'

'Perhaps,' said Robyn, belatedly remembering her reticence to give him the wrong impression. 'Perhaps,' she repeated, and consoled herself with the thought that she hadn't actually said yes.

'Why did you say you'd go to his silly rehearsal?' demanded Daniel, as soon as the door had closed behind the visitor. 'You know Grandpa won't like it, after what happened last night——'

'That will do, Daniel.' Robyn used her most quelling tone, her dark brows drawn together ominously. 'I suggest you leave me to manage my affairs and go upstairs and run your bath, before I remember you haven't been to school today and decide to give you some homework!'

'Mum!' Daniel was indignant. 'You know Uncle Jared promised we could go and see my snowman after Mr Kingsley had gone!'

'I doubt if Uncle Jared will be too distressed if you forget that promise,' retorted Robyn shortly, only to press her lips together in frustration as Jared himself emerged from the library.

'Ready, Dan?' he asked, infuriatingly, and the boy looked from one to the other of them in a pained demonstration of confusion.

'Oh, very well. Go and look at your snowman,' said Robyn tersely, taking pity on him. 'But I expect you to spend no more than fifteen minutes outside, do you hear me? It's dark and it's cold, and I don't want you going down with a cold for Christmas.'

'I'll see he doesn't,' said Jared, forcing her to look at him, though her eyes slid away from the challenge in his. 'By the way,' he added, as she turned towards the stairs, 'I'd like to talk to you later.' His lips twisted. 'Privately.'

Robyn stiffened. 'Very well.'

'Shall we say—after supper? In the study?'

'The study?' Robyn couldn't prevent the involuntary exclamation, and Jared inclined his head.

'It seems a suitable place to discuss business,' he averred, putting a familiar hand on Daniel's shoulder. 'So—come on, cobber. Let's go see this snowman.'

Robyn heard Daniel asking what 'cobber' meant as she went upstairs, as well as Jared's explanation that it was an Australian word meaning 'mate', but for once the casual affection in his voice didn't grate on her nerves. She was too involved with the prospect of what he intended to discuss with her later, and she thought how typical it was of him to startle her into divulging something incriminating, before revealing his own hand. He must know she had expected a discussion of a more intimate nature, but he had deliberately turned aside from the obvious conclusion.

Supper was a trial, so far as Robyn was concerned. She wasn't particularly hungry to begin with, and the awareness of what was to come after had affected what little appetite she had. Besides which, she had the beginnings of a headache, and the awful shivery feeling one developed immediately prior to going down with a cold. Of course, she thought impatiently, she would have to be the one to suffer for what had happened the night before. In more ways than one, she added, somewhat cynically. Having sex meant very little to a man, whereas she had never been able to regard it lightly. And, despite her determination not to let him get to her, she was unwillingly aware that he had. She had known that, the minute he had walked through the door that evening. Even furious with him as she was, she couldn't prevent the unwilling surge of heat that flooded her body every time she looked his way, and sitting opposite him at the table was the purest kind of mental torture. But, aside from everything else—the incongruousness of her infatuation for him, the difference in their ages—whatever he said, whatever he did, she must not forget that his real reason for coming to England in the first place had been to be near Daniel. It was Daniel he wanted, not her. Because of Daniel, she couldn't trust him. And without trust there was no future together, for any of them.

With thoughts like these for company, it was very difficult to concentrate on her meal, and she was inordinately relieved when it was over. She just wanted to get the upcoming interview done with, so that she could escape to bed, and she made no demur when Jared rose from the table and made their excuses to his father.

'I could remind you that it's still my company,' muttered Ben, when he heard what his son had to say. 'Anything you have to say to Robyn can be said in front of me.'

'I know that.' Jared had changed for dinner, and now he tucked his hands into the pockets of the dark brown suede jacket he was wearing. 'But I'd prefer to discuss this in private, if you don't mind. We don't want to embarrass Robyn, do we? Let me put her in the picture on my own.'

Robyn longed to wipe the complacent smile from his face, but she refrained from any overt retaliation. Instead, she contented herself with confining her resentment to a heated glare, wondering how she could be so stupid as to be attracted to him still.

With the door of Ben's study closed behind them, Jared lost no time in coming to the point. Robyn had barely crossed the floor to reach the desk, set squarely in the middle of the carpet, before his hands descended on her shoulders, hauling her back against him, and her stomach hollowed sickeningly as his mouth found the sensitive hollow below her ear.

'I've been wanting to do this ever since I got home,' he confessed huskily, his hands moving sensuously up and down her arms. His tongue searched for the nerves beneath her skin. 'My God, I'm shaking like a schoolboy! What a pity the door doesn't have a lock. I'd like to have you here, right now, just to prove a point, so to speak.'

Robyn was trembling, too, but somehow she managed to drag herself out of his arms and turned to face him with flushed cheeks and a cold-eyed dignity. 'You—you have a bloody nerve!' she choked, moistening her dry lips and avoiding looking at the unmistakable proof of his arousal. 'My God, indeed! And you said it was business! I wonder what your father would say if he could see you now!'

Jared stared at her furiously for several seconds, his eyes hot and undisguisedly savage. Then he looked away. Taking deep, steadying breaths, he directed his attention to the patterned whirls of the carpet, not trusting himself to lift his head until he was sure he was firmly in control again.

'All right,' he said, and she shrank away as he brushed past her, making for the desk with an obvious effort. Ignoring her involuntary withdrawal, he circled the desk to where a leather briefcase lay innocently on the pad. 'Business first,' he averred, flipping open the briefcase and extracting a file of papers. 'A matter of some two hundred thousand pounds, to be exact. The sum systematically withdrawn from the company assets over the past thirty months, and to which Maurice Woodhouse was allowed to draw my attention.'

CHAPTER TEN

ROBYN had to force her brain to start functioning again. 'Allowed?' she echoed stiffly. 'How—allowed? I'm sorry, but I don't think I understand what you're saying.'

'I'm sure you do.' Jared's eyes were cool and remote now, very different from the impassioned gaze he had subjected her to earlier. 'You did know there were some discrepancies in the figures, didn't you? In spite of what Woodhouse says, I can't believe even you could be that naïve!'

'Thank you.' Despite being strangled, Robyn's tone was taut with resentment.

'So—why did you let Woodhouse take the initiative? Why didn't you report the matter to me yourself? Surely it must have occurred to you that someone had to be responsible.'

'Have you overlooked the fact that you've been away?' Robyn exclaimed, struggling to compose herself, and Jared's mouth thinned.

'For two weeks only,' he informed her flatly. 'You had at least ten days to bring the matter to my attention before I left the country. I realise you still feel you have to protect Steve's memory, but for Christ's sake, did you have to give Maurice Woodhouse the chance to score?'

Robyn blinked. 'Maurice Woodhouse?'

Jared expelled his breath impatiently. 'You did discuss it with him, I assume?'

'No.'

'No?' Jared frowned. 'Are you sure?'

'Of course I'm sure.' Robyn sniffed. 'Look, what has Mr Woodhouse been saying? If he thinks he can blame me for——'

153

'Don't be silly,' Jared cut in shortly, giving her a belittling look. Tossing the file on to the desk, he sprawled into his father's chair and regarded her frustratedly. 'No one's putting the finger on you. This has been going on for a lot longer than the three months you've been in the chair. In any case, you had no reason to do it. You haven't been running up debts at the bookmakers, have you?'

Robyn swallowed. 'Are—are you saying that—that Stephen did?'

Jared looked up at her through his lashes. 'Is that what you thought?'

'No.' Robyn was defensive. 'I—I hadn't come to any conclusion.'

'But it must have crossed your mind that Stephen was the most obvious candidate for suspicion,' said Jared thinly. 'Is that why you didn't tell me? Because you hoped I wouldn't find out?'

Robyn bent her head. 'I knew you'd find out—eventually. I—I would have told you——'

'But?'

'—I wanted to be sure, that's all.'

'And you didn't discuss it with Woodhouse?'

'No.'

'Why not?'

Robyn shrugged. 'He doesn't like me. He never accepted me as acting managing director. We never—talked. Not properly.'

Jared leaned forward suddenly, his arms along the arms of the chair, his hands resting on the rim of the desk. 'But he did consult you on fiscal matters? I mean, he would have to have your signature on any outlay of finance.'

'No.' Robyn squared her shoulders and looked at him. 'Your father left that responsibility to him.'

'Did he, by God?' Jared snorted disbelievingly. 'And no one expected I'd come back, least of all old man Woodhouse.'

Robyn said nothing. There was nothing she could say. It was obvious that Stephen was involved, and nothing she did now could prevent that from becoming public knowledge. She shivered. Even beyond the grave, it seemed, Stephen's reputation could still reach out to her and Daniel. She had hoped it could be avoided, but now Daniel was bound to learn his father had been a swindler, as well as a womaniser.

'I—I suppose there's no mistake?' she ventured, clinging desperately to that final straw, and she saw Jared force his attention back to her from whatever line of reasoning he was following.

'What? Oh, no, Stephen was involved all right,' he said, dashing any faint hope she may have had. 'I spoke to Manny Prince on the phone this afternoon. You do know who Manny Prince is, I suppose? You did know Stephen—occasionally made a bet?'

There was irony in his tone, and Robyn held up her head. Everyone had heard of Manny Prince's chain of betting shops. 'Does he—does Stephen still owe him some money, then?' she asked, holding on to her dignity, and Jared met her defensive gaze with weary resignation.

'I'd say that was the least of our worries, wouldn't you?' he declared, and Robyn had to steel herself not to give in to a totally futile surge of self-pity. 'But there may be a way to salvage something out of this mess. Tell me, are you sure Woodhouse never brought his suspicions to you?'

'I've said so, haven't I?' Robyn could see no way to salvage anything, and her throat felt tight. She was getting a cold, she thought miserably; as if she didn't have troubles enough already!

'What if I told you he says that you were always too busy to discuss the figures with him?' Jared volunteered suddenly, and Robyn blinked.

'Why would he say a thing like that?'

'That's what I'm wondering.'

She shook her head. 'Do you think he's trying to cover himself for not noticing what was going on?'

'He says he'd had his suspicions for some time.'

'Oh.' Robyn nodded. 'Well—he would, I suppose.'

'Hmm.' Jared frowned. 'I'm thinking that, too.'

Robyn made a helpless gesture. 'I wish he had said something to me. I might have been able to do something about it.'

'What?' Jared was sceptical.

'I don't know.' Robyn lifted her shoulders. 'Sold something, perhaps. I do have some jewellery, and there's a necklace my grandmother left me, which ought to be worth something.'

'Two hundred thousand pounds?' suggested Jared drily, and she flushed.

'All right. So it wouldn't have been enough. It might have been possible to arrange a loan——'

'Loans have to be paid back,' put in Jared cuttingly, and Robyn nails dug painfully into her palms.

'You're not very helpful!'

'And you're not very bright,' retorted Jared, with asperity. 'Don't you see? Hasn't it dawned on you yet? Woodhouse knows more about this than either you or I gave him credit for.' He lifted his hand and pressed the heel of his wrist against his forehead. 'Of course. That's why he brought his suspicions to me. He waited to see if you were going to say anything, and when you didn't he couldn't believe his luck. As soon as he heard I was coming back for good, he knew he had to do something. And who's going to suspect the man who points out the errors to you?'

'You mean—you think Stephen and he— together——'

She couldn't go on, and Jared nodded. 'It stands to reason, doesn't it? Look, Woodhouse is near to retiring age. Stephen had all kinds of monetary problems. And there's no one else likely to catch on to what they were doing. Not immediately, anyway. I guess Steve was always hoping for the big winner to solve his problems for him.'

Robyn stared at him. 'But—wouldn't he—Woodhouse, I mean—know that you'd guess what had been going on?'

'He might have. And then again, he might not. In any case, it was worth the gamble. What did he have to lose? As far as he was concerned, you knew nothing about it.'

Robyn was appalled. 'I can't believe it!'

'Why not?' Jared was laconic. 'This sort of thing goes on all the time, believe me.'

'And—and Stephen was—was swindling his own father.'

'I guess he'd argue it wasn't his father's company any longer.'

'But the shareholders!'

'Got smaller dividends. Times are hard. I suppose he thought they'd never notice.' He shrugged. 'Obviously, they didn't.'

Robyn's tongue circled her lips, and she frowned suddenly. 'What you said—about Mr Woodhouse believing I knew nothing about it—why did you think I did?'

'I found some calculations you'd been making in a drawer. I didn't know what they were at first, but, when old Woodhouse came with his tale of woe, I checked.'

Robyn pressed her lips together. 'I see.'

'It is my desk now, you know,' Jared reminded her gently. 'Don't look so dismayed. You don't want me to think you're involved in this, too, do you?'

Robyn gasped. 'I would never——' she began, her face blazing, and with a muffled imprecation, Jared got up and came round the desk towards her.

'And I'd never think it,' he exclaimed, catching her heaving shoulders and pulling her round to face him. 'For heaven's sake, Robyn, I'd trust you with my life, you know that. I've trusted you with my son's life all these years! Do you think I want to change that now?'

'I don't know what you want, do I?' Robyn cried frantically, struggling to be free of him before he overwhelmed her resistance yet again, and Jared swore angrily as her nail caught his unguarded cheek.

'You do know what I want,' he argued fiercely. 'I want you—and I want my son! It's what I've wanted ever since I was sixteen years old and you know it! So when are you going to stop fighting me and tell me what we both know to be the truth: that you want me, too?'

'I don't!' With an inhuman effort, Robyn tore herself away from him, putting the width of the floor between them as she rushed towards the door. 'I don't want anything to do with you, Jared, and I'll never let you take my son away from me. Just keep away from me, do you hear? Or Daniel and I will leave here, with or without your permission!'

Robyn would have liked nothing better than to pack her and Daniel's bags, and to get away from Saddlebridge for ever. Everything was getting much too much for her, and what had once been a sanctuary was fast becoming a prison.

But, whatever she might have liked to do, for the next few days, at least, she was compelled to abandon any thought of escape. The morning after that scene in Ben's study with Jared, she awakened with streaming eyes and a runny nose, and as soon as Janet saw her she ordered her back to bed.

'You don't want to infect everybody in the house before Christmas, now, do you?' she asked reasonably. 'Daniel can go to school, and I'm sure Jared is quite capable of running the mill without your help. You get back into bed. Dr Harrington is coming to see Mr Morley this morning, and I'll ask him to take a quick look at you, too.'

Robyn's protests that she didn't need a doctor fell on deaf ears, but she couldn't deny the feeling of relief she felt to be sliding back between the sheets. Maybe that was why she felt so defeated, she thought, seizing on that possibility as another bout of sneezing left her feeling weak. Colds could be quite exhausting, and she was sure she would feel better when her head stopped aching and her eyes stopped watering.

Daniel didn't come in to see her before he left for school. He simply shouted 'Goodbye' from outside, and she had to summon all her strength to answer him.

'Have a good day, darling,' she called huskily, wishing he was older and therefore less vulnerable. She dreaded to think what would be said at school when it came out that his father was an embezzler, as well as an unfaithful husband. She might even be asked to remove him. Adultery was one thing, fraud was another.

Dr Harrington came during the morning and pronounced she had a severe case of coryza. 'In other words, the common cold, young woman,' he remarked, folding his stethoscope back into his bag. 'Janet tells me you've been standing about in draughty church halls, without proper protection, and that a long evening walk in the snow has aggravated your condition.'

'She would,' said Robyn miserably, glad to pull the covers over herself again. 'I've just been helping the curate with his Christmas show, that's all. And my car broke down when I was on my way home.'

'A little bird told me you ran it into the ditch,' observed Dr Harrington, with the familiarity of a long association. 'Never mind. You'll survive,' he added humorously. 'I'll pop in and see you again at the weekend. You should be feeling much better by then.'

Robyn hoped so, although she wasn't optimistic. The way she felt right now, it didn't seem possible that she would ever feel better, and when her eyes streamed again there were tears mixed with the outflow.

Of course, there were some advantages to being confined to her room. It meant she was not expected to face any visitors for several days, and the dual problems of Stephen's dishonesty and Daniel's parentage could be temporarily set aside.

Eventually, she knew, she would have to face the damaging results of what her husband had done. There was no avoiding it, and in her lower moments she thought how smug Jared must be feeling in the present situation. That Stephen, who had always been his father's favourite and therefore above reproach, should have let him down so badly, must be a bitter pill for Ben to swallow, and she supposed it was only natural that Jared should enjoy his vindication. Nevertheless, she was glad she didn't have to be there to see it.

So far as Daniel was concerned, her feelings were rather less unequivocal. On the one hand, she welcomed the opportunity of a breathing space before having to speak to Jared again, but on the other, when both Jared and her son were in the house and therefore possibly together, she fretted over what might be said between them. She couldn't deny that what had happened on the night of the storm had upset all her preconceived ideas about a lot of things, but she still clung to the premise that Jared was simply using her to gain his own ends. Nothing he had done before or since had convinced her there could be any other reason for his behaviour. Every kiss, every caress, every intimate moment between them, seemed to have been engineered to persuade her to commit the ultimate folly of admitting the truth and, no matter what he said, she couldn't believe he really wanted her. He might have done once—but that was many years ago. She was older now, *much* older.

One other outcome of her illness was that she was obliged to abandon any hopes of continuing with the church pageant. In spite of the fact that, on Thursday afternoon, a steady thaw cleared most of the roads, Robyn was forced to accept Janet's offer to telephone Mark with the news.

'There's no way you're going to be fit enough to spend several hours in that draughty old place,' the housekeeper asserted firmly, when Robyn ventured that she might be well enough to attend Saturday evening's performance. 'He'll have to manage without you. Mr Morley's adamant about that.'

'*Mr* Morley is?' Robyn was tempted to ask what Mr Morley had to do with it, but she was too worn out with sneezing and blowing her nose to start an argument.

'That's what I said,' declared Janet, not realising she was pushing her luck. 'So—how about a nice poached egg on toast, hmm? That won't take much eating, now, will it?'

Robyn made a weary gesture. 'I'm not really very hungry, Janet,' she murmured, feeling as if everything—her own body included—was combining to balk any plans she might have for asserting her independence. Even her friendship with Mark was being thwarted by circumstances totally beyond her control, and she felt completely helpless.

By Saturday, however, she had recovered a little of her strength. The worst effects of the head cold had left her, and only a harsh cough remained. She still felt weak, and a little heady after spending two full days in bed, but her brain was functioning again. She no longer had the muzzy sense of viewing herself from outside her body and, although to her own eyes she looked ghastly, Janet insisted she had a little more colour in her cheeks.

'Another couple of days and she'll be right as rain, don't you think, Doctor?' she suggested, when Dr Harrington returned on Saturday morning, and the elderly physician had to concede that she was right.

'Yes, two more days should make a world of difference,' he agreed, although his expression was curiously troubled as he met his patient's anxious gaze. 'And then perhaps you could come and see me at the surgery, Robyn,' he added, and Robyn knew a disturbing sense of foreboding at his unexpected invitation.

'There's nothing wrong, is there, Doctor?' exclaimed Janet at once, voicing Robyn's own fears. As if realising his words could be misconstrued, Dr Harrington attempted to reassure her.

'Nothing wrong, no,' he said, closing his bag and giving a hearty smile that was, nevertheless, forced. 'It's just a little matter I wanted to—discuss with you, Robyn,' he added, and as Janet showed him out, Robyn guessed exactly what that little matter must be. *Jared!* she thought sickly. It had to be something to do with Jared— and Daniel! For heaven's sake, had Jared voiced his suspicions to Dr Harrington? Was that why the doctor wanted to talk to her? To ask her about the premature delivery of a baby that had been born almost eight years ago?

It was a horrifying proposition, but now she could think of no alternative. But that Jared should do such a thing! She could hardly believe it. What must Dr Harrington be thinking? Oh, she had been so right not to trust Jared, *ever*.

When Janet came back, Daniel was with her, and with her recent insight into Jared's character foremost in her mind, Robyn pulled her son towards her and gave him a fervent hug.

'Hey!' protested Janet, as Daniel struggled in some embarrassment to free himself. 'You're still contagious, Robyn. Let the boy go. He's not going to run away, are you, Daniel?'

Daniel grimaced, somewhat awkwardly, and settled himself on the foot of his mother's bed. Then, brushing a hand over his flushed cheeks, he muttered, 'How are you, Mum? Janet says you're feeling better.'

Robyn was going to reprove him for using the housekeeper's Christian name, but somehow it was too much of an effort. Instead, she assured him she was feeling much better, and then, in a guarded voice, she added, 'And where's your uncle this morning?'

'Uncle Jared?' exclaimed Daniel in some surprise, and Robyn bit back the obvious rejoinder. 'Oh, he's downstairs. D'you want to see him?'

'No.' Robyn gave Janet an awkward smile. 'I—just wondered, that's all.'

'I expect both he and Mr Morley will be glad to see you up and about again,' remarked the housekeeper severely. She was not unaware of the antipathy that existed between her mistress and her employer's younger son, and this was her way of letting Robyn know she didn't endorse it. 'But now, young man, you'd better ask your mother what you came to ask her, and then we'll go and let her get some rest.'

'Oh! Oh, yes.' Daniel looked somewhat discomfited now, and Robyn gazed at him with sudden anxiety.

'What is it?' she asked. 'What do you want to ask me?'

Daniel looked at Janet, then at his mother, and then down at his hands, clenching over the knees of his jeans. 'Um, well—would you mind if I went Christmas shopping with Uncle Jared?' he mumbled awkwardly. And then, with more confidence, 'He says he'll take me into Sheffield.' He lifted his head, his eyes shining. 'Can I go, Mum? Please?'

Robyn's eyes moved to the housekeeper's now, too, and Janet gave a little dismissing shake of her shoulders. It was obvious she saw nothing out of the ordinary in Daniel's request, and Robyn knew an overpowering feeling of frustration at her own helplessness.

'I—well——' Avoiding Janet's gaze now, Robyn shifted uneasily. 'I'll take you into Sheffield on Monday. Now that you've finished school, we can go whenever we like. It'll be Christmas Eve on Tuesday. We could go then.'

'I think it's highly unlikely you'll be going anywhere before Christmas,' put in Janet flatly. 'For heaven's sake, Robyn, you're not going to be strong enough to trail around Sheffield shopping. Let him go with his uncle. Jared will enjoy it, and so will he.'

Robyn had no doubt about that, but she dared not allow it. After what Dr Harrington had said, how could she trust Jared not to betray his suspicions to her son?

'I'm sorry,' she said now, and Daniel gave a cry of dismay. 'It's no use, Daniel. My mind is made up. In any case, Uncle Jared has—has more important things to do than take you shopp——'

'No, he doesn't.'

The quiet rejoinder came from the doorway and, turning her head, Robyn was infuriated to see Jared standing in the opening, watching them. Then, without waiting for an invitation, he walked casually into the room, smiling reassuringly at Daniel and exchanging an understanding glance with Janet.

But when he came to the bed, his smile disappeared. 'So,' he said, pushing his hands into the pockets of the brown cord jacket he was wearing, 'I understand you're feeling better. Perhaps you'll be fit enough to get up this afternoon, hmm? I won't be here, but I know my father would like to see you.'

Was that a warning? Or a threat? Looking up into Jared's enigmatic face, Robyn couldn't be sure. But it had brought the memory of Stephen's dishonesty sharply back into focus, and she guessed that had been his intention.

'I—may get up,' she ventured tightly, irritably aware that it mattered to her that he was seeing her at her worst. It wasn't important, she told herself fiercely, resisting the urge to touch her braid or check that the buttons of her nightshirt were securely fastened. But the trouble was, it *was* important, and she despised the treacherous emotions that fed such an unworthy weakness.

'And you are feeling better?' he prompted, as Daniel got up and came to stand beside him. 'Dr Harrington says you've been lucky. It could have turned to pneumonia.'

'Aren't I the lucky one!' Robyn's lips were tight. 'But now, if you don't mind——'

'But what about Sheffield?' protested Daniel, clearly not prepared to give up now he had an ally. But, before Robyn could repeat what she had said before, Jared put a warning hand on her son's shoulder.

'Let me talk to your mother, Dan,' he said, pushing the boy gently towards the housekeeper. 'You go downstairs with Janet. I'll be with you in a minute.'

Robyn wanted to protest, too, but she was loath to create a scene in front of Daniel. Besides, Janet, too, was all ears, and there were things she wanted to say to Jared which were not fit for anyone else to hear.

The door closed behind the others a few moments later, and Robyn wished she could have conducted this conversation anywhere else than in her bed. As if Jared didn't have advantages enough, she brooded, aware of his dark-skinned strength and harsh good looks with every fibre of her being. He looked young and virile, while she felt pale, and unhealthy, and decidedly old. How could she hope to compete, when it came to Daniel's affections?

'Before you start, I should tell you that I know all about what you've been doing?' she burst out, before he could say anything. 'And—and I want you to know, I think you're disgusting! Disgusting, and—and contemptible!'

'Really?' Jared frowned. 'For inviting Dan to go to Sheffield with me?'

Robyn's lips curled. 'No! No, of course not. You— you know what I mean. How—how dare you stand there and pretend you don't?'

Jared took his hands out of his pockets and ran weary fingers through his hair. 'Well, I'm sorry, but you're going to have to enlighten me,' he said flatly. 'Are you talking about what happened the other night? Are you going to tell me that what happened was all a mistake? I guess, after what happened the last time, I should have expected——'

'Damn you, this has nothing to do with what happened the other night!' cried Robyn, fairly simmering with frustration. 'Oh, for heaven's sake, you can stop acting now. You don't have to pretend any more. Didn't it occur to you that Dr Harrington might say something to me? He's an old man, and an old friend; naturally, he must be wondering what's going on.'

Jared's brows arched. 'And what is?'

Robyn gasped. 'You tell me.'

Jared shrugged, and then, to her astonishment, he lowered his weight on to the side of the bed, the hard bone of his hip taut against her thigh. Then, ignoring her efforts to evade him, he took her left hand between both of his, and smoothed his thumb over the narrow band of her wedding ring.

There was a shocked silence as Robyn absorbed the fact that Jared was struggling with some emotion, too, and then she tugged her hand away, and thrust it under the covers. She was trembling, as much with her awareness of him as with any sense of confusion she might be feeling, and she wondered somewhat blankly what he expected her to say.

Taking a deep breath, she began again. 'Why did you go to see Dr Harrington?' she asked unsteadily. 'You might as well admit it. He's virtually said as much to me.'

'Has he?' Jared seemed unperturbed. 'And what did he say, exactly?'

'Well——' Robyn was annoyed to find she was on the defensive again. 'He said—he said he wants me to go and see him. At the surgery. As soon as I'm fit enough to go into the village.'

'And what has that got to do with me?' Jared was so reasonable, she wanted to scream.

'Don't pretend, Jared.'

'I'm not.'

'You're not denying you went to see him, I notice.'

'I—went to the surgery a couple of weeks ago, yes.'

'A couple of weeks—*why*?'

'He asked me to come in. We spoke about Dad. I asked him if there was any chance of him recovering sufficiently to go back to the mill.'

Robyn swallowed. 'And?'

'And he said no. But I'm sure you could have answered that yourself. I don't think it was such a contemptible thing to do. I wanted to know the score, before I severed all ties with Australia.'

Robyn stared at him. 'What else did you ask him?'

'What else?' Jared shook his head. 'Nothing else.'

'*Liar!*'

'Now, listen to me——' With a roughening of his voice, Jared leant towards her then, grasping her shoulders in a painful grip, and staring at her with tormented eyes. 'Suppose you tell me what all this is about, hmm? What am I supposed to have done? What could Dr Harrington tell me that I don't already know?'

Robyn trembled. 'You know!'

'About Dan?' Jared's lips twisted, and with a violent gesture he set her free. 'What do you think he could tell me, do you suppose? I hate to disillusion you, Robyn, but doctors can't prove conclusively who a child's father might be.'

Robyn blinked. 'They can't?'

'No, they can't.' Jared regarded her coldly. 'Did you really think I might ask Dr Harrington about something like that?'

Robyn swallowed. 'Well——'

'You did think it, didn't you?' Jared's mouth tightened. 'My God! You must hate me, Robyn. I didn't want to believe it, but gradually you're convincing me.'

Robyn shook her head. 'I don't—hate you, Jared——'

'But you don't like me much, either,' muttered Jared harshly, getting abruptly up from the bed. 'But don't worry, Robyn. I've finally got the message. Anything I thought there was between us all those years ago—it's over. I'm through with trying to persuade you that we could still have a life together. You've got your memories, such as they are, and you've got your son! That's all you ever wanted, only I was too stubborn to realise it before.'

Robyn looked up at him. 'And—and you won't—you won't tell Daniel?' she ventured unsteadily.

'Tell him?' Jared was bleak. 'Tell him what?'

'Oh, please...' Robyn knew she was pleading with him, but she couldn't help it. 'You're not—you're not going to tell him who his father really is, are you? I—I'll do anything you say, just don't tell him the truth.'

If anything, Jared looked even colder. 'I doubt if you'd recognise the truth if you heard it,' he said savagely. 'In any case, I don't have to tell Dan anything about his father. He knows.'

'He knows!' Robyn's face grew even paler than it already was. 'How—how does he know? Have you already told him?'

Jared swore. 'I didn't have to tell him,' he declared harshly, and then, at her gulp of despair, he added, 'He's always known, Robyn. Stephen *was* his father. Believe me, I know what I'm talking about. If you'd made a few simple enquiries yourself, you could have saved both of us a lot of anguish. What I said about doctors not being able to distinguish who a child's father might be is only half the story. Stephen and I had different mothers; we had different blood types. I'm sorry to disappoint you, but Dan isn't my son!'

Robyn was stunned. She couldn't believe it, after all these years, to learn she had been living a lie. It couldn't be true. Was Daniel really *Stephen's* son? Had he really been three weeks premature, and not the one week overdue that she had always assumed? Oh, how could she have been so stupid? How could she have been so naïve? Jared had *known*, yet, if she hadn't brought it up, he hadn't been going to tell her!

He was at the door when she found her tongue. 'How—how could you?' she choked. 'How could you let me go on believing—believing——'

'What?' Jared was contemptuous. 'That Dan was my son? You denied he was, remember?'

'But you knew——'

'No. I didn't *know* anything. I thought I did, but I didn't. Not until the other night, when you made me so mad. I decided to make some enquiries for myself. Oh— not from Harrington,' Jared added scornfully. 'Even I couldn't go that far. But I already knew Stephen's blood type, and my own, and the private maternity home in Sheffield still had the records they made when Daniel was born.'

CHAPTER ELEVEN

FOR the rest of the morning, Robyn felt numb. Even when Janet came to tell her that Jared had taken Daniel into Sheffield, she made no demur, and she guessed the housekeeper was curious at her apparent change of heart.

But she couldn't help it. For so long she had lived with the fear that someone else would find out Daniel was not Stephen's son, that now that fear had been removed she felt incapable of absorbing it. It was as if it was all a dream, as if she had imagined that scene with Jared, and soon she would wake up and find everything was as it was before. It wasn't possible that she had been mistaken. Daniel wasn't Stephen's son, he was Jared's.

At lunch time, Janet brought her tray, and the suggestion that she might get dressed and go downstairs afterwards. 'I know Mr Morley would like to see you,' she said. 'And you know it's impossible for him to come upstairs.'

Robyn gave a thin smile. 'I might do that,' she said, realising that was one problem that would not go away. Sooner or later, she had to talk to Ben about Stephen's embezzlement. It wasn't going to be easy, but no doubt Jared had told him what had been going on in his absence.

'You're all right, aren't you, Robyn?' Janet persisted, lingering even after her mistress had picked up her spoon and was making a brave effort to tackle the bowl of creamed soup she had brought her. 'I mean,' she added, when Robyn looked up at her a little warily, 'you don't really mind that Jared's taken Daniel into Sheffield, do you? I know Jared said you wouldn't, and you didn't object when I told you earlier, but—well, you seemed so—tense, somehow. I hope you're not worrying about the boy.'

Robyn expelled her breath on a sigh. 'No,' she said at last. 'No, I'm not worrying about Daniel.'

'But you are worrying about something else?' Janet was quick to notice the qualification.

'I—no.' Robyn knew that, however attractive the proposition might be, she could not discuss her present problems with Janet. 'But—er—thanks for your concern. I do appreciate it, honestly.'

Janet gave a rueful smile. 'Oh, well... So, I'll tell Mr Morley you'll be down later, shall I?'

Robyn hesitated a moment, and then she nodded. 'Why not?' she agreed flatly. 'I don't have anything else to do.'

Robyn took a shower and washed her hair before attempting to get dressed. It was a foolish notion, she knew, after all that had gone before, but she wanted to look her best the next time Jared saw her. There was not a lot she could do to mask the puffiness around her eyes, and the hollows in her cheeks were the result of more than just a few days' loss of appetite. Ever since Jared had come home, she had lived on the knife edge of her emotions, and it was no surprise that it was beginning to show. Nevertheless, she was determined to show him that his words had not devastated her, even if, deep inside her, the knowledge that Daniel was not Jared's child had been a shattering revelation.

But the real truth was, she was not relieved. Not really. After all this time, and all this soul-searching, she was only just beginning to understand her real feelings. She loved Jared. She knew that now. She probably always had. Only always, in the back of her mind, she had blamed him—and herself—for something that had never been their fault. Jared had not made her frigid with Stephen; Stephen had done that for himself. But until the guilt she had always felt about Daniel's conception had been removed, she had been unable to accept it.

Ben was in the library when she eventually went downstairs. With a rug across his knees, he was seated in his usual position beside the fire, and his eyes took on a grudging approval as his daughter-in-law came into the room.

'Well,' he said, as she bent to kiss his cheek, 'you're looking a great deal better, if I'm to believe what Janet's been telling me.'

Robyn smiled. 'Tactful as ever,' she remarked, taking the seat across from him. 'I've just had a shower and washed my hair, that's all. I felt like smartening myself up. Do you mind?'

'Why should I mind?' retorted Ben irascibly. 'I'm just the resident geriatric here, that's all. Nobody tells me anything. I'm not considered intelligent enough to understand the simplest problem!'

Robyn's smile disappeared. 'That's not true, Ben——'

'It is true.' He sniffed. 'Anyway, how are you feeling? I could say, I told you so, but I don't suppose you'd want to hear it.'

'Ben——'

'Well, at least that fool, Kingsley, hasn't been pestering us again since Janet gave him his marching orders.'

'Ben!'

'Now, don't look like that.' Ben grimaced. 'I had Jared send a sizeable contribution to the vicar's favourite charity, so I don't suppose old Tomlinson will be complaining.'

'Even so...'

'Even so, nothing. No wishy-washy curate is good enough for my daughter-in-law, no matter how attractive he might be. Even if she does treat me like an imbecile, she's family. And whatever her faults, that's the important thing.'

Robyn sighed. 'Ben, I realise you think I've been deceiving you——'

'Damn right!'

'—but it's not true.' She sighed, searching for the right words to tell him how she felt. 'I—I wasn't sure. I wasn't certain I was right. It wasn't until—until——'

'—until Jared had the sense to see through Woodhouse's lies!' snapped Ben harshly. 'I know, I know. He's told me all about it. At least he still thinks I've got a brain in my head!'

'Oh, Ben——'

'What I can't understand is how Stephen didn't notice what was going on,' the old man continued, and Robyn's features froze. 'Still, I suppose he never was much of an accountant, was he? And a clever man like Maurice Woodhouse—well, I reckon he must have run rings around him.'

Robyn caught her breath. 'Stephen—didn't—know?' she ventured faintly, and her father-in-law shook his head.

'Well, it stands to reason, doesn't it? Stephen would have told me if he'd noticed anything amiss. But Jared says Woodhouse must have been too sneaky for him, and if, as he says, there was a second set of books——'

Robyn was breathing shallowly now, and it wasn't easy to hide her reaction from the old man. She couldn't believe what she was hearing; she couldn't believe Maurice Woodhouse had been prepared to take all the blame; it didn't gell with what she knew of him. And, in any case, Jared had known the truth and had intended to act upon it.

'Thank God Jared came home when he did,' Ben was saying now. 'Although I'm not sure I entirely agree with the way he's handling it.'

Robyn swallowed. 'No?' she managed croakily.

'No.' Ben gnawed at his lower lip. 'You see, he's got some fool notion that a scandal at this time could do more harm to the company than it would to Maurice Woodhouse. He's an old man, like myself; he's near to retiring. There's no doubt that he'd go to prison if it got out, but Jared reckons it's not worth it for the satisfaction it would give us.'

'I see.' Robyn nodded.

'Well?' Ben gazed at her impatiently, and when she didn't immediately respond he added sharply, 'What do you think? What's your opinion? As acting managing director of Morley Textiles, you ought to have an opinion.'

Robyn swallowed again. 'Um—oh, I agree with Jared,' she got out in a little rush. 'That is—it does seem more sensible not to—not to rock the boat.'

'Huh!' Ben snorted. 'I suppose I should have expected that. Women! They always take the easy way out. Oh, well, if that's your decision, I'll go along with it. I don't have much choice, do I? But I'll tell you one thing, Robyn, Stephen wouldn't have let him get away with it. Not Stephen. He was too much like me!'

Jared came to bed at about half-past eleven. Robyn heard him come upstairs. She had been listening for him. Even if she hadn't, she was sure she would have sensed it in her present state of tension. She had been wanting to talk to him alone all evening, ever since he and Daniel got back from Sheffield. But for once he had proved annoyingly elusive. Despite several thwarted efforts, she had had no opportunity to say what she wanted to say, and she had begun to wonder if he was deliberately avoiding her.

She had stayed up for supper, even though Janet had expressed the view that she might be overdoing things by doing so. But she had been sure that, at some point in the evening, she would get Jared on his own, and her frustration had known no bounds when her son proved to be the obstacle. Allowed to stay up for supper because of his mother, Daniel had succeeded in monopolising the conversation both during and after the meal. He had entertained his grandfather by recounting every minute of his day in Sheffield, even telling him about the cars, and the multi-storey car park, and the self-service cafeteria where they had had their lunch.

By the time the meal was over, Robyn's nerves were stretched as taut as violin strings and, when Janet eventually offered to take her son away to bed, she had held her breath. But, although Jared had often said goodnight to Daniel after he was tucked up, tonight he didn't. Instead, he said he was going to have a nightcap with his father, and Daniel had to be content with a promise to take him riding the next day. 'If your mother doesn't object, of course,' Jared had added, with an unsmiling glance in Robyn's direction. 'He does have a pony, doesn't he? And the roads around the estate are fairly dry.'

In consequence of which, Robyn had said her goodnights, too, and gone to bed. But not to sleep. For the past two and a half hours, she had been lying awake, wondering if she dared intercept Jared on his way to bed. In the event, she heard the door of his room close while she was still considering her options, and the silence of the house seemed to mock her good intentions.

With an exclamation of impatience, she came to a decision. Jared hadn't had time yet to get undressed, and there was no way she was going to sleep without speaking to him first. She had to know what he had said to his father; she had to thank him, if thanks were adequate, for what he had done for Daniel. How he had succeeded in keeping Stephen's name out of the accusations, she couldn't imagine, but somehow he had done it, and she had to tell him she was grateful.

Sliding out of bed, she slipped her feet into furry mules and reached for her dressing-gown. Its dark red velour folds were warm from lying across the foot of her bed, and she cast a rueful glance at her reflection in the mirror before opening the bedroom door. So much for the efforts she had made with her appearance, she thought wryly. Now, without make-up, and with her hair pulled back into a single braid, she had no delusions of glamour, but perhaps that was just as well. The last thing she wanted was for Jared to get the wrong impression.

As she had expected, a ribbon of light showed beneath the bottom of Jared's door; summoning all her confidence, she knocked lightly on the panels. Then, she waited, her fists balling in the pockets of her dressing-gown, endeavouring to marshall all she wanted to say, without giving away either her nervousness or her feelings.

As on that other unforgettable occasion when she had come to his room, Jared didn't immediately respond to her summons. On the contrary, she was obliged to knock again before she attracted his attention, and she was glad Daniel's apartments were at the other end of the corridor.

However, much to her relief, when Jared did open the door, he was still fully clothed. He had shed the black suede jacket he had worn to supper, but he was still dressed in matching trousers, and a beige silk shirt. And, although the cuffs of his shirt were folded back over his forearms, most of his tanned brown skin was hidden from her gaze.

'Well, well,' he said, with just a faint edge to his voice. 'Surprise, surprise! Why did I know it would be you? Could it be because there's nobody else in the house?'

Robyn moistened her lips. 'That's not true——'

'No.' He conceded the point with an inclination of his head. 'Mac and Janet are in their flat downstairs, and my father is asleep in his ground-floor apartments. Oh—I suppose it could have been Dan, but somehow I didn't think so.'

Robyn let him finish, and then she said quietly, 'Can I come in?'

'In here?' Jared arched a mocking brow. 'Is that wise? You know what happened the last time. Aren't you afraid that I might compromise you?'

Robyn sighed. 'Must you be so sarcastic?'

'Perhaps I feel sarcastic,' retorted Jared shortly. And then, meeting her troubled stare, he made a frustrated gesture. 'Of course, of course. Come in, why don't you?

It wouldn't do for anyone to see us. They might get the wrong impression.'

Robyn stepped past him as he stood aside, and then took a few steps more as he closed the door behind her. Curiously enough, she didn't feel at all nervous now she was here, though she suspected her confidence could evaporate if Jared chose to take the advantage.

'So,' he said, walking past her and halting at the end of his bed. He folded his arms, and waited. 'I assume this visit has a purpose. It's not just a—social call.'

Robyn straightened her spine. 'I suppose you can guess why I'm here.'

'Maybe.' He was non-committal. 'Suppose you tell me.'

Robyn caught her lower lip between her teeth. 'I wanted to thank you. For—for keeping Stephen's name out of the trouble at Morley's. I don't know how you did it, but Daniel and I will never be able to thank you enough.'

Jared shrugged. 'I didn't do it for you. I did it for my father. He's had enough shocks lately. One more might have killed him.'

Robyn nodded. 'Of course. But—even so——'

'Forget it.' Jared was dismissive. 'It was no big deal. Woodhouse was pathetically eager to save his own hide. He'd have done anything to avoid going to prison.'

'But—he is leaving, isn't he?'

'He's taking an early retirement.'

'And won't that cause some talk?'

'I shouldn't think so.' Jared was laconic. 'He's an old man. He's been seeing a doctor about high blood pressure for some time. It'll look perfectly natural. Even if it was probably aggravated by the stress of what they were doing.'

Robyn expelled her breath slowly. 'Thank God!'

'For what? Saving Stephen's memory?' Jared looked scornful. 'That's not something that gives me any pleasure. But, if it makes you happy, then so be it. And at least Dan doesn't have to know anything about it.'

Robyn hesitated. 'You really—care about him, don't you?'

'Dan?' Jared's lips twisted. 'I suppose you think I'm a fool, hmm?'

'No!'

'No?'

'No, why should I?'

'Because he's not my son.'

Robyn caught her breath. 'Does that matter. You're still his uncle.'

'It matters,' said Jared heavily, turning away. 'But it doesn't alter my feelings for him, if that's what you mean.'

Robyn licked her lips. 'I'm glad.'

'Are you?' Jared looked at her over his shoulder, his expression sceptical. 'Just so long as he's not mine, you don't mind if I care about him. When you thought he was my son, you couldn't bear me to be near him.'

'That's not how it was.' Robyn gazed at him unhappily. 'I—I was afraid. Afraid of what you might do to him.'

Jared swung back to face her again. 'What I might *do* to him? What the hell do you mean?'

'Oh——' Robyn shook her head. 'You don't understand.'

'No, I bloody don't!'

'I'm expressing myself badly.' Robyn made a helpless gesture. 'I thought you might try to—to take him away from me. I thought if you knew he was yours, you might take me to court to prove it.'

Jared looked aghast. 'Why in God's name would you think a thing like that?' He shook his head. 'Did I ever threaten you?'

'No.'

'Did I ever give you any reason to think I might take legal steps to prove myself his father?'

'No.'

'Then what the——'

'You wouldn't leave me alone!' burst out Robyn painfully. 'When—when you saw you weren't getting anywhere by normal means, you started coming on to me. You—you pretended you cared about me, just to get me to admit that Daniel was yours!'

Jared swore then, his face contorted with emotion. 'You—fool!' he muttered. 'You crazy little fool! Do you really think I'd marry you just to claim my rights as Dan's father?'

Robyn quivered. 'Well—I thought—that is, when you came back——'

'Oh, I know.' Jared remembered. 'When I came home, I let you think I hated you. Perhaps I did hate you then. I certainly hated you when I went away. When you had the baby and I thought he was mine, I think I wanted to kill you!'

Robyn swallowed. 'I'm sorry.'

'Yes. So was I.' Jared spoke bitterly. 'But that's all water under the bridge now, as they say, isn't it? What's past is gone, and you don't have to be afraid of me any more,' he finished sardonically.

Robyn held up her head. 'I'm not afraid of you.'

'Not now,' jeered Jared scornfully.

'All right. Not now.' Robyn drew her hands out of her pockets and linked them together. 'As—as a matter of fact, I think I love you.' She paused. 'Is it too late to tell you that? Will you even believe me?'

Jared uttered a choking sound. 'What did you say?' he demanded, staring at her as if she had taken leave of her senses, and Robyn wondered if she had made a terrible mistake.

Clearing her throat, as if the obstruction had been hers, she said, 'I think you heard me,' in low uneven tones. 'I—love you. I think I always have. But you were so much younger than me, and I dared not take the chance that you might change your mind.'

Jared blinked. 'And—what makes you think I might not change my mind now?' he asked in a strangled voice. 'I mean—you are still older than me, aren't you? And, as you pointed out earlier, I do have proof now that Dan's *not* my son.'

Robyn trembled slightly, but she held her ground. 'You—you said you wouldn't marry me just to claim your rights as Daniel's father.'

Jared inclined his head. 'So I did.'

'Well, then?'

'Well, then, what?'

Robyn fists clenched. 'Jared!'

'Did I ask you to marry me?' he asked infuriatingly. 'I'm sorry, I don't remember that.'

Robyn stared at him for a moment longer, and then her shoulders sagged. 'I see.'

'What do you see, I wonder?' Jared's voice was rough now, and the mockery he had exhibited moments before had completely disappeared. 'You have a nerve, do you know that? For the past few weeks you've treated me like dirt, telling me things you didn't believe to be true, and making me feel like an intruder in my own home!'

'That's not true!'

'A favourite cry of yours, but it *is* true, Robyn! You did your best to turn Dan against me——'

'No!'

'—and you rejected every move I made towards you.'

'You know why!' she exclaimed defensively.

'I know what you've told me,' retorted Jared, a muscle jerking at the corner of his mouth. 'But now, how do I know you're not just approaching me because of Dan, hmm? I mean, now that he's not my son, perhaps you're afraid I'll not make him my heir?'

Robyn gasped. 'I—I would never do such a thing!'

'Wouldn't you?'

'You know I wouldn't.' She shook her head. 'That—that's a foul thing to suggest!'

'No worse than what you accused me of, remember?' Jared reminded her harshly. 'How do you like it, Robyn? How do you like being made to feel a louse?'

Robyn shook her head. And then, moving a little dazedly, she turned towards the door. 'I'm sorry,' she

said, swallowing back the lump of emotion that seemed
to have balled in her throat as he spoke. 'I—er—I seem
to have made a mistake. I'm sorry. I'll leave you now.
I shouldn't have come——'

'Oh, for Christ's sake!' Before she could reach the
door, Jared moved after her, his hands capturing her
arms and halting her progress. 'You're not going anywhere,' he added, the warmth of his breathing stirring
the hairs on the back of her neck. 'All right, it was cruel,
but I had to do it. You've hurt me so many times, don't
you think I deserve a little restitution?'

Robyn bent her head. 'What do you mean?' she asked
in a small voice, and Jared uttered a self-derisive laugh
as he pulled her back against him.

'Don't push your luck,' he advised, his lips soft against
the side of her neck. 'You know what I mean. I mean
I'm fool enough to forgive you anything. Even ruining
eight years of our lives, just to prove I really knew what
I was doing.'

Robyn's breathing quickened. 'Do you mean it?' she
asked huskily, tilting her head to facilitate his caressing
exploration of her nape. She felt his rueful amusement
whisper against her skin.

'Would I lie to you?' he demanded, turning her to
face him. And then, cupping her face in his hands, he
added, 'Does this mean you will marry me, as soon as
a decent interval has elapsed?'

'If that's what you want.' Robyn covered his hands
with her own.

'It's what I want,' Jared confirmed, stroking his lips
against hers. 'It's what I've always wanted. So long as
this isn't some misguided sense of gratitude because Steve
is off the hook.'

'Oh, Jared!' With a cry of protest, she wound her
arms round his neck, bringing his mouth hard to hers
and sliding her tongue between his lips. 'Does this feel
like gratitude?' she panted, when they were both weak
and short of breath, and Jared gave a muffled oath as
he swung her up into his arms.

'At least you came ready for bed,' he teased softly, setting her down on his own quilt, and rapidly tearing off his shirt and tie. 'Although I don't think much of this nightshirt,' he appended, growing impatient with the neat row of buttons that confronted him. With a groan of impatience, he snapped the buttons from their holes and sent half a dozen of them tumbling on to the floor. 'Mmm, that's much better,' he approved, lowering his face into the hollow between her breasts. 'Ah, Robyn, Robyn,' he breathed, 'how I love you! Will you believe me now if I tell you that this is the most wonderful Christmas gift of all?'

It was in July of the following year that Robyn discovered she was expecting Jared's baby.

There was no mistake this time. She and her husband had been married for almost three months, and, although some people had expressed the opinion that six months was an inordinately short period of mourning, most had approved the match and offered their congratulations. Anyone who had known Stephen, and the humiliating existence Robyn had led with him, was more than willing to give them their good wishes. And everyone, without exception, applauded her choice, for Jared had always inspired the most affection.

For Robyn, the past six months had been the happiest six months of her whole life. Ben was happy, Daniel was happy, and she was happy, undeservedly so, she sometimes thought, considering the way she had almost ruined both hers and Jared's lives.

But, as to that, she was doing her best to make up for all the years she had wasted, and she knew she was succeeding. Jared had never looked more attractive or more content, and she knew he was happy, too, because he never ceased convincing her.

Even so, it was quite a traumatic prospect, to tell Jared he was going to be a father at last. She didn't quite know how he would take it, particularly as they had originally agreed that they should not have any children for the first couple of years.

'We'll let Dan get used to having a new father first,' Jared had suggested gently. 'I know he likes me, and I don't think he minds us getting married. But coping with a new half-brother or sister—well, let's take it one step at a time, shall we? We can wait. We've got all the rest of our lives.'

And they did. And just being together had proved to be all she could ever have wished. Their honeymoon— a week in Venice, which was all the time Jared could take away from the business—might not have been as glamorous as the honeymoon in the Bahamas she had spent with Stephen, but it had been so much more enviable. In spite of the fact that April had proved to be rather a chilly month, with the occasional downpour for good measure, Robyn and Jared had scarcely noticed. They had spent most of their time alone in the splendid isolation of the suite Jared had booked for them at the Danieli Hotel, and only the pealing bells from the city's many *campaniles* reminded them where they were. Oh, they had done a little sightseeing, and Jared had taken her for a romantic ride on a gondola. But mostly they were content to spend their time together, and Robyn knew they attracted many smiles from the friendly, sentimental Italians.

In consequence, Robyn broached the subject of her pregnancy with some reluctance. What if Jared didn't want a child? What if he was quite content as Daniel's stepfather? Would he still love her when she became bloated and ungainly? Had she made a terrible mistake by not taking care that it didn't happen?

Daniel was the first person she encountered when she got home from the doctor's. He was playing in the garden with the puppy Jared had bought him for his birthday, and Robyn saw with some misgivings that one of them had trampled all over Janet's herb garden. Oh, well, she thought resignedly, the McClouds had been as keen as

Daniel to buy the young Dalmation, and Janet was perfectly capable of chastising him for herself.

Daniel himself looked fit and healthy. Since Jared's advent into his life, he had joined the local cub pack, and rode regularly with his stepfather. Jared was even talking about getting him a bigger pony at Christmas, and Robyn was really delighted that they got on so well together.

It had been Jared's suggestion, too, that they abandon all ideas of sending Daniel away to school until he was at least thirteen. The prep school he attended had an excellent reputation and, as neither she nor Jared wanted him to go away, it was a very satisfactory arrangement. Besides, they were a real family now, and Robyn had seen her son's growing confidence since Jared came into his life.

Now, he followed her indoors, poking into the shopping bag she set down in the hall, and begging a chocolate biscuit that he found there. 'You've been a long time,' he said, accompanying her into the sitting-room and flinging himself on to one of the pair of sofas that faced one another across the hearth. 'Grandpa said you had an appointment at the doctor's. Did you? *Did you*?'

Robyn was glad she could be truthful. 'I had to go and get a prescription for your grandfather's new tablets,' she said, producing the bottle she had got from the chemist's from her handbag. She remembered that other occasion Dr Harrington had asked to see her to discuss her father-in-law's medication. That was when she had accused Jared of spying on her. How foolish she had been then.

'Is that all?'

Daniel's voice interrupted her reverie and she sighed. 'Well, I had to get the prescription filled, and there were one or two other things I had to buy.'

'Like these biscuits,' agreed Daniel enthusiastically, peeling off the wrapper and taking a bite. 'A pity. I thought there might have been another reason for you

to see the doctor. Lester—one of the chaps at school—
his mother's going to have a baby, and I know she goes
to see the doctor regularly.'

Robyn managed to hide her start of surprise. 'And—
would you like that?' she ventured tentatively. 'If I had
a baby, I mean?'

'Well, I think so.' Daniel grimaced. 'I wouldn't like
its crying, of course, but they don't do that all the time,
do they?'

'No...'

'And it's quite natural, isn't it?' Daniel continued. 'I
mean, you and Uncle Jared—that is, *Dad*—are married,
aren't you? And married people do have babies. I was
really quite expecting it.'

Robyn decided to tell Jared her news while he was
taking a bath that same evening. He usually left the
bathroom door open while he was in the tub, and Robyn
positioned herself just beyond the door so she wouldn't
have to look at him when she said it.

'Jared?' she called, pressing her shoulders back against
the wall of their bedroom. 'I've got something to tell
you.'

'I've got something to tell you, too,' remarked Jared,
and Robyn's brows drew together uncertainly.

'You do?'

'Yes.' She heard him sigh. 'Look, why don't you come
in here, hmm? To save me having to shout at you. I
thought you were going to take a shower.'

Robyn caught her breath. 'I was.'

'Well, then?'

She hesitated. 'In a minute.'

There was a sudden movement from the bath, and the
swoosh as water overspilled the tub, but before Robyn
could anticipate what he was doing Jared appeared in
the bedroom doorway. He was in the process of drying
himself as he came, and the soft folds of a creamy apricot
towel half covered his chest and were caught between
the muscular strength of his thighs. He looked so attractive at that moment, his blond hair artificially

darkened by the water, and his body still tanned several shades darker except below his waist, that Robyn wanted to go to him and wrap her arms around him. But what she had to tell him had to be said and, subduing her instincts, she turned away from the sensual beauty of his physique.

'I'm—pregnant,' she said, her nervous fingers busy with the ribbons of the silky beige teddy she was wearing. Still without looking at him, she bent to pick up a stocking she had discarded earlier and threaded it through her hands like a lifeline. Realising several seconds had gone by and he had not said anything, she was compelled to find out why and, turning her head again, she added, 'I know we didn't plan it, but—well, are you mad?'

Jared threw the towel into the bathroom behind him. 'Are you?'

Robyn lifted her slim shoulders. 'Why should I be?'

'That's not an answer.'

'Nor was yours,' she countered unevenly, forcing herself not to dwell on his lean powerful body. 'If—if there's a problem——'

Jared uttered an expletive. 'Why should there be?'

'Oh——' Robyn made a helpless gesture. 'Oh—you're making me nervous, Jared. I knew this wasn't going to be easy. That was why I wanted to get it over with.'

'By shouting it from the bedroom,' observed Jared flatly.

Robyn shrugged. 'Perhaps.' She glanced his way briefly, and then away again. 'Um—oughtn't you to put some clothes on? You'll get cold.' She paused. 'What was it you wanted to tell me?'

'Later,' said Jared, abandoning his stance by the door and coming towards her. 'Now, come on,' he said, pulling her away from the wall and into his arms. 'What's your problem, hmm? Don't you want another baby, is that it? Or are you afraid Daniel might object?'

Robyn linked her arms around his neck, gazing up at him with anxious eyes. 'I don't have a problem—not with the baby, anyway,' she admitted huskily. 'And, as far as Daniel is concerned, he told me this afternoon, he was disappointed I wasn't pregnant.'

'So did you enlighten him?'

'No.' Robyn was indignant. 'No one knows but you.'

'And I'm your problem?'

Robyn bent her head, pressing her forehead against his chest. 'I don't know.'

'What don't you know?' Jared's voice roughened as he put his fingers beneath her chin and tilted her face upward. 'Surely you don't really believe I wouldn't be delighted? My God, Robyn, I can think of nothing more exciting than the prospect of you carrying my child inside you. So long as that's what you want, I want it, too.'

'But you said——'

'Yes, what did I say?'

'Well—I thought you wanted to wait.'

'I thought that was what *you* wanted,' admitted Jared roughly. 'After—after everything that had gone before, I didn't want to rush you. I didn't want you to think I'd married you just to have my child.'

'Oh.'

'Is that all you can say? Oh?'

Robyn bit her lip. 'You won't mind when I get fat and ugly?'

'You may get fat, but you'll never be ugly to me,' retorted Jared.

'But I will get big—and clumsy——'

'And I'll love you just the same. Now, stop fishing for compliments.'

'I'm not.' Robyn hesitated. 'All right. Tell me what you wanted to say, then.'

Jared pulled a wry face. 'Would you believe I was going to tell you that I'm planning to expand, too? I'm going to buy the land next to the mill and put up another weaving shed.'

'Oh!' Robyn dimpled. 'How appropriate!'

'But now,' he said huskily, pressing a kiss to the corner of her mouth, 'now I'm going to finish my bath.'

She gasped when he swung her up into his arms then, and carried her into the bathroom. 'What are you doing?' she exclaimed, when he deposited her, still in her teddy, in the bath of soapy water.

'I'm taking a bath—and you—at the same time,' responded Jared, stepping into the deep round tub with her. Then, peeling the wet straps of her bodice down off her shoulders, he covered her mouth with his, sinking down into the water with her and pulling her fully against him.

'I—we can't!' moaned Robyn, feeling the lacy teddy floating around somewhere near her hips, but his touch was unbearably exciting and it was only a token protest.

'Of course we can,' he murmured thickly, his hands busy under the water. Seconds later, the teddy floated away, removing the last barrier. 'My wife, my mistress, my lover,' he breathed softly. 'And the mother of my children. What more could any man ask?'

DON'T MISS EUROMANCE

1992 is a special year for European unity, and we have chosen to celebrate this by featuring one Romance a month with a special European flavour.

Every month we'll take you on an exciting journey through the 12 countries of the European Community. In each story the hero will be a native of that country–imagine what it would be like to be kissed by a smouldering Italian, or wined and dined by a passionate Frenchman!

Our first **EUROMANCE**, *The Alpha Man'* by Kay Thorpe is set in Greece, the land of sunshine and mythology. As a special introductory offer we'll be giving away *'Hungarian Rhapsody'* by another top author, Jessica Steele, absolutely free with every purchase of *'The Alpha Man'*.

And there's more . . .

You can win a trip to Italy simply by entering our competition featured inside all Romances in September and October.

Published: September 1992   Price: £1.70

Next Month's Romances

Each month you can choose from a world of variety in romance with Mills & Boon. Below are the new titles to look out for next month, why not ask either Mills & Boon Reader Service or your Newsagent to reserve you a copy of the titles you want to buy — just tick the titles you would like to order and either post to Reader Service or take it to any Newsagent and ask them to order your books.

Please save me the following titles:		Please tick √
A HONEYED SEDUCTION	Diana Hamilton	
PASSIONATE POSSESSION	Penny Jordan	
MOTHER OF THE BRIDE	Carole Mortimer	
DARK ILLUSION	Patricia Wilson	
FATE OF HAPPINESS	Emma Richmond	
THE ALPHA MAN	Kay Thorpe	
HUNGARIAN RHAPSODY (This book is free with THE ALPHA MAN)	Jessica Steele	
NOTHING LESS THAN LOVE	Vanessa Grant	
LOVE'S VENDETTA	Stephanie Howard	
CALL UP THE WIND	Anne McAllister	
TOUCH OF FIRE	Joanna Neil	
TOMORROW'S HARVEST	Alison York	
THE STOLEN HEART	Amanda Browning	
NO MISTAKING LOVE	Jessica Hart	
THE BEGINNING OF THE AFFAIR	Marjorie Lewty	
CAUSE FOR LOVE	Kerry Allyne	
RAPTURE IN THE SANDS	Sandra Marton	

If you would like to order these books from Mills & Boon Reader Service please send £1.70 per title to: Mills & Boon Reader Service, P.O. Box 236, Croydon, Surrey, CR9 3RU and quote your Subscriber No:...(If applicable) and complete the name and address details below. Alternatively, these books are available from many local Newsagents including W.H.Smith, J.Menzies, Martins and other paperback stockists from 11th September 1992.

Name:...

Address:..

....Post Code:......................

To Retailer: If you would like to stock M&B books please contact your regular book/magazine wholesaler for details.

You may be mailed with offers from other reputable companies as a result of this application. If you would rather not take advantage of these opportunities please tick box ☐

Forthcoming Titles

DUET
Available in August

The Emma Darcy Duet   **STRIKE AT THE HEART**
     THE POSITIVE APPROACH

The Anne Mather Duet   **BURNING INHERITANCE**
     TRIAL OF INNOCENCE

BEST SELLER ROMANCE
Available in September

HIDDEN TREASURES Emma Goldrick
THE KISSING GAME Sally Wentworth

MEDICAL ROMANCE
Available in September

GYPSY SUMMER Laura MacDonald
THE BECKHILL TRADITION Lilian Darcy
THE DOCTORS AT SEFTONBRIDGE Janet Ferguson
A MIDWIFE'S CHOICE Margaret Holt

Available from Boots, Martins, John Menzies, W.H. Smith, most supermarkets and other paperback stockists.

Also available from Mills & Boon Reader Service, P.O. Box 236, Thornton Road, Croydon, Surrey CR9 3RU.

Readers in South Africa - write to:
Book Services International Ltd, P.O. Box 41654, Craighall, Transvaal 2024.